Stephen Chambers

POMPEII
AD79

Sponsored by Imperial Tobacco Limited in association with *The Daily Telegraph* in support of the arts.

Royal Academy of Arts Piccadilly London
20 November 1976 – 27 February 1977

Catalogue compiled and written by
John Ward-Perkins and Amanda Claridge

© John Ward-Perkins and
Amanda Claridge 1976

ISBN 0 905692 00 4

Produced for Pompeii AD79 by
Carlton Cleeve Limited,
13 New Quebec Street, London W1

Published by Imperial Tobacco Limited,
Lombard Street, Bristol

Designed by Dennis Bailey

Photography by Eric de Maré
Maps and diagrams by Michael Robinson

Printed in England by Westerham Press

Photographs of the exhibits loaned by the
British Museum, London (who also provided
the illustration on page 64), the Musée du
Louvre, Paris, and the Musée de Mariemont,
Belgium, were very kindly supplied by the
museum concerned.
Grateful acknowledgement is also made to
the following:
Amanda Claridge: pages 34 (both), 39 (below
right), Nos. 106–108, 195, 252, 258, 276, 277
279, 280
Deutsches Archäologisches Institut, Rome:
pages 69, 71 (top left), 74 (both), Nos. 129, 131
Hans Eschebach: map of Pompeii pages 43
and 44
Foto Alinari, Rome: pages 37, 39 (top),
57 (top), 70 (both), 71 (below left and above
far right), No. 26
Sheila Gibson: plan for No. 100
Edgar Hyman and Peter Chorley: pages 69,
71 (centre), Nos. 33, 122, 204, 250, 288, 290,
291, 293–298, 338
Alan Irvine: No. 46 (profile)
Dr Ann Laidlaw: sources of plans for page 47
Museo della Civiltà Romana, E.U.R.: Nos. 16,
17
Museo Nazionale Archeologico, Naples:
pages 52, 55, 58, 66, 75, 76 (all three), 77
(below), Nos. 8–15, 18, 35, 47, 81, 92–96, 98,
103, 120, 128, 132, 142, 152, 157, 159, 169,
186–187, 189, 202–203, 207, 208, 210, 211, 227,
229, 256, 259–262, 287
Pubbli Aerfoto, Milan: page 45

Patrons

Her Majesty The Queen
The President of the Republic of Italy, Giovanni Leone

Committee of Honour

On. Arnaldo Forlani
Minister of Foreign Affairs

On. Mario Pedini
Minister of Cultural Heritage

H.E. Roberto Ducci
Italian Ambassador in London

Avv. Galileo Barbirotti
President of the Region of Campania

Dr Vittorio Cordero de Montezemolo
Director General for Cultural, Scientific and Technological
Co-operation, Ministry of Foreign Affairs

Dr Salvatore Accardo
Director General for Antiquities and Fine Arts, Ministry of
Cultural Heritage

Prof. Massimo Pallottino
President of the Consiglio Superiore, Antichità e Belle Arti,
Section for Antiquities

Prof. Alfonso de Franciscis
lately Superintendent of Antiquities, Naples and Caserta

Prof. Mario Montuori
Director of the Italian Institute in London

The Rt. Hon. Anthony Crosland, MP
Secretary of State for Foreign and Commonwealth Affairs

The Lord Donaldson of Kingsbridge, OBE
Minister for the Arts

The Baroness Birk
Parliamentary Under-Secretary of State
Department of the Environment

H.E. Sir Alan Campbell, KCMG
H.B.M. Ambassador at Rome

Sir Guy Millard, KCMG, CVO
Lately H.B.M. Ambassador at Rome

The Lord Ballantrae, KT, GCMG, GCVO, DSO, OBE
Chairman, The British Council

The Lord Gibson
Chairman, The Arts Council of Great Britain

Dr Arnold Taylor, CBE
President of the Society of Antiquaries of London

J. A. L. Morgan Esq
Head of Cultural Relations Department
Foreign and Commonwealth Office

Committees

Policy Committee

Sir Hugh Casson	President of the Royal Academy
Mr R. A. Garrett	Chairman, Imperial Tobacco Limited
Mr Roger de Grey	Treasurer of The Royal Academy
The Lord Hartwell	Chairman, *The Daily Telegraph*
Mr Sidney C. Hutchison	Secretary of the Royal Academy
Mr C. G. Knowles	Public Affairs Manager, Imperial Tobacco Limited
Mr Peter Saabor	Carlton Cleeve Limited, Organizer, Pompeii AD79 Exhibition
Mr H. M. Stephen	Managing Director, *The Daily Telegraph*
Mr P. A. Taverner	Carlton Cleeve Limited
Mr John Ward-Perkins	Academic Adviser, Pompeii AD79 Exhibition

Executive Committee

Mr Colin Bayley	Imperial Tobacco Limited
Mr Sidney C. Hutchison	The Royal Academy
Mr Alan Irvine	Buzas and Irvine
Miss Pauline Kennedy	Exhibition Manager
Mr John Mannings	Security Adviser
Mr D. J. Miller	*The Daily Telegraph*
Mr Peter Saabor	Carlton Cleeve Limited
Mr Kenneth J. Tanner	The Royal Academy
Mr Nicholas J. Usherwood	The Royal Academy
Miss Julia Vickerman	Carlton Cleeve Limited

Contents

8 Preface by Sir Hugh Casson, President of The Royal Academy

9 Forewords by Mr R. A. Garrett, Chairman,
Imperial Tobacco Limited
and by Lord Hartwell, Chairman, *The Daily Telegraph*

11 Acknowledgements by Peter Saabor, Exhibition Organizer

12 Introduction

15 Campania

17–32 Colour plates

33 History of Pompeii

38 The town: government and people

42 The town: planning and architecture

47 The Pompeian house and garden

52 The economy: agriculture and industry

55 Cults and beliefs

62 Entertainment, sport and leisure

68 Painting

75 Sculpture

77 The other arts

79 Herculaneum

81–88 Colour plates

89–204 Catalogue:

   exhibits 1–22   I History and the volcano

        23–73   II The people

        74–99   III The garden

        100–185   IV The house

        186–226   V Cults and beliefs

        227–299   VI Trade and occupations

        300–338   VII Leisure

205 Glossary

206 Bibliography

Preface

About 2000 years ago a modest provincial town in
southern Italy was buried, almost overnight, by the ash
and cinders of a volcanic eruption. For nearly 1700 years it
remained undiscovered, the miraculously preserved
tomb of 20,000 people together with everything they
owned, used or enjoyed. No event in history perhaps has
caught so sharply the human imagination or been held so
firmly in our memory. Why is this?

Psychologists tell us that the capacity to imagine
disaster is a primitive but essential part of our human
capacity to survive, part of our need to confront death
when we are not ourselves dying.

True as this may be, it does not entirely explain the
continuing fascination for all of us of the story of Pompeii.
The answer, I believe, lies in the fact that we remember
Pompeii not just for its human tragedy, nor even for the
strange accident which kept its secret so perfectly and for
so long, but for the wealth and quality of its art – the
paintings and furniture, the mosaics and sculpture, the
architecture, jewellery and treasures, the whole
man-made environment of its legendary life-style.

It is from this rich hoard (most of it now cared for in the
Museo Archeologico Nazionale in Naples) that this
exhibition has been chosen and arranged in a setting
designed to show them at their best. It is the most
ambitious and comprehensive exhibition of these
treasures, we believe, ever to have been shown outside
Italy.

We are honoured that H.M. The Queen and the
President of the Italian Republic have consented to be our
Patrons. We are grateful to the Italian Government and
particularly to the Ambassador in London,
H.E. Roberto Ducci, for consistent and practical help,
and to the many scholars and experts who have brought
this project to fruition.

Finally I must pay the warmest tribute to the
generosity of our joint sponsors, Imperial Tobacco
Limited and *The Daily Telegraph*, who have made possible
this unique and marvellous exhibition.

Hugh Casson
President of The Royal Academy

Forewords

When we first commissioned a study of the feasibility of mounting an exhibition about Pompeii, we were motivated by the belief, held in common with much of British industry, that a company should try to make more than just a strictly economic contribution to the society by which it is sustained, and, by doing so, go some way to replace the great individual patrons of the past. Happily, this is a point of view shared by our co-sponsor, *The Daily Telegraph*, and welcomed by The Royal Academy of Arts. That early study has thus been encouraged to blossom into a cultural event of some magnitude.

'Pompeii AD79', with its fascinating blend of education and arts, takes its place as part of Imperial Tobacco's contribution to the arts – which ranges from our Awards for Radio Writing to the production, in December 1976, of *Ariadne auf Naxos* at the Royal Opera House through the annual Celebrity Series in Bristol and our Museum Development Fund.

To learn how one segment of European society went about its daily affairs almost 2000 years ago is a unique experience. To examine the treasures of Pompeii, many of them displayed in the context of their everyday setting, is both rewarding and stimulating.

The exhibition will engage the mind and delight the eye of all who see it, and I am sure that many thousands will come to The Royal Academy to be enriched as well as informed by their visit.

R. A. Garrett
Chairman
Imperial Tobacco Limited

The Pompeii Exhibition also includes relics from the neighbouring small town of Herculaneum. The fascination of the two is that, unlike any other historical sites in Europe, both of them disappeared, one engulfed in cinders, the other in mud. Within a matter of days there was hardly anything man-made to be seen.

Other sites decayed, or were built over, or were plundered, only slowly, so that a great deal of imagination is needed to recreate them in the mind's eye. Here a whole bit of civilization came to a dead stop, and it is possible to reconstruct it to some extent as all of it existed on 24 August AD79.

Moreover we are showing here how ordinary people lived then – not the gilded society of Imperial Rome. Pompeii and Herculaneum can be compared to Brighton in the summer rather than to Monte Carlo. The Exhibition will thus capture the atmosphere of life in an ordinary town in the greatest country of its time; the domestic architecture, life in the home, the cults and religions and leisure pursuits.

The bringing together of so many valuable treasures gives an indication of the detailed organization which has been put into the Exhibition, and *The Daily Telegraph* is proud to have co-operated with The Royal Academy and Imperial Tobacco Limited in its planning.

Lord Hartwell
Chairman
The Daily Telegraph

Authors' note

We could not have produced this catalogue had it not been for the unstinted help we have received from many friends, among them Simon Bendall, Joanna Bird, John Callaghan, Maria Giuseppina Cerulli-Irelli, Anna Fazzari, Martin Frederiksen, Antonio Giuliano, Wilhelmina Jashemski, Anne Laidlaw, Dimitrios Michaelides, Massimo Pallottino, Toby Parker, Enrica Pozzi Paolini, Dale Trendall, Luciana Valentini, Angela Wardle, Helen Whitehouse and Fausto Zevi. But there have been many others as well, too numerous to name individually. To all of them we offer our sincere thanks.

   We would also like to take this opportunity of expressing our deep sense of personal gratitude to our Italian friends, both in Naples and in Rome, who gave us so much of their time and trouble in resolving the thousand and one difficulties, great and small, that inevitably arise in the preparation of an enterprise of this sort and size. But for their patience, understanding and unfailing kindness, it would have been a very different story. We are very conscious of our debt.

   This is not the first time, and it will surely not be the last, that the authors of an exhibition catalogue have had to do their work far more hurriedly than they would have wished, often without any possibility of reference back to the objects themselves to resolve doubtful points. We have aimed at accuracy, but we are all too aware that we have not always achieved it.

John Ward-Perkins
Amanda Claridge

Acknowledgements

This Exhibition is presented by kind permission of the President and Council of The Royal Academy of Arts, and is sponsored by Imperial Tobacco Limited in association with *The Daily Telegraph*. Representatives of the Royal Academy and of the sponsoring companies served on the various committees, and their active involvement and support made a major contribution to the organization of the Exhibition. In this regard, a special tribute should be paid to Colin Knowles of Imperial Tobacco Limited, who has been the architect of their arts sponsorship programme.

We are most grateful for the advice and co-operation of the Museo Nazionale Archeologico in Naples, from which museum most of the exhibits were loaned, and in particular Professor A. de Franciscis (Superintendent of Antiquities, Naples and Caserta), Dr M. G. Cerulli-Irelli (Director of Excavations, Pompeii) and Dr E. Pozzi Paolini (Director of the National Archaeological Museum, Naples). They worked very closely with John Ward-Perkins, the Academic Adviser to the Exhibition, and his assistant, Amanda Claridge, and it was their joint responsibility to select all the art and artifacts on view at the Exhibition.

We also gratefully acknowledge the loan of important items by the Musée du Louvre, Paris, the Musée de Mariemont, Belgium, the Trustees of the British Museum, London; the Walker Art Gallery, Liverpool, kindly loaned Sir E. J. Poynter's *Faithful Unto Death*, and the Society of Antiquaries, London, the watercolour of the Temple of Isis.

A special word of thanks is due to John Letts, Chairman of the Executive Committee of National Heritage, who has been associated with the Exhibition since the inception of the idea. The generous assistance of the Italian State Tourist Office in London has also been much appreciated.

The Exhibition has been designed by Stefan Buzas and Alan Irvine, Architects, assisted by Esther Hayter. The Exhibition contractors were Messrs F. W. Clifford Ltd.

Special photography for the Exhibition of the Villa of the Mysteries and Oplontis is by Edgar Hyman and Peter Chorley. The model of the City of Pompeii has been made by Richard Powell & Associates, and that of the House of the Menander by H. R. Allen from drawings by Sheila Gibson.

The transport and packing of the exhibits from Italy was handled by Dr E. de Marinis, with the assistance in the UK of Ian Pearson of W. Wingate & Johnston (South) Limited. The consultant on security is John Mannings, formerly security adviser to National Museums in the UK.

MacKay and Partners are the advertising agents to the Exhibition, and Fay Jenkins is the Account Manager responsible.

A great deal of work has gone into the selection of the publications and merchandise for the Exhibition. Special thanks in this regard are due to Pauline Kennedy (Manager of the Exhibition), Moira Cook, Julia Vickerman, and Candida Hunt, who also helped to produce this catalogue.

We are most grateful to Jaeger, who have very generously provided the clothes worn by the sales girls; and also to Gross, who kindly loaned the British electronic sales registers.

The Exhibition was organized on behalf of the sponsors by Carlton Cleeve Limited.

Peter Saabor

Introduction

On the morning of the twenty-fourth of August, AD 79, the long-dormant volcano of Vesuvius blew up, and by the evening of that day the two flourishing towns of Pompeii and Herculaneum and the nearby coastal resort of Stabiae were dead, already half-buried by the rain of ash, pumice and volcanic mud beneath which they were to lie entombed for more than sixteen centuries. Before long their very locations were lost. It was not until 1709 that well-diggers hit upon the theatre of Herculaneum, and it was another thirty years before, in 1738, the Bourbons put in hand the programme of organized treasure hunting (*zufälliges raüberisches Nachwühlen*, 'haphazard, predatory grubbing', is how Goethe described it) which furnished the first nucleus of the royal collections that were eventually to come to rest in the National Museum of Naples. Then in 1748 attention was diverted to another Vesuvian site, where peasants had recently made promising finds and where digging was easier. This proved to be the lost Pompeii. Here too exploration was at first haphazard and destructive, and it was really only with the appointment of Giuseppe Fiorelli (1860–75) that systematic excavation may be said to have started. It was he who hit upon the idea of making casts of the victims of the eruption, and who introduced the system of nomenclature, still in use today, whereby any building in the town can be located in terms of its Region, its city block, and the serial numbers of its street entrances. It was again he and his successor, Michele Ruggiero, who first adopted the modern principle of restoring buildings and of conserving finds in place, instead of ripping out the more spectacular and leaving the rest to disintegrate.

The first and overwhelming impression which these sites leave on the modern visitor today is the immediacy of this ancient tragedy. As one gazes on the table set for breakfast, on the posters for the next municipal elections, on the pathetic huddle of bodies clustered in a cellar, the intervening centuries fall away. It is just as if yesterday some sudden and dreadful natural catastrophe had overwhelmed all the familiar things of Surbiton or Ealing, preserving every intimate detail of the semi-detached and the supermarket for the archaeologists of future millennia. This sense of yesterday, this powerfully enduring presence of all the little everyday things that constitute the externals of a way of life, this is something unique to Pompeii and Herculaneum.

But it is not the tragedy of 24 August AD 79 as such which is the subject of this exhibition. We are concerned with one particular aspect of this event, namely to present, so far as is possible in terms of objects that can be transported, a cross-section of the art and craftsmanship of the buried cities, as it stood at the moment when the clock of history was so dramatically stopped: that of Pompeii in the first instance, because the setting is there more complete and the range of available material wider, but supplemented where necessary from Herculaneum, from Stabiae, and from material now in the National Museum of Naples of which the precise Vesuvian source is no longer known.

Art and craftsmanship: one uses the double term advisedly because the modern distinction between artist and craftsman would have had very little meaning, at any rate with reference to contemporary artists. Throughout most of classical antiquity, and very much so in Roman times, the artist was by definition a craftsman, working to supply the specific needs of a patron or, more generally, the demands of public taste. This fact is bound to influence any modern attempt to present his work. Certain categories and certain individual products of ancient art may be timeless, transcending all accidents of time and place. It does not really matter that a fifth-century Athenian viewed the Parthenon frieze under very different conditions from ourselves, and with very different eyes: the quality still shines through. Even so, there can be very few products of ancient art which do not gain an added dimension from being viewed within their historical and social context. This is emphatically true when the objects in question are the products of a society as complex and many-sided as that of Rome, and doubly true when they represent, not some single, homogeneous masterpiece, nor the accumulated artistic treasure of some single great patron, but a selection of the objects which just happened to be assembled on the walls and in the streets of a town of provincial Italy on that fateful August day when, without warning, history stood still.

One has therefore to present the art of Pompeii in its context. In the case of the paintings this is quite literally true, physically as well as metaphorically. The Romans did possess panel paintings, as we do; but very few of these have survived, and the paintings that now adorn the walls of museums and galleries were all once parts of much larger decorative complexes, detached from which they have much the same artistic significance as a panel cut from a Tiepolo ceiling. We can still enjoy many of their qualities, but viewed in isolation they have certainly lost something of their original artistic intention. One has to remember too that the artists who painted them, most of them simple craftsmen, both slaves and freedmen, were operating within a context of ideas very different from our own. Many of the presuppositions of the society for which Tiepolo and his assistants worked are still common currency, making it relatively easy for us to enter into the spirit of their work. Roman society is a very different matter. It is true that certain aspects of the daily life of Pompeii do strike a startling note of modernity. Water supply and sanitation; paving and street drainage, and the organization of such public services as markets and the disposal of refuse; the mechanisms of commerce and banking; the life of the tavern and bar; the addiction to spectator sport; all of these are still quite near enough to our own recent past (and indeed in some cases to our present) to strike an immediate response of comfortable recognition. But the moment one scratches a little deeper, one is aware also of a number of profound, underlying differences. The position of the family within the social structure, religious beliefs and ethics, the status of the professions, the accepted functions and duties of patronage, these are some only of the aspects of Pompeian life without some awareness of which it is very hard to arrive at any true evaluation of the material remains. The art of Pompeii was an integral part of this wider culture.

An exhibition can and should concentrate on allowing the objects displayed to speak for themselves. We hope that by our selection and our presentation we may have conveyed something also of the wider message which, unbeknown to itself, Roman Pompeii was busy compiling for us to read.

Map of Roman Campania.

Campania

Today, a century after the unification of modern Italy, it is not always easy to recall that what was achieved in 1870 was not the restoration of a natural, self-evident state of affairs that had been briefly disrupted by external forces; it was the re-creation of a national entity that had been laboriously built up by classical Rome, only to disintegrate into its component parts as soon as the authority of the Western Roman Empire collapsed. One of the geographical units that make up Italy is Campania, the region of which Naples is today the capital. Long before it was a part of Roman Italy Pompeii had been a city of Campania, and for two of the three thousand-odd years since central Italy first emerges into history Campania has been independent of, and frequently in conflict with, Rome. Somewhere between Rome and Naples the South begins. This is still one of the salient facts of Italian political and economic life, and it is a truth rooted in history.

The heart of Campania has always been the Bay of Naples, together with the fertile coastal plain that is bounded on the north by the river Volturno and on the east and south by the western slopes of the Appenines and the mountains of the Sorrento peninsula. Both geographically and historically it constitutes a remarkably well-defined unit. Except for the mountains to the south and east, this is all very fertile country of recent volcanic origin, and it first took historical shape when in the eighth century BC the Greeks, finding themselves debarred from further progress up the western coast by the Etruscans, and later by the Romans, established here a number of thriving settlements. During the course of the fifth century BC these Greek colonies and trading stations, together with the Etruscan outpost of Capua, lost their independence, passing under the control of Italic tribesmen who had moved down from the mountains of the interior. The latter were quick to learn the lessons of civilization and the union was a fruitful one, resulting in a culture which in varying proportions was both Greek and Italic. Campania never lost either its Greek cultural roots or its Greek commercial contacts and aptitudes; but at the same time the Italic component remained strong enough to enable this mixed society to adapt without too much difficulty to the consequences of the inexorable southward advance of Rome. Whereas over much of southern Italy the Roman conquest was a sorry story of pillage, disruption and catastrophic economic decline, Campania was the exception. Power and authority had moved to Rome, but in terms of commerce, culture and the arts Campania enjoyed a prosperity fully equal to, and in certain respects in advance of, that of Rome itself.

The history of Pompeii, summarized in the following section (pages 33–37), is in most respects that of Campania in miniature, but we may perhaps single out two aspects of the broader scene

which were especially important for the cultural and artistic life of the Campanian cities. One was the fact that, until the emperor Claudius created his new, artificial harbour at the mouth of the Tiber, the chief sea-going port of Rome was Puteoli, the modern Pozzuoli. With the establishment of Rome as a world power in the second century BC, this inevitably brought great material prosperity, one facet of which was the settlement at Puteoli of a large and prosperous commercial community, derived very largely from the Hellenistic east. It is symptomatic that as early as 105 BC Puteoli should already have had a temple of the

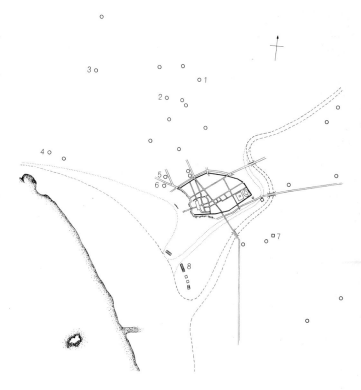

Sketch map to show the possible position of the port, the mouth and ancient course of the river Sarno in relation to Pompeii. Country villas in the neighbourhood are indicated by an open circle.

1. *Villa Rustica, Boscoreale.*
2. *Villa of P. Fannius Synistor, Boscoreale.*
3. *Villa of Agrippa Postumus, Boscotrecase.*
4. *Oplontis (see No. 338).*
5. *Villa of the Mysteries.*
6. *Villa of Diomedes.*
7. *Temple of Dionysus, S. Abbondio.*
8. *Large storerooms, shops and other buildings belonging to the port.*

Egyptian divinities, Isis and Serapis, and there are many traces of other oriental cults. Puteoli was where St Paul landed on his journey to Rome.

Another aspect of the Campanian scene that was very closely related to Rome's new-found position as a world power was that of the changes which the sudden access of wealth inevitably brought about in Roman upper class customs. Among these was one which calls for no comment today, namely the determination of every well-to-do Roman to acquire a seaside property. Gaius Marius had a villa at Misenum, Sulla the Dictator one near Cumae. Among the many prominent Romans known to have possessed such seaside retreats during the last half-century of the Republic were Julius Caesar, Pompey, Lucullus, the notorius Clodia, Varro the historian, many distinguished ex-consuls, and several of Cicero's clients; Cicero himself had no less than three Campanian properties, at Cumae, at Puteoli and at Pompeii. By the time the emperor Augustus established himself on Capri, the Bay of Naples was ringed around with the playgrounds of the rich. As we shall see, these *villae marittimae* constituted a natural field for imaginative architectural experiment, while at the same time they ensured that the decorative tastes and fashions of Roman society found an almost immediate expression in Campania, and vice versa. They were also a bountiful source of artistic patronage. Each year there is fresh evidence to show that the Bay of Naples, and especially the area around Puteoli, was busy with the workshops of sculptors, potters, stuccoists and painters. Late Republican Campania was one of the most active creative centres of the late Hellenistic world.

The area to the south and east of Vesuvius lay somewhat on the fringes of all this creative activity. It contributed to and profited from the general prosperity, and the latest contemporary artistic fashions were reflected on its walls. But its own interests were predominantly agricultural and its population, as the family names of Pompeii clearly show, was very largely Italic, many of the families being of Samnite origin but with a generous admixture of newcomers from other parts of Italy, reinforced in 80 BC by the establishment of colonies of Sullan veterans at Nola and Pompeii. Compared with Puteoli or Baiae Pompeii was perhaps a trifle provincial, and it lacked the Hellenic sophistication of Naples. Nevertheless, it was a prosperous and lively member of the Campanian community, at a moment when Campania was itself in the forefront of contemporary architectural and artistic progress.

A villa beside the sea (7).

Portrait of a man and his wife (23). Portrait of a woman (24).

Mosaic portrait of a woman (72).

Mosaic of rehearsal for a Satyr Play (314).

Garden painting detail (97).   A still life detail (257).

A rustic sanctuary (125).

Rocky landscape with herdsman and goats (136).

overleaf
Pan and the Nymphs (128). Europa on the Bull (132).

Dionysiac scene in marble intarsia (161).

A chariot race detail (311).

Mosaic of fishes (253).

History of Pompeii

The earliest history of Pompeii must remain a matter of conjecture until the relevant archaeological levels have been more systematically explored. Finds made in the city's two Archaic sanctuaries, that of Apollo beside the Forum and of Hercules (the Doric Temple), show that by the sixth century BC Greek influence was very strong, and it may very well be that the site was actually first colonized by Greeks from Cumae, who recognized its advantages as a river-mouth station for trading with the native Italic agricultural communities of the Sarno valley. Pottery characteristic of the latter has been found in the same contexts, suggesting close association if not intermarriage with the local peoples; and Etruscan wares indicate commerce also with Etruscan Capua. From the outset the geographical position of Pompeii made it a meeting place of cultures.

The middle years of the fifth century, after the decisive defeat of the Etruscans in 474 by Cumae in alliance with Syracuse, were a period of Greek prosperity. The original 24-acre settlement of Pompeii on the spur overlooking the river mouth was at this time greatly enlarged, to include the whole area of some 160 acres enclosed by the surviving city walls. But the period of undisputed Greek authority was short-lived. The walls themselves were symptomatic of the threat from the hardy Italic tribesmen of the interior, who were already spilling down across the coastal plain. By the end of the century the entire Greek coastland, from Cumae in the north to Poseidonia (Paestum) in the south, had succumbed to the invaders: only Neapolis (Naples) managed to retain its independence.

The newcomers were part of a loose confederation of peoples, the Sabellians, who shared a common language, called Oscan, a member of the same Indo-European group of languages as Latin. These peoples appear in the literature variously as Sabellians and as Samnites, from the name of the particular tribe around which resistance to Rome's southward advance was soon to crystallize; in the Sarno valley they merged with the Oscans, a closely related Italic tribe already settled in the coastal area. At the time intertribal disputes and alliances bulked large – it was one of these Sabellic tribes, the Campani of the area around Capua, who first called in the Romans in 343 BC; but seen in historical retrospect, the most important thing about them was the broad common heritage of Italic peasant culture and language which they shared with each other and, at one remove, with the Romans. Without this common element the story of the union of central Italy under Roman rule would have been very different. Another gift which these peoples shared with the Romans was that of taking on the externals of the more advanced peoples whom they conquered. The Greek component in the resulting mixed culture was to be a very important factor in the success story of Republican Campania.

During the Samnite wars, which ended in 290 BC with the establishment of Roman authority over the whole of central Italy, Pompeii was still a small country town. Its economy was predominantly agricultural, based on wine and oil, with some local industry, and supplemented by a flourishing commerce in wool and woollen goods. Such other importance as it had at this stage was as a harbour town for its more important neighbours, Nola and Nuceria (Nocera), and for the smaller towns of the Sarno valley. But times were changing fast. The consolidation of Roman authority, the defeat of Carthage in the Second Punic War (218–201), and Rome's triumphant advance eastwards into Greece, Asia Minor and Syria, opened up rich fields of economic enterprise of which the Campanians, with their mixed Graeco-Italic background, were ideally placed to take advantage. Puteoli (Pozzuoli) was now the principal port of Italy. Roman traders, prominent among them the Campanians, began to appear in large numbers all over the eastern Mediterranean; and while a steadily increasing proportion of the financial capital was probably put up by wealthy Romans, there were rich prizes for the Campanian merchants and middlemen and for those of the Campanian landed gentry who had money to invest. By the second half of the second century BC Pompeii was, as its monuments show, already a very prosperous city.

The last century of the Roman Republic was a period of almost continuous civil strife and deep social unrest, during which the political and economic forces loosed by Rome's conquest of Italy, Carthage, and the Hellenistic kingdoms of the eastern Mediterranean, battled their way to the new state of institutional equilibrium which we call the Roman Empire. In such troubled times Campania could not escape involvement: cities and individuals found themselves caught up in larger events, and many people lost their lives or property. Pompeii itself was very far from being the happy small town without a history which it is sometimes painted; but despite temporary ups and downs, it was still able to maintain a surprising level of economic well-being. Because of its privileged economic position, Campania was better able than a great many parts of Italy to adjust to the successive new situations, and when in 31 BC Caesar's nephew and heir, Octavian (or Augustus, as he was to be known from 27 BC), finally succeeded in reimposing peace and unified rule upon the Mediterranean world, Pompeii was still a very prosperous town, well placed to take advantage of the opportunities offered by the new Pax Romana.

From the earlier part of this period two closely related series of events stand out as directly affecting the fortunes of Pompeii. One was the Social War of 90–89 BC, in which Pompeii, with its fine walls, was one of the Campanian strongholds of the Italian allies in their struggle to achieve full Roman citizenship. There

The town walls of Pompeii, originally built in the fifth century BC but repaired and heightened during successive crises. Top: the Nola Gate; below: stretch of early masonry on the north wall.

was heavy fighting, during which Herculaneum was occupied, Stabiae captured and sacked, and Pompeii itself besieged by the future dictator, Lucius Cornelius Sulla: one can still see the damage wrought by his artillery in the walls near the Vesuvius Gate. We do not know the immediate local outcome of those events, but the long-term result of the Social War was the unification of Italy south of the Po valley within the broad framework of the Roman polity.

The conclusion of the Social War did not, however, resolve the immediate local problems. It was left for Sulla to complete the Italian settlement after his return to Italy in 83 BC from Asia Minor at the head of a victorious army. Having eliminated all political opposition in Rome itself, he turned his hand to the larger problem with characteristic ruthlessness and efficiency. One of the most effective instruments to hand was the establishment of citizen colonies of loyal military veterans on land expropriated from past opponents. Many such colonies were planted in Campania, among them a group of possibly as many as two or three thousand families on the territory of Pompeii. It was a neat solution, satisfactory to all parties except the dispossessed, and, in extreme cases, it must have meant the virtual annihilation of the old Italic upper classes. At Pompeii, as we shall see, the long-term results were nothing like so drastic. But the immediate result was to give Pompeii and other similar colonies a new civic status, a new ruling class, and a new stake in the events of the world around them.

With the establishment of the Colonia Cornelia Veneria Pompeianorum in 80 BC we turn a page in the city's history. The historical perspectives shift, slightly but decisively. As a Hellenized Italic city Pompeii, though irrevocably involved in the fortunes of Roman Italy, had retained a certain measure of independence. Now, for better or for worse, she found herself a full partner in the great Roman adventure. For the next fifty years the death throes of the Roman Republic continued to offer the politically ambitious plenty of scope for direct involvement in larger events. We catch an occasional glimpse of such happenings in the pages of Cicero, who owned a property in the neighbourhood: in 62 BC he successfully defended the founder of the colony, the dictator's relative Publius Cornelius Sulla, on a charge of involvement in the conspiracy of Catiline; and in 49 BC Cicero himself, on his way to join Pompey in Greece, found himself approached by the commanders of the three cohorts stationed in or near the town (an offer which he discreetly declined). Again, during the Servile War (73–71 BC), Spartacus's army remained for a long time in the countryside near Pompeii, and actually destroyed Pompeii's neighbour, Nola. But such incidents were the inevitable by-products of troubled times. For the last century and a half of the city's

Oscan inscription recording the building of the Samnite Palaestra (see page 62) in the later second century BC. 'Vibius Adiranus, son of Vibius, left money in his will to the men of Pompeii; with this money the quaestor of Pompeii, Vibius Vinicius, son of Maras, with the consent of the council had charge of the construction of this building and approved it.'

existence, the inhabitants of Pompeii, in company with those of countless other colonies and municipalities in Italy, were fully engaged in reaping the material advantages of their new status.

From 80 BC onwards the real history of Pompeii is that of the city and its inhabitants, and that can only be told in terms of the city's civic institutions, which are the subject of the section that follows (pages 38–41). Here it must suffice to refer to the three remaining occasions on which Pompeii found itself front-page news outside Campania.

The first of these was the riot which took place in AD 59 after a gladiatorial spectacle in the amphitheatre, as a result of which a number of visiting spectators from Nuceria were killed or wounded. The matter reached the Senate in Rome, and as a punishment all spectacles in the amphitheatre were banned for a period of ten years – a sentence comparable today to a ten-year

closure of the local football stadium. The scene is vividly portrayed in a contemporary picture, now in Naples Museum (see below), which was found in a house near the Theatre.

Then, on the fifth of February 62 there was a severe earthquake. Though nobody at the time knew it, this was Act One of the tragedy of AD 79, and like many earthquakes of a volcanic nature its effects were localized but intense, and Pompeii was the epicentre. The town was very badly damaged; quite how badly can be judged from the fact that when, seventeen years later, disaster hit again, only two of the city's public monuments (the Amphitheatre and the Temple of Isis) and a handful of private houses had been completely restored. Of the Forum and the buildings round it, only in the Temple of Apollo was the work near completion: even allowing for the fact that after the eruption this whole area was ransacked for its metals, its

The Amphitheatre riot of AD 59. Naples Museum.

Graffito of a triumphant gladiator, drawn by a Pompeian after the riot of AD 59. 'Campani (probably the inhabitants of a suburb of Pompeii) you too were destroyed in the victory over the Nucerians.'

CAMPANI VICTORIAVNA
CVMNVCERINIS PERISTIS

marbles and its building materials, it is quite evident that the only buildings where reconstruction work was not still in progress were those, like the Capitolium, where it had not yet started – presumably because of plans to rebuild them in a more opulent, contemporary manner. In 79 the whole Forum area was a gigantic builders' yard. The same story is repeated all over the city: in the public bath buildings, the theatres, the Doric temple, the water supply, a great many of the private houses. As we shall see, this was not the only problem which Pompeii was having to face in its last years; but the earthquake of 62 was in itself undoubtedly a major disaster.

The great eruption of Vesuvius of 24 August 79 came out of a clear sky. The volcano had been inactive since well before historical times and it was universally believed to be extinct. Villas and vineyards crowded up the slopes, and in a land where earthquakes are common the warning of AD 62 had passed unheeded.

For the course of the eruption, which followed a classic pattern, we have two contemporary sources: the analysis of the deposits

Map showing the area affected by the hail of pumice stones and the relative depths of ash ejected by Vesuvius in AD 79.

of ash and cinders beneath which the whole city was buried, and the eye-witness account of Pliny the Younger, contained in two letters addressed to the historian Tacitus. At the time Pliny was staying with his uncle, the famous scientist and writer, who happened to be in command of the Roman fleet at Misenum, nineteen miles to the west, at the mouth of the Bay of Naples. It was about one o'clock in the afternoon when their attention was called to the cloud, shaped like a gigantic pine tree, which had appeared across the bay:

'I cannot describe its appearance and shape better than as resembling an umbrella pine tree, with a very tall trunk rising high into the sky and then spreading out into branches. I imagine this was because where the force of the blast was fresh it was thrust upwards, but as this lost impetus, or indeed as the weight of the cloud itself took charge, it began to thin out and to spread laterally. At one moment it was white, at another dark and dirty, as if it carried up a load of earth and cinders.'

(Pliny, *Letters* vi, 16)

Allied troops who witnessed the far less destructive eruption of March 1944 will at once recognize the description – nature's equivalent of the mushroom cloud released by an atomic bomb.

Summoning ships, the Elder Pliny headed straight for the coast near Herculaneum, where he found it already impossible to land. Instead he put in at Stabiae, at the coastal villa of a friend, Pomponianus, where he spent the night. In the small hours of the following morning a succession of violent earthquake shocks and the steadily falling ash drove the party down to the beach, where during the course of the morning of the 25th Pliny was overcome by the fumes and died. Meanwhile, Misenum was feeling the same earthquake shocks, and when a shift of wind into the east brought with it a cloud of darkness and falling ash the whole population took to the open countryside: it was not until the following day that the ashes began to cease falling and that a fitful daylight broke through once more.

The eruption must have started between 10 and 11 o'clock on the morning of the 24th, and by the evening of that day some 6 feet of ash had already fallen on Pompeii. Here the first 8 or 9 feet of deposit consist of a thin scatter of lava pebbles (*lapilli*), the debris of the plug of solidified basalt which had for so long sealed the volcano, followed by successive layers of almost pure pumice. This represents the body of volcanic magma which was ejected up the throat as soon as it was clear, under conditions of great heat and enormous pressure, to a height of several thousand metres (the trunk of the 'pine tree'); on reaching the upper atmosphere the drops of magma were able to expand, releasing some of the gases which they contained, and to fall as a dense, spreading cloud of incandescent, gaseous pumice. More than two thirds of the deposits at Pompeii represent this first, cataclysmic series of events, after which the gases of the interior were free to escape upwards with a much smaller admixture of pure magma, its place being taken by increasing quantities of alien material, as the old volcanic matter of the existing cone collapsed inwards upon itself, causing a series of convulsive blockages and explosions. This was the peak moment of the eruption, involving a tremendous release of gaseous pressure and causing the earthquakes which destroyed Pomponianus's villa at Stabiae and spread panic at Misenum. But although the deadly rain of gas and cinders continued, the body of actual solid matter that fell was already tailing off rapidly. In terms of its power to destroy, by the afternoon of the 25th the eruption had already done its worst.

The city of Pompeii had ceased to exist, buried beneath twelve feet of lethal ash. We have no means of estimating the casualties, but in the town itself and the immediate countryside they must have run into many thousands. Those who got away did so in the first few hours, the lucky ones by sea, the rest striking inland before the roads were blocked and the air became unbreathable. Those who dallied to collect their valuables or who took shelter in the houses and cellars died miserably, some when the roofs and upper stories collapsed upon them under the weight of the ash, most of them suffocated by the steady accumulation of deadly, sulphurous fumes. The ash solidified round their bodies, leaving for posterity the pathetic record of their death agonies amid the darkness of that terrifying August day.

When something like normality had been restored a commission was sent to Campania to report; but there was nothing to be done. Herculaneum and many of the villas of the coast along the foot of Vesuvius had vanished from sight beneath an engulfing torrent of volcanic mud, washed down the mountainside by the torrential rains that accompanied the eruption. Pompeii and Stabiae were slightly better off in that the upper parts of many of the taller buildings were still visible above the mantle of ash. Here it was at least possible to do some salvage. The Forum area was ransacked for its bronze statues and its fine building materials, and many houseowners – and others – grubbed their way down into the houses, hunting for strong boxes and caches of valuables. But the town was beyond resurrection. The survivors drifted away or were settled elsewhere and, as has happened many times in Campanian history, nature took over and what had been Pompeii became once more rich agricultural land. The knowledge that there had once been a town here lingered on in folk memory: in the eighteenth century the area was still known as Città (*civitas*, or 'city'). But as far as the learned world was concerned Pompeii, like Herculaneum, had been wiped off the map and had laboriously to be rediscovered.

The eruption of Vesuvius in 1879.

The town: government and people

A great deal of our information about life in Pompeii is derived from inscriptions. In addition to the ordinary everyday uses of writing that distinguish any advanced society, the Romans seem to have had a strong portion of the common human passion for self-commemoration. Three main categories of inscriptions may be distinguished. One is that of formal monumental epigraphy on stone or bronze, ranging from long, elaborate, formal texts down to the simple tombstones of the domestic slave and his family. To this category belong dedications to divinities and records of religious events (Nos. 202, 205, 206); inscriptions in honour of members of the Imperial family and distinguished citizens (No. 47); building inscriptions (Nos. 14, 15, 229) and funerary inscriptions (No. 30). A second category is that of the inscriptions used in commerce and private life to denote the source of ownership of certain goods, or to facilitate accounting. These might be an integral part of the object inscribed, as were the maker's stamps on many sorts of pottery or lamps (Nos. 106–108), or they might be scratched or painted on the object, as frequently for example on silver ware or the painted tally marks on amphoras. A third group, in which by the circumstances of its destruction Pompeii is unusually rich, is that of *graffiti* (literally 'scratches'), a term which may be used to denote any sort of ephemeral sign or text scratched or painted on plaster or other appropriate surfaces. Many of these are the work of the inevitable idle scribbler, but a very unusual and important group consists of electoral posters painted on the fronts of the houses of the candidates or their supporters (see page 41). The evidence is not evenly spread: for the final period of the city we have a great deal of electoral propaganda, but few formal inscriptions setting out the names and careers of the successful candidates. Even so, as a Who's Who to the personalities of local politics it remains an invaluable source of information.

Another unusual group of inscriptions is that of the *tabulae ceratae*, the wax-surfaced wooden tablets upon which a local banker, Lucius Caecilius Jucundus, kept his business records. These were buried in the earthquake of 62 and never recovered; and not only do they throw light on aspects of contemporary life about which we normally hear very little, but they tell us a lot about the people involved. Because of the rigid rules of precedence prevailing in Roman society, even a list of witnesses can be an eloquent document.

Most of these inscriptions record the names of individuals, a great many of them in some public capacity, and to understand their significance it will be helpful at this point to glance briefly at the Roman rules governing the use of names, which fortunately for us were remarkably precise. By the end of the Republic it was standard practice for a Roman citizen to bear three names. Thus the full name of the most distinguished citizen of Augustan Pompeii was M(arcus) Holconius M(arci) f(ilius) Rufus. His middle name, Holconius, was that of the *gens*, the family of which he was a member, the equivalent of a modern surname. His first name (*praenomen*) was given to him at birth, and in normal Roman practice it was written in abbreviated form (A. for Aulus, L. for Lucius, Gn. for Gnaeus, etc.) and in official documents a man would normally also give his father's *praenomen*, which in the case of Holconius Rufus was the same as his own. In early Republican times two names had sufficed; but a developed society can only carry a limited number of plain John Smiths, and quite early it became the practice in aristocratic circles to add a third name, or *cognomen*, a practice which spread steadily down the social scale to all levels of citizen society. These *cognomina*, when first adopted, were very commonly descriptive (*Ahenobarbus*, 'Brazenbeard'; *Calvus*, 'Baldhead'; *Faventinus*, 'from Faventia' (modern Faenza), but they very soon became conventional names which ran in families. M. Holconius Rufus ('Redhead') was no more necessarily himself red-headed than his brother Celer ('Swift') was fast-moving. To his friends he was probably known as Rufus, although on this point there were no hard and fast rules. Cicero was M. Tullius Cicero, but Pliny the Elder was Caius Plinius Secundus, while his nephew on his sister's side, Publius Caecilius Secundus, whom he adopted, became Caius Plinius Caecilius Secundus, (taking on his adopted father's family name but retaining his own (Caecilius) as a *cognomen*).

Women used a simpler form of the same system, usually at this period just their family name together with that of the father or husband whose legal dependents they were, while household slaves carried a single name, which was normally Greek, a convention which reflects the fact that the overwhelming majority of such slaves were of Greek-speaking extraction. Slaves, it must be remembered, were members of the family. If they were given their freedom (see below) they took their former master's name and forename, usually retaining their own slave name as a *cognomen*. A hypothetical slave of M. Holconius Rufus, named Narcissus, would have become officially M. Holconius M(arci) l(ibertus = freedman) Narcissus, whereas the son of the latter would have been (say) M. Holconius M. f(ilius) Primus, born free and from his name indistinguishable from any other free-born citizen. There were innumerable possible nuances of the system, and with the passage of time names tended to become more complex and many fresh names came into circulation. But down to AD 79 the main rules still broadly applied.

From the inscriptions we learn that M. Holconius Rufus had been a *duovir* of the colony five times (the fourth time in 2/1 BC) and *quinquennalis* twice; he was a *flamen Caesaris Augusti*; he was

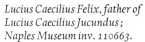

Lucius Caecilius Felix, father of
Lucius Caecilius Jucundus;
Naples Museum inv. 110663.

Marcus Holconius Rufus.
Naples Museum inv. 6233.

fessions were ineligible (an odd list, including innkeepers, auctioneers, comedy actors, gravediggers, gladiators, trainers) and others (shopkeepers and small traders) only eligible under conditions that at this date would have been prohibitive; tenure was for life, unless a holder was specifically disqualified for some breach of the conditions; and – a very important provision – there was a high property qualification. A decurion, and *a fortiori* a magistrate, was expected to spend money on the community. The *ordo* in effect constituted a moneyed municipal aristocracy, and as long as money was plentiful membership was a valued privilege. It was a Roman senate in miniature, but – as Cicero remarks to a friend who had asked his support in getting his stepson appointed to the *ordo* of Pompeii – it was rather harder to get into.

The senior elected magistrates were a pair of *duoviri*, who between them presided over the meetings of the *ordo*, handled all important financial business and administered local justice. Amongst other privileges certain senior priesthoods were reserved for members of the duoviral families, and a magistrate with good connections at the imperial court might aspire to the honorary but prestigious position of *patronus*. The *duoviri* were supported by a pair of junior magistrates, aediles, who dealt with such day-to-day administrative matters as the maintenance of streets and public buildings, the management of markets, and the issue of licences and permits. These were young men at the beginning of their careers, and since election to a magistracy carried with it membership of the *ordo*, there was no shortage of candidates. Every five years the *duoviri* had special powers and were known as *quinquennales*, with the special task of carrying out a municipal census and of reviewing the qualifications of the members of the *ordo*. This last power must have greatly reinforced the tendency for municipal power to fall into the hands of a small self-perpetuating group of wealthy families. Only if things went badly wrong was central authority (i.e. from the time of Augustus onwards, the emperor) likely to intervene. A properly qualified newcomer could in theory seek popular election, but in practice the only sure access was through marriage or adoption into the ruling families and the best key to that door was wealth.

The magistrates were elected annually by the whole body of free citizens, who were for the purpose divided into voting districts. As the electoral propaganda shows (most of it admittedly from the last period of the town's history, when the hold of the old families had largely broken down) this was a duty which the population entered into with gusto; and while many of the supporters were no doubt simply friends, neighbours and clients of the candidates, others were organized bodies which may be presumed to have had a serious economic

an official patron of the colony; and he was one of the three known Pompeians to have been appointed a *tribunus militum a populo*, an honorary office which gave him equestrian rank in Rome, a position of privilege second only to senatorial rank. Together with his brother, Celer, he modernized the Large Theatre after the model of the Theatre of Marcellus in Rome. This was a very distinguished municipal career. What did these titles signify, and how did the system work?

When a Roman colony was founded it was given its own written constitution and, because the Romans were an orderly-minded people, such constitutions tended to follow a broadly uniform pattern, with relatively minor variations to meet special local circumstances. There is no direct record of the law with which in 80 BC Sulla established the Colonia Cornelia Veneria Pompeianorum, but we do have fragments of several other late Republican or early Imperial constitutions, and it is evident that that of Pompeii followed conventional lines.

The colony was established initially by an official (*deductor*) who was appointed by the central government and who in this case was the dictator's relative, Publius Cornelius Sulla. His tasks included the appropriation and allocation of lands for the new settlers, the establishment of a municipal council and the appointment of the first body of magistrates. The council, a body usually of some 80–100 members, was known corporately as the *ordo decurionum* and its individual members as decurions (*decuriones*). Decurions had to be freeborn citizens; certain pro-

or social interest in the outcome. Religious associations, such as the *Isiaci* and the *Venerii*; influential trade associations, such as the fullers (*fullones*); bodies of people involved in agriculture or transport; the fishermen; the bakers; the goldsmiths; various sorts of small shopkeepers or stallholders; all of these are attested, together with a number of other groups of a less serious character – 'the draughtsplayers', 'the theatregoers', 'the late drinkers', and so on. Elections were evidently lively affairs.

There were also a number of organizations of a partly administrative, partly social or religious character (the distinction is not always an easy one to draw), which offered an outlet to citizens or other residents who were not qualified to become ordinary magistrates. It has to be remembered that there were also substantial groups of resident foreigners. But although, slave or freeborn, a man's position was rigidly defined by his civil status, this was also a surprisingly fluid society. Not only could slaves of ability rise to positions of very considerable responsibility as stewards, bailiffs, managers of large estates, and the like, but slavery was actually one of the recognized roads to social advancement. A Roman citizen had the right of bestowing freedom upon any slave who had given faithful service, a right that was freely exercised; and although a freedman, or *libertus*, was debarred from holding certain positions which called for free birth, his children born after he obtained his freedom were the equals at law of any other Roman citizen.

A great many of the domestic slaves came from the Greek-speaking east, as prisoners of war, as the victims of a flourishing slave trade along and across the frontiers, or even as children sold into slavery by their families. Many of them had natural abilities and aptitudes in fields where the Romans were by temperament and position less qualified, and by the first century AD a very high percentage of the professional and commercial skills of a town like Pompeii were in their hands, either as trusted slaves working for their masters, or else as freedmen operating on their own behalf or as agents of their former masters. Doctors, teachers, accountants, secretaries, architects, decorators, barbers, cooks; small craftsmen and tradesmen of every sort; the overseers and technicians of commerce and industry; the staffs of the city offices: by the first century AD almost all of these would have been slaves or descendants of slaves; and because of their natural ability and training, many of them were well-to-do and some of them were very wealthy. Trimalchio, the millionaire freedman of Petronius's *Satyricon*, is a caricature, but he is a caricature which everybody would have recognized as drawn from life.

It was, as we have seen, the regular practice for a freedman to adopt his former master's family name, and by the second generation it is often quite impossible to distinguish the descendants of freedmen from members of the parent family. Statistics elude us, but by AD 79 a very substantial proportion of the free urban population of Pompeii must have been descended from freedmen, and in many cases from the freedmen of freedmen. (In the countryside the proportion would have been less.) Much of the economy of the town was in their hands, and many of them were socially ambitious. The election posters of the last period include a lot of the old names, and although some of these were doubtless still the lineal descendants of the old Samnite and Roman families, a great many others were unquestionably the second- and third-generation products of this extraordinary ethnic melting pot.

For a vivid glimpse of the system at work we may turn to the inscription recording the rebuilding of the Temple of Isis after the earthquake of 62 (No. 15). The restoration was paid for by N. Popidius Celsinus, who bears the name of one of the most distinguished of the pre-Roman families of Pompeii, the Popidii. It must have cost a lot of money, at a time when the town was in serious financial difficulties, and in return the council was doubtless glad to elect him to their number. The only surprising feature is that at the time Popidius was a boy of six. The truth is, of course, that the real donor was the boy's father, N. Popidius Ampliatus, who happened to have been born a slave and who, being himself debarred from membership of the *ordo*, chose instead to buy his son's way into it. But for the eruption, Celsinus, with his family's wealth behind him, might well in due course have become the town's chief magistrate.

The case of the restoration of the Temple of Isis is obviously in some respects exceptional, but it illustrates admirably the intent behind the system. Without doing violence to the inherited Roman prejudices in favour of free birth and against most forms of direct commercial activity, a real effort was made to engage the loyalties of the socially underprivileged and to direct their energies and wealth into socially useful channels. One such outlet was in the local administration of the *vici* and *pagi*, the subdistricts into which the town and its territory were divided (see p. 65). There were bodies known as *ministri*, who were mostly freedmen, but who might include freeborn citizens and in some cases even slaves. In origin the duties of the *ministri* may have been mainly religious, but, as organized bodies, they constituted a useful peg on which to hang other local responsibilities; they carried status, and we find them contributing financially to such municipal enterprises as building and the provision of games. Another important outlet was provided by the institution of the imperial cult in the time of Augustus (see page 61). Here again, although the forms were ostensibly religious, the objectives were in reality far wider. The *Augustales* in particular were recruited from the most prominent freedmen

M HOLCONIVM
PRISCVM·II·VIR·I·D· POMARI·VNIVERSI CVM·HELVIO·VESTALE·ROG

of the community. They ranked immediately after the members of the *ordo* and, in addition to a large statutory payment on election, they were expected to use their wealth liberally on behalf of the community. In AD 79 the golden age of the *Augustales* was still to come, but even so they were already a powerful force within the community.

At Pompeii as nowhere else outside Rome we can follow the issues of local politics in terms of the individuals directly involved, the man in the street as well as the candidate for whom he voted. We must be content, however, to summarize the broad conclusions that emerge from the study of this mass of detailed information, in so far as it illustrates the history of the town during the 160 years of its existence as a Roman colony.

The first fifty years (80–31 BC), as reflected in the names of those who held municipal office or who were candidates for office, were closely influenced by the play of events elsewhere in Rome and Italy: the shifts of power and of allegiance in Rome itself following the rise of Caesar and, striking deeper and more lastingly, the break-up of the old tribal Italy and the steady emergence of a more urbanized, more broadly-based Roman Italy. In this respect the founder of the colony, P. Cornelius Sulla, seems to have acted with considerable statesmanship and foresight. Although the colony was in intention founded as a closed electoral society from which the old Samnite families were excluded, within barely a generation we find members of the latter already back in the *ordo*, and they were joined there by an increasing number of families from other parts of Campania or from the impoverished inland districts of central Italy. The pattern is a familiar one. The product of a society that was out of balance, with large sections of the population adrift socially and seeking fresh opportunities within the enduring framework of Italian geography, there are many analogies with modern times.

If the first fifty years were, therefore, a time of rather rapid change, the next sixty to seventy years were characterized by a no less remarkable stability. Towards the end of the previous period many of the newcomers seem to have been partisans of the future emperor Augustus, and with the firm establishment of central authority after his victory at Actium in 31 BC they found themselves very comfortably placed. For a couple of generations the control of Pompeii seems to have lain in the hands of the small group of closely interrelated families to which M. Holconius Rufus and his brother belonged. As large landed proprietors, with profitable outlets in wine production, the tile industry and sheep farming, much of the local economy was in their hands; their wealth is attested by the sums which they spent on buildings, games and other municipal amenities; and they had secured an almost complete monopoly of civic office. Because of their close ties with central authority – the

establishment of the imperial cult and the institution of the *Augustales* are symptomatic – it was a period during which any lingering Campanian eccentricities (for example, the use of the old Samnite weights and measures) were quietly eliminated. As the ferment of the Civil Wars settled, the processes of Romanization begun in 80 BC came to fruition. By the death of Augustus's successor, Tiberius, in AD 37, Pompeii was as fully Roman a city as were Mantua, Sulmona and Venusia (Venosa, in Apulia), the birthplaces of Vergil, Ovid and Horace.

The last forty-odd years of the city's history were by contrast a period of change and of urban crisis. The earthquake of AD 62 was a serious aggravation of a difficult situation; another must have been the loss of imperial favour after the amphitheatre riot of AD 59. But the underlying causes were political and economic. For one thing, Italy in general and Campania in particular were beginning to lose out economically to some of the developing provinces overseas; for another, the monopoly of wealth formerly exercised by the old landed classes was facing ever-increasing competition from the emergent middle class to which the wealthy freedmen belonged. Exactly how the crisis developed and on whose authority it was resolved we do not know. There are signs of imperial intervention (the normal procedure when the affairs of a municipality got out of hand) and perhaps of a temporary suspension of the normal civic institutions during the forties. It is not until after the adoption of Nero by his stepfather, the emperor Claudius, in AD 50, that we begin once more to find records of appointments to the normal magistracies and priesthoods. But from then on the record is extensive, and the message is clear. It shows that there had been an almost complete break with the recent past and with the group of families which had virtually controlled the city for more than half a century. Instead, many of the office-holders of the last period are from families with no previous political record; others are from old families which had long been excluded from office, and yet others are manifestly of freedman descent.

The monopoly of local authority by the established landed families had gone, and its place was being taken by a society in which privilege and wealth were more widely spread, but which found it difficult to fill the gap left by the withdrawal of the old, comfortable municipal paternalism. Pompeii was still a busy city, but it had fewer resources. It is no accident that in AD 79, seventeen years after the earthquake, only two major public buildings had been completely restored or that many of the fine old houses were being subdivided and converted into commercial premises. Another generation, and a great deal more of the older, wealthier Pompeii would have vanished. If it was the city's destiny to be preserved for posterity as a monument to a way of life, the eruption of 79 came just in time.

The town: planning and architecture

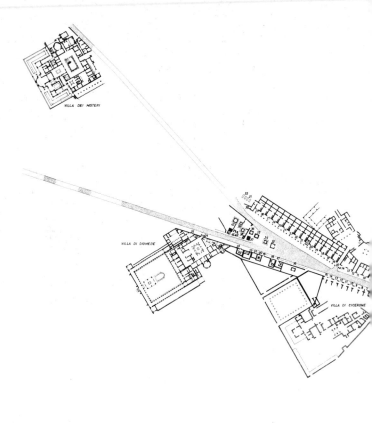

The early history of Pompeii is faithfully reflected in its town plan. The original settlement, which occupied the south-west corner of the later town, was situated on a spur of higher ground, projecting from the lower slopes of Vesuvius and looking out over the mouth of the river Sarno and the Bay of Naples. It was defended by a circuit of walls which on the south and west sides followed the cliffs above the river mouth, and which on the land-ward side faced out across the saddle that carried the coast road from Naples towards Stabiae and the Sorrento peninsula, following a curving line still clearly visible in the street plan of the later town. Within this circuit the early town was laid out on orderly, though not mathematically precise, lines. Of the early buildings, the positions of two can be established: the sanctuary of Apollo, which lay beside the reserved open space which was later to become the Forum, and that of Hercules (?), finely situated on a rocky spur which projected south-eastwards above the river (later the 'Triangular Forum'), possibly outside the city walls. This early settlement covered some twenty-four acres, and the population is estimated at about 2000 to 2500 people.

With its command of local land and river traffic and its ready access to the sea, the settlement prospered and grew rapidly, and in the fifth century BC it was greatly enlarged northwards and eastwards, within a new circuit of defensive walls enclosing a roughly oval area of some 160 acres. These walls, several times strengthened and repaired, were to remain the effective boundary of the city throughout its subsequent history: any subsequent expansion (and the inscriptions and excavation confirm that there was such expansion) was into suburban areas outside the gates.

The new town was laid out in the Greek manner. This consisted ideally of long, narrow, rectangular residential blocks separated by narrow access-streets (*stenōpoi*) running at right-angles to the main traffic avenues (*plateai*), and it can be seen at its simplest and most orthodox in the area south of the Via dell'Abbondanza, towards the Amphitheatre. Elsewhere there are many irregularities of layout, but all of them make good sense as a rationalization of the already existing road-system outside the walls of the early settlement: the main coast road running south-eastwards from the Herculaneum Gate and down the well-marked valley that led to the Stabian Gate; and, radiating outwards, a web of roads heading for Naples and Herculaneum, the farms on the slopes of Vesuvius, Nola, and Stabiae and Nuceria. With a little tidying-up at important intersections, it is all there, a classic instance of an orderly planning system superimposed upon an existing topographical situation in such a way as to cause a minimum of disruption to established suburban street frontages and property rights.

The original settlement at Pompeii.

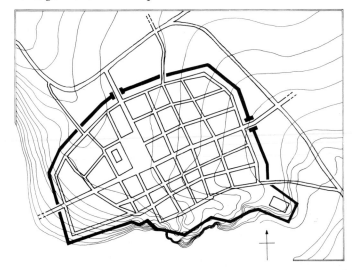

Aerial view of the Forum from the south, showing also the houses terraced out over the town walls.

The Forum

1. Temple of Jupiter.
2. Provisions market (Macellum).
3. Sanctuary of the City Lares.
4. Temple of Vespasian.
5. Cloth traders hall (Eurnachia Building).
6. Voting hall (comitium).
7. Chief magistrates' (duovirs') office.
8. Council chamber.
9. Junior magistrates' (aediles') office.
10. Basilica.
11. Temple of Apollo.
12. Control of weights and measures.
13. Cereals market.
14. Commemorative arches.

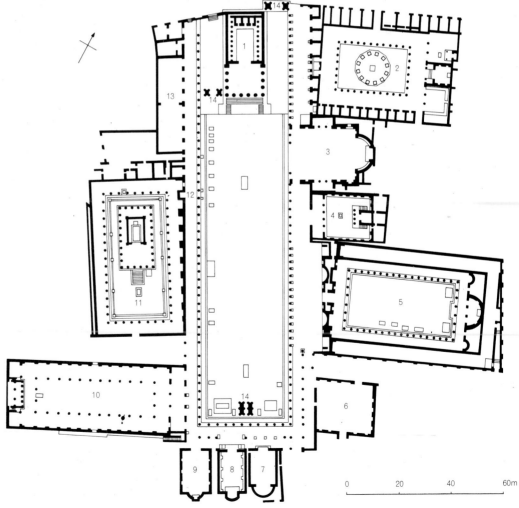

Pompeii

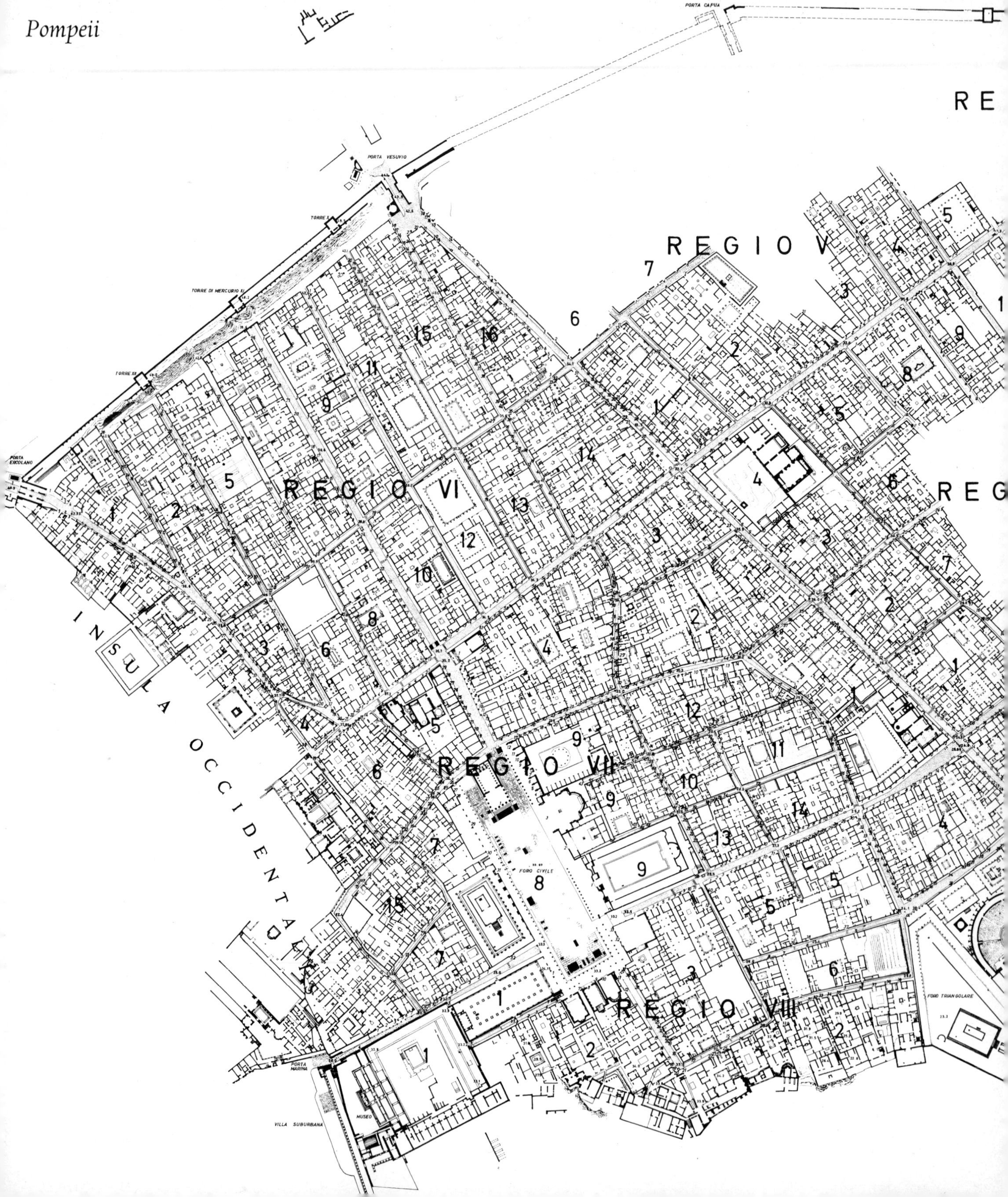

PORTA CAPUA

PORTA VESUVIO

R E

REGIO V

REGIO VI

PORTA ERCOLANO

INSULA OCCIDENTALE

REG

REGIO VII

FORO CIVILE

REGIO VIII

FORO TRIANGOLARE

PORTA MARINA

VILLA SUBURBANA

MUSEO

TORRE DI MERCURIO

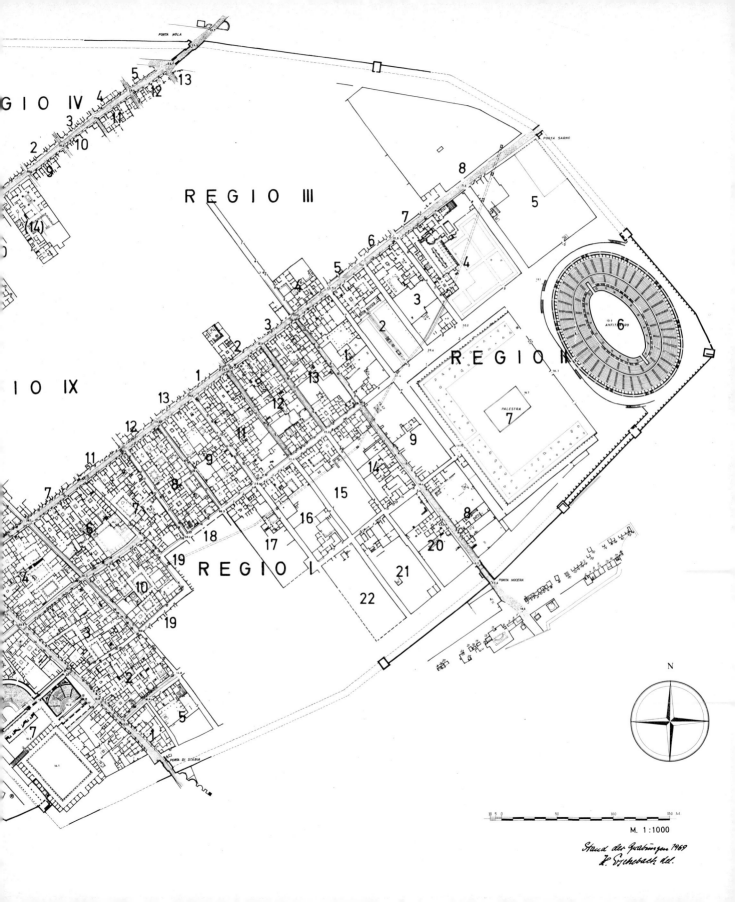

REGIO IV

PORTA NOLA

5
13
4
12
3
11
2
10
9
(14)

REGIO III

PORTA SARNO

8
5

7
6
4
5
3
4
2
3
2
1

REGIO IX

REGIO II

ANFITEATRO
6

PALESTRA
7

3
2
1
13
12
11
9
8

13
12
11
9
8
7
6

18
19
17
16
15
14
9

21
20
8

22

PORTA NOCERA

REGIO I

4
10
19
3
2
5
7
1

PORTA DI STABIA

N

10 5 0   50   100   150 M.
M. 1:1000

Stand der Grabungen 1969
L. Eschebach del.

1. Forum.
2. Temple of Venus.
3. Forum Baths.
4. House of the Tragic Poet.
5. House of Sallust.
6. Villa of Diomedes.
7. Villa of the Mysteries.

8. Temple of Fortuna Augusta.
9. House of the Faun.
10. Insula VI, 13.
11. House of the Vettii.
12. House of the Gilded Amorini.
13. Fullery.
14. House of the Silver Wedding.

15. Central Baths.
16. House of the Centenary.
17. Bakery of Modestus.
18. Stabian Baths.
19. Temple of Isis.
20. Theatres (see p. 62).
21. House of the Menander.

22. Caupona of Euxinus.
23. House of the Ship 'Europa'.
24. House of Julius Polybius.
25. House of Pinarius Cerialis.
26. House of 'Loreius Tiburtinus'.
27. 'Praedia' Julia Felix.
28. Palaestra.

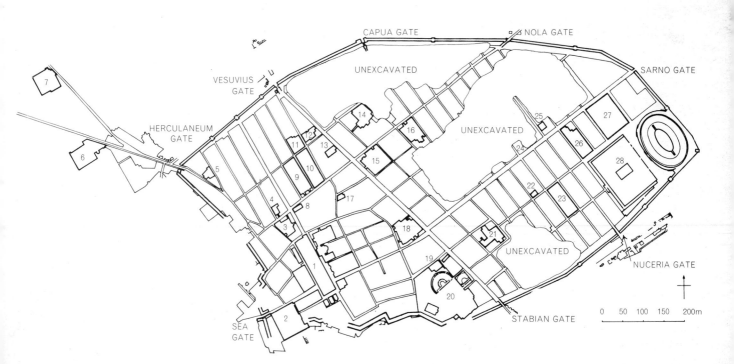

Of the architecture of the earliest town we have little more than the scanty remains of the two Greek temples, including the platform of one of them and a selection of the gaily-painted terracotta architectural ornament which once covered the superstructures of both. The earliest substantial surviving structures belong to the turn of the fourth and third centuries BC, and it is not really until the last century of Samnite rule, in the second century BC, that we begin to get any coherent picture of the town as such. At this time there was still plenty of room: among the several wealthy houses of the period still standing in AD 79 was the House of the Faun, which occupied an area of some six acres, covering a whole city block. During this period there was also a lot of public building. The Forum was enlarged and monumentalized by the addition of enclosing porticoes; at the north end it was dominated by a large, upstanding temple of Jupiter, and off the south-west corner there now opened a grandiose new basilica. To this same period belong also the first bath buildings of the new Roman type, the Large Theatre in its original form, the elegant Doric colonnades of the Triangular Forum and, very probably, the predecessors of such later temples as those of Venus, of Zeus Meilichios, and of Isis. Typical of this late Samnite-period architecture are the use of the brown tufa stone of Nocera, especially for house frontages, and of the First Style ('Masonry Style') painted stucco ornament to cover all the more important interior wall surfaces.

Although the establishment of the Sullan colony in 80 BC was achieved without any radical change to the existing urban structure, it was, as one would expect, followed by considerable building activity. The city walls were repaired; the temple at the head of the Forum was rebuilt and rededicated in honour of the Roman Capitoline triad, Jupiter, Juno and Minerva; the Stabian Baths were enlarged and modernized; and a number of new public buildings were erected, including a smaller, covered theatre (*theatrum tectum*) beside the existing open-air theatre, an amphitheatre (inaugurated in 70 BC) and a second public bath building, near the Forum. The list is an interesting one, illustrating as it does not only the initial contribution of the new colonists, but also their rapid assimilation to local ways. For all its top-dressing of Roman colonial forms, Pompeii was still a Campanian city.

Full Romanization came only under Augustus and his immediate successors, a process neatly symbolized by the formal adoption of the Roman system of weights and measures in place of the old Sabellian system, which the Sullan colony had retained. Once again, however, it was a process of organic development and mutual assimilation within the existing framework rather than one of radical change. The Forum was progressively modernized by the addition of a meat and fish market (*macellum*),

a group of city offices, and a voting precinct; by the construction of the 'Eumachia Building' by the patroness of the most powerful of the city's trade associations, the wool merchants; and by the rebuilding in limestone of the Forum porticoes – this last still in progress at the time of the earthquake of AD 62. Other major public works of this period include provision for the newly-established imperial cult; the creation of a huge exercise ground (*palaestra*) near the Amphitheatre; an elaborate remodelling of the old Samnite-period theatre, undertaken by the wealthy brothers Holconius (see p. 38-39) in conscious imitation of the Augustan Theatre of Marcellus in Rome; and by the building of an aqueduct and a city-wide system of public water points. To this same period, between 80 BC and the middle of the first century AD, belong most of the large private houses, with their elaborate schemes of Second and Third Style painted decoration. Both in the public and the private sector, this was a time of great and varied architectural activity.

By contrast, the last thirty years before the eruption were a time of economic stress and of gathering urban crisis. After the earthquake many of the large private houses were abandoned as residences; seventeen years later only two public monuments (the Amphitheatre and the Temple of Isis) had been completely restored and there was little or no new public building. In 79 the Forum was a vast builder's yard, and even the water supply was still under repair. Of the few exceptions, the building usually identified as a public *lararium*, in honour of the city's protecting divinities, and the small temple in honour of Vespasian, could both have been considered necessary acts of propitiation towards religious and secular authority, following the disaster of AD 62. The only major new project of a utilitarian nature was a large new bath building, the Central Baths, still incomplete in AD 79.

In its use of building materials and constructional techniques the architecture of Pompeii lies rather on the fringes than at the centre of contemporary Italian building history – rather surprisingly so when one considers that the event which changed the face of classical architecture, the discovery of the unique properties of the mortar based on the volcanic sand of west central Italy, took place little more than 20 miles away, at Puteoli (Pozzuoli), and that some of the outstanding early manifestations of its use are still to be seen at Baiae. At Pompeii there was evidently a considerable prejudice in favour of the familiar Greek constructional traditions still to be overcome. It was only in such frankly innovating building types as the amphitheatre and the bath building that the arch and the vault (the forms in which the new Roman 'concrete' found its ideal expression) could be used freely and explicitly without doing violence to the conventions of established monumental taste. Viewed in context, the amphitheatre in particular appears as one of the outstanding early examples of the emergence of an architectural aesthetic based on the candid exploitation of the visual properties of the arch. At the time this was something quite new in classical architecture.

Another conspicuous innovation, in this case well represented at Pompeii, was the emergence during the last two centuries BC of a number of the new building types that were to figure so prominently in the later history of Roman architecture. Pompeii, though surely not a major creative centre in its own right, was in this respect right in the mainstream of progressive architectural thinking. The stone-built Amphitheatre, the upstanding, Roman-type theatre, the Basilica, the bath building, the market building with a circular pavilion of the type here represented beside the Forum: all of these important and distinctive architectural types seem first to have taken monumental shape in southern Italy rather than in Rome itself, and to have been products of the new social needs and opportunities created by Roman wealth and power operating within a setting of sophisticated local building skills and technical know-how. Although the amphitheatre as an institution came from central Italy, Rome itself did not have a permanent amphitheatre building until 29 BC; the first permanent theatre in the capital dates from 55 BC, and the first public bath building not before 19 BC. There had been a basilica, the Basilica Porcia, beside the Roman Forum as early as 184 BC; but even in this case there is good reason to believe that the prototype came from South Italy, and the Basilica beside the Forum at Pompeii is the earliest example surviving anywhere. In this respect Campania during the second and first centuries BC was fertile soil, and by the accident of its preservation Pompeii offers us a unique vision of Imperial Roman architecture in the making.

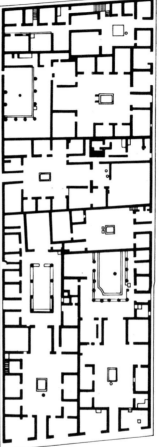

A typical residential insula (city block) VI, 13.

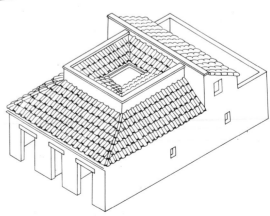

Restored view of an early atrium house.

The Pompeian house and garden

No survey of the art of Pompeii can be complete without some knowledge of the wealthy houses in which so much of it found its natural place. Buildings such as the House of the Faun, the House of the Menander, and the House of the Vettii figured as prominently in the local artistic life of their time as they do today in the itinerary of the modern visitor. They were not, of course, the only type of urban dwelling. There were many small, simpler family houses; there were modest upper-storey apartments, particularly in the later period; and there were one-room or two-room *tabernae* which opened directly off the street, and which served both as workshops and as living quarters for the poorest families. But, given the family-centred nature of traditional Italic society, the large, well-to-do houses did in fact bulk far larger than their equivalents would do in any advanced modern society, or indeed in the later urban architecture of Rome itself; the owners of these houses constituted the major source of patronage for local artistic enterprise.

As an architectural form the Pompeian house was very much a phenomenon of its age and place, occupying a midway position between the great hall of archaic Italic practice and the luxurious town residences of the wealthy Roman families of the Imperial age. Like any such term, 'the Pompeian house' represents an abstraction, a convenient label for a page of architectural history torn from what was in fact a continuously developing historical

narrative: but the use of this term may be justified by the strong element of formal continuity that runs right through the three centuries and more separating the earliest from the latest surviving examples. It does, moreover, greatly simplify description. Although by the end of the period the names and functions of some of the rooms were changing or had become obselete (as in our own times such names as 'parlour', 'powder room' or 'cloak-room'), it is still broadly possible to use the same terminology to describe the individual members of the whole series.

As late as the early second century BC a typical Pompeian atrium house such as the House of Sallust (VI, 2, 4) was still essentially an inward-facing building, enclosed by bare walls and lit almost exclusively from within. The dominant feature of the plan was a large centrally-lit hall, the *atrium*, the roof of which might in earlier times still have taken on one of the several forms described by later writers, although by the second century BC it seems invariably to have been of 'compluviate' form, sloping downwards and inwards towards a rectangular opening (*compluvium*) situated above a rectangular basin (*impluvium*), so as to admit more light and at the same time to replenish the cisterns which were the house's principal water supply.

Grouped around the atrium were the other rooms of the house. The entrance was originally set back within an entrance porch (*vestibulum*) beyond which lay a short corridor (*fauces*). To

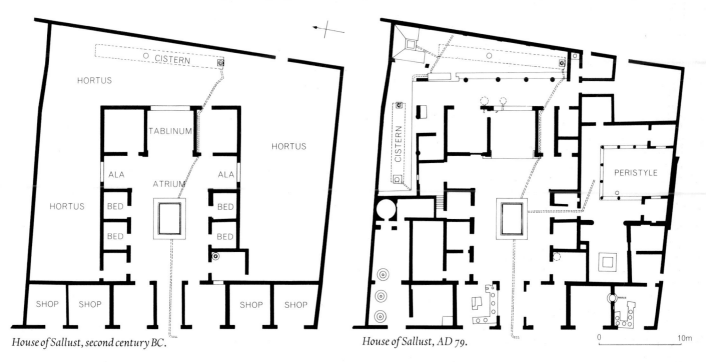

House of Sallust, second century BC.

House of Sallust, AD 79.

0   10m

Atrium in the House of the Silver Wedding.

can conveniently be summarized in terms of what was clearly felt to be a normal type.

The most important single innovation was a direct result of the ever-increasing exposure of Campania to the sophisticated civilizations of the Hellenistic world, where the standard type of wealthy house was one built around a rectangular, cloister-like, colonnaded courtyard, known as the peristyle. These Hellenistic contacts made themselves felt at every level, notably in the character and wealth of the architectural detail and in the transformation of the old cavernous atrium by the incorporation of columnar supports for the central opening, at first four columns and later whole colonnades, until in extreme cases it came to resemble a miniature peristyle. But the most dramatic and far-reaching innovation was unquestionably the conversion of the old garden area beyond the house into a formal peristyle complex, accessible from the atrium by a corridor or corridors leading past the *tablinum*, which itself tended also to be opened up towards the peristyle.

For much of the year the rooms around the peristyle offered far more agreeable living conditions than the small, rather cramped rooms around the atrium, and there was an inevitable tendency for the main living rooms to migrate outwards. One recurrent form, known as an *oecus* (a Greek name, which suggests that it was introduced in the same context as the peristyle itself), was an elaborately decorated room open towards the portico and often used as a fair-weather dining room. Another common innovation was the introduction of a private bath suite; yet another, wherever the slope of the ground involved a measure of terracing, was the introduction of a cryptoportico, a long, narrow, vaulted chamber or chambers, lit obliquely from above and useful for storage, or even as a hot-weather residential amenity. Above ground the open area of the peristyle was regularly equipped with fountains and pools, and with formal gardens in which plants and trees alternated with statuary and garden furniture.

The atrium-peristyle house needed plenty of space, and in the second century BC most of the wealthy householders could still achieve this by building out over their existing gardens. But in parts of the town one can already detect signs of what was to be a growing problem, that of increased population pressures and rising property values. Galleries and upper stories began to be added along the facade and around the atrium and, as street frontages became more valuable, more and more of the service rooms on either side of the main entrance were converted into independent single-room shops (*tabernae*) opening directly off the street, just as has happened to the frontages of so many of the palaces of post-mediaeval Italy, and for identical reasons.

A third and more insidious change was inspired by the villas of

right and left were service rooms (in the House of Sallust their place was already taken by shops facing outwards on to the street), and along the two longer sides of the atrium itself a series of small, square bedchambers (*cubicula*), in which the position of the couch was usually marked by the pattern of the floor and often also by the shape of the ceiling. Along the fourth side two lateral wings (*alae*) extended outwards, giving access to a range of rather larger rooms. In the centre, opposite the entrance and structurally open towards the main hall, from which it could be closed off by a wooden screen or a curtain, lay the *tablinum*. This was the principal reception room of the house and, unlike most of the other rooms, it was often lit by a window, which opened on to the garden plot (*hortus*) beyond. Of the two rooms on either side of it, one was often used as a dining room or *triclinium*, so named from the □-shaped arrangement of three couches (*klinai*) which constituted the normal dining pattern in classical times, and like the *cubicula* often identifiable from the layout of the floor-patterns. Within the atrium one would have looked for such features as the family strong-box and the household shrine (*lararium*). Furnishing was by modern standards scanty, but it might include wooden couches and cupboards and small tables of wood or later of marble, as well as wooden doorways and screens. After dark the rooms were lit by means of oil lamps, often on tall bronze stands, and they were heated by braziers of bronze, iron and terracotta.

This was the basic pattern of the atrium house, and with the passage of time it was developed and elaborated in a number of ways. The precise forms and layouts of such development obviously depended upon the particular circumstances of each house in relation to its neighbours, but once again the process

House of the Tragic Poet (VI, 8, 3)
an early peristyle plan.

1. Shops.
2. Fauces.
3. Atrium.
4. Bedrooms.
5. Ala.

6. Tablinum.
7. Oecus.
8. Peristyle garden.
9. Lararium.

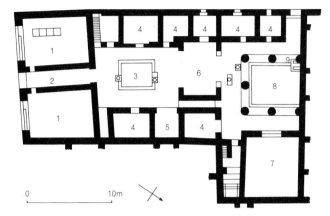

0   10m

House of the Vettii, (VI, 15, 1)
a late peristyle plan.

1. Vestibule.
2. Atrium.
3. Staircase to upper storey.
4. Kitchen.
5. Dining room (triclinium).

6. Dining room (triclinium, 'Pentheus room').
7. Peristyle garden.
8. Oecus.
9. Small peristyle.
10. Dining room/sitting room.
11. Bedroom.

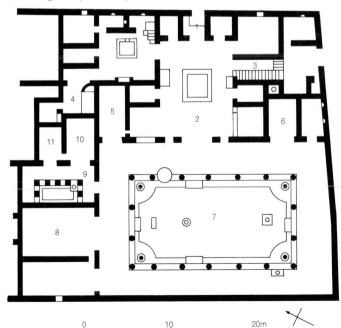

0   10   20m

the contemporary countryside. One of the more attractive aspects of Roman culture was its appreciation of natural beauty and of landscape. The town houses perforce looked inwards towards their gardens, but by the second century BC it was already customary among well-to-do Romans also to maintain a country house (*villa*) – or indeed several of them. Although these were normally working farms (*villae rusticae*), many of them were also equipped to serve as occasional residences, and we regularly find these villas situated and designed so as to take full advantage of their setting, with terraces and garden rooms facing outwards over the adjoining landscape. Within the towns scope for such development was obviously limited, but both at Pompeii and at Herculaneum we do in the later period find a number of fine houses terraced out over the walls so as to take full advantage of the views over the Bay of Naples, and during the first century BC the seaward facade of the Villa of the Mysteries was remodelled in the same sense. In practical terms, this opening-up of the house was greatly facilitated by the widespread introduction of window glass, and although its full effects would not be felt in urban architecture until after AD 79, it was already a factor in the later planning of Pompeii.

The villas on the slopes of Vesuvius, at Boscoreale for example, and at Boscotrecase, were of the sort described, centres of working estates which were also residences. But there were also the *villae marittimae*, the luxurious seaside residences which studded

Peristyle garden in the House of the Gilded Amorini (VI, 16, 7).

49

the coastline of the Bay of Naples ever since, in the first century BC, Campania had become the preferred playground of the wealthy Roman. Inevitably their proximity affected standards of luxury and taste in the neighbouring towns. Moreover, they were picked up by the painters of the Third Style wall paintings and used as one of the stock subjects for the smaller secondary panels of their large wall compositions. The seaside villa landscapes which one sees on the walls of a house such as that of Marcus Lucretius Fronto (illus. below) were *genre* pieces, but it was a *genre* rooted in actuality. Waterside villa platforms, jetties, harbours, single-storied or two-storied colonnaded facades with projecting wings or outcurving *belvedere* rooms, towers and balconies, temples and rustic shrines, grottoes, fountains and statues: these were the commonplaces of a landscaped architecture as rich in contrived fantasy as any eighteenth-century English park. One of the sources of such paintings was undoubtedly a real, three-dimensional, luxury architecture, which itself owed much to what was obviously a very widely felt contemporary taste for romantic landscape – a taste which turns up again in the so-called 'sacro-idyllic' landscapes (e.g. No. 9) and again in the conventions of the popular Egyptianizing 'Nilotic' idiom. In painting we meet it already in the mythological land-scapes of the late Second and early Third Styles of painting – the same trees and rocky outcrops, the same grottoes, the same towers, the same rustic shrines. Whatever the ultimate source of the individual motifs, these were all very much part of a contemporary Roman artistic fashion which affected architecture and painting alike.

Finally, a word about the gardens. In origin no doubt these were simply those parts of the individual building plots which were left over after the building of the houses, and which were planted with fruit and vegetables for domestic consumption. In AD 79 there were still, behind the built-up street frontages, surprisingly large areas of open green, notably within the south-eastern perimeter of the city, on either side of the Amphitheatre and the Palaestra (which had no doubt been sited here because of the available open space). Here, as recent excavation behind the House of the Ship Europa (I, 15, 1) has shown, there were large stretches of market garden, in which vegetables were combined (as they still are in Campania today) with orderly rows of fruit trees and areas for bedding out young plants; there was also at least one sizeable vineyard, in the block immediately north of the Amphitheatre.

With time, however, and in the more densely populated

Seaside villa landscape, in the House of Marcus Lucretius Fronto.

Market garden in the House of the Ship 'Europa' (I, 15, 1) Small dots indicate grapevine roots; black circles indicate roots of various sizes; empty circles indicate plants in pots.
1. Vegetable gardens.
2. Path.
3. Water cistern.

0   10m

The upper garden terrace in the house of 'Loreius Tiburtinus'; at the far end is the open-air dining-room.

quarters, there was an inevitable tendency for the garden to be absorbed within the architectural complex of the house itself. At one extreme were small, tree-planted courtyards, areas of shaded green upon which the occupants of the *tablinum* and the *triclinium* could look out: this was the logical development of the old Italic *hortus*. And at the other extreme, from the second century BC onwards and, it seems, like the peristyle itself a newcomer from the Hellenistic east, we have the sort of highly organized, formal garden which one finds in the peristyle court-yards of such buildings as the House of the Vettii and the House of the Gilded Amorini.

It has long been known that these gardens were lavishly planted with trees and shrubs, and recent work is beginning to tell us a great deal not only about the layouts but also about the actual plants used. Not surprisingly, these included a great many of those still familiar in Campania today: olives, lemons, soft fruits, pomegranates, walnuts and filberts, chestnuts, and vines grown on trellises. Vegetables leave fewer traces that are readily identifiable, but here we have the evidence of wall painting and, most recently, a beginning of the results of the analysis of pollen remains. Paintings such as the garden room at Prima Porta (page 70) show that there were also cultivated garden flowers, but not it seems on any very substantial scale.

Perhaps the most surprising result of recent work is to show how large many of the trees were. Modern replanting has tended to follow the model of the later 'Italian' garden, with low trimmed hedges and shrubs; and in the formal peristyle gardens, where the plants were a setting for fountains and statuary, something of the sort might indeed seem reasonable. But many of the smaller, courtyard gardens evidently followed simpler, more luxuriant patterns, including substantial trees. This has been demonstrated in the recently-excavated House of Julius Polybius (IX, 13, 1–3), and also at Oplontis (see No. 338).

Within the town there was little room for landscaping: that had to be left to the villas of the seaside and the suburbs. But we do get a glimpse of it in the garden of the House of 'Loreius Tiburtinus' (II, 1, 2), which sloped downhill from the Via dell'-Abbondanza towards the open ground within the southern walls. Here the whole rear frontage of the house opened on to a transverse terrace, with a marble-lined water channel and a trellised pergola. At the east end of this terrace there was an open-air dining room, while a fountain in the middle dropped its water into a second, architecturally embellished water chan-nel which ran down the length of the garden. Terrace and fountain basins were adorned with statuary, while serried lines of trees carried the eye down the garden towards the view across the Sarno plain and the mountains of the Sorrento penin-sula beyond – a fine example of a studied formal design used to emphasize the beauties of natural landscape.

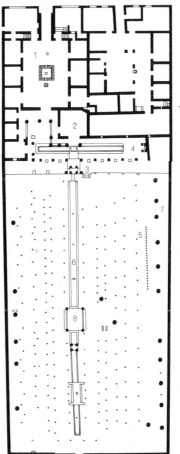

Plan of the House of 'Loreius Tiburtinus'.

1. Atrium.
2. Oecus.
3. Peristyle garden terrace.
4. Open air dining area.
5. Line of plants in pots.
6. Ornamental water channel.
7. Large trees.
8. Small pavilion.

0   10   20m

The economy: agriculture and industry

Dionysus and Vesuvius. Naples Museum.

The economy of Pompeii was based primarily on two factors: the boundless fertility of the Campanian soil and the town's position as the harbour for the whole area south and east of Vesuvius. Although industry was mainly geared to local needs, the proximity of large numbers of wealthy seaside villas must at the same time have furnished a steady market for surplus produce, for everyday tools and equipment, and for building materials. In addition to these local possibilities, Campanian prominence in the markets of the eastern Mediterranean offered rich outlets for spare capital, as well as numerous fringe opportunities for the smaller operators in which this region has always abounded and still abounds.

Fruits and vegetables of almost all sorts familiar in the area today (except, of course, for such post-Roman intruders as the potato and the tomato) are attested in the wall paintings and in many cases by the organic remains recovered during the recent excavations. In these, as in grain and other market produce, the city would have been self-sufficient. But the two outstanding agricultural products were undoubtedly wine and olive oil. Both of these, particularly the former, were widely exported, and they must between them have furnished a high percentage of the wealth of the rich landed families. Large numbers of wine amphoras have been found in southern France bearing the name of two of the prominent indigenous families, the Lassii and the Eumachii. Another of the leading local families, the Holconii, gave its name to a special quality of vine, while another prized vine was known simply as the Pompeian Vine (*vitis pompeiana*). The best known local wines came from the Sorrento peninsula and from Vesuvius; those of Pompeii itself were said to leave a

hangover. The only surviving ancient picture of Vesuvius, from the household shrine of the House of the Centenary (see illus., left), does portray the god of wine, Dionysus, decked with grapes, and beyond him the lower slopes of the mountain covered with trellised vines; and the remains of the villas recovered on these slopes, like those of Boscoreale and Boscotrecase (see plan, right), show that they were not only the occasional residences of their rich owners but also the centres of working estates, equipped with all facilities for pressing wine and oil. Even within the city, excavation has recently revealed small vineyards, and the huge oil-storage jars are everywhere a familiar feature.

The one major exception to this predominantly agricultural, or agriculture-oriented, economy was the production of woollen goods. The wool was produced in the highlands of Samnium and Lucania, where some of the indigenous families still had ties and where many wealthy Romans had acquired large absentee estates. The family of M. Numistrius Fronto, for example, who was chief magistrate (*duovir*) in AD 2/3, evidently came from Numistro in northern Lucania (Muro Lucano, near Potenza) in the heart of the sheep-rearing country; and it was his widow, Eumachia, the heiress to a big local family, who built the large courtyard building near the south-east corner of the Forum to serve as the headquarters of the trade association (*collegium*) of the wool-traders and fullers. It was used among other things as a cloth market, and periodic auctions of raw wool were held in the forecourt, towards the Forum. The continuing importance of this woollen industry even after the earthquake of AD 62 is shown by the number of fulleries (*fullonicae*) that have been found in the city, some of them installed in what had previously been well-to-do private residences. The election posters too reveal the members of the association of fullers as active and influential supporters of the candidates for municipal office.

The same election posters give us the names of a great many other trade associations, and these confirm the impression left by the excavated remains, namely that within Pompeii commerce was geared very largely to local needs. The associations named include agricultural labourers and smallholders, men engaged in various types of transport, dealers in poultry, fruit and vegetables, fishermen, bakers, goldsmiths. The list is not exhaustive – there is no mention, for example, of the important building and decorating trades – but it helps us to people the markets and the small one-room workshops in which, in the immemorial Mediterranean manner, many of them earned their livelihoods. A few local specialities went further afield. Cato, who farmed in northern Campania, advises sending to Pompeii for oil mills, or to Rufrius's yard at Nola. The building stone of the Sarno valley was shipped extensively to sites around the Bay of Naples, while the amphoras made in the local potteries travelled wherever their contents took them, including Spain, Gaul and North Africa.

About industry it is less easy to generalize in terms that are readily comprehensible today. In the absence of mechanical power the factory even for a product with a world market, such as the red-gloss 'terra sigillata' pottery of Arretium (Arezzo, in eastern Tuscany), was little more than a large group of related workshops, differing from those that supplied the local markets mainly in their number and organization. The only Campanian industry organized on this sort of scale about which we hear in the sources was the fine bronzework produced under the late Republic in and around Capua. It awaits detailed study, but it was evidently based on Greek experience and technical know-how, as already practised in several well-known South Italian centres, notably Tarentum (Taranto), supported by ready access to the output of the Spanish mines, made available by Rome's defeat of Carthage in the Second Punic War. Already in the second century BC Cato advises going to Capua or Nola for bronze pails, water-jugs, and urns for oil or wine; and for a

couple of centuries this area supplied much of the western Mediterranean, spreading its products up into central and northern Europe, often far beyond the Roman frontiers. At Pompeii itself considerable traces of bronze working have come to light outside the Vesuvius Gate; the Capuan factories and their Campanian subsidiaries must have been the source of a great deal of the fine bronzework in local circulation. Pottery was another flourishing local industry, both for domestic use and to supply the containers (*amphorae*) in which wine, oil, *garum* and other local products could be stored and shipped.

Such in outline was the economy on which the manifest prosperity of late Republican and early Imperial Pompeii was based. But there are many signs that by the middle of the first century AD things were changing, and changing fast: the earthquake of AD 62 hastened, but was not itself the root cause of, what could well be termed a state of urban crisis. The prosperity of the recent past, based on Campania's privileged position in the markets of the Mediterranean world, was being rapidly eroded by the growing prosperity of many of the provinces. Spanish and North African oil were beginning to dominate the markets of

Feltmakers at work. Painted on the outside wall of a shop on the Via dell'Abbondanza.

Plan of a villa rustica at Boscoreale.

1. Courtyard.
2. Wine presses.
3. Wine vats.
4. Barn.
5. Threshing floor.
6. Oil press.
7. Olive crushing room.
8. Bedrooms.
9. Kitchen.
10–12. Baths.
13. Bakery.
14. Dining room.

Plan of a fuller's workshop installed in a private house (VI, 14, 21–22).

1. Shop with treading vats and fuller's press
2. Kitchen.
3. Atrium.
4–7. Living quarters.

8. Corridor full of fuller's earth.
9. Peristyle with three large basins (A–C) for soaking the cloth, on three different levels, water draining from one to the next. D is a high walk at level of top of basins from which steps lead into the basins E. Treading vats.

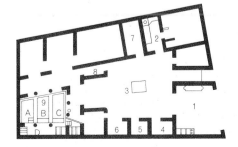

0   10   20m

0   10m

the west. Gaul too was beginning to develop not only its own vineyards but also its own industries. Henceforth the bronze-work of Capua found itself competing with workshops established in Gaul and, for the Danube market, in North Italy. A dramatic illustration of what this process of devolution could mean is provided by a crate of South Gaulish red-gloss pottery which was found at Pompeii, newly imported and not yet unpacked (Nos. 106, 107, 108). Under Augustus the prototypes for such wares had been shipped from Italy all over the known world, from Britain to the Indian Ocean. But already under Tiberius an enterprising potter from Arezzo had set himself up in South France, nearer to his markets, and by AD 79 these South Gaulish wares were beginning to be shipped to Italy.

The results of this economic decline inevitably made themselves felt also in the social sphere. The established landed families were rapidly losing their virtual monopoly of local wealth and, with it, of local political office. During the last period of Pompeii we find their place increasingly taken by new men, many of them of quite recent servile origin. As we have seen (page 41), awareness of some aspects of the process goes back at least to the beginning of the century; but while many of the new men no doubt retained their newly-won family connections (it was common for patrons to invest capital in the enterprises of able freedmen), or indeed set about establishing themselves as landed proprietors, in the last phase of Pompeii there clearly was a considerable shift in both the distribution and the use of property. Some of the new men were very well-to-do: witness the reconstruction of the Temple of Isis after the earthquake at the expense of a man who had been born a slave (see No. 15). Nevertheless a surprising number of the old town houses were abandoned as residences and were being taken over piecemeal for commercial purposes. Of the private houses in the insula that contained the House of the Menander only one was actually being used as a private residence at the time of the eruption. The gentry were moving out. There was still vitality in the processes of municipal life, as the election posters show, but by AD 79 new social patterns were rapidly emerging.

Bakery of Modestus (VII, 1, 36).

Terracotta plaque set into a wall north of the Forum, showing two men carrying an amphora strung from a pole.

Painting of a baker's shop. Naples Museum.

Cults and beliefs

As might be expected in a society that was in a state of rapid transition, the religion of Pompeii during the last century and a half of its existence was a stream of many currents. The traditional state religion was one of practice rather than of religious experience. It satisfied certain enduring everyday needs both of the individual and of society; but in the absence of any consistent body of doctrine or of any fount of written authority comparable to the Bible, to the Koran, or to the works of Karl Marx, for example, it had little or nothing to offer those in search of higher truth. An old order was passing away, an order that was rooted in the needs of the family and of a simple agricultural community; and the new order that was to replace it, an order geared to the needs of the multi-national society that came into being as a result of Alexander the Great's conquests, had still to take definitive shape. Everywhere we are confronted by a confusion of beliefs and practices. All that we can hope to do is to single out a few of the more consistent threads that went to make up the larger pattern.

One such thread was that of the popular beliefs and practices, many of them inherited from a remote past, which were, and were to remain, one of the enduring aspects of Mediterranean society. At one end of the scale there were the great gods of Olympus and their Italian counterparts, divinities whom the accidents of history and a powerful literary tradition had singled out for universal dominion; and at the other end there were the countless little local gods who so often lurk behind the well-known names. Great and small, together they represented the classical world's first attempt to come to terms with the forces of nature and the vagaries of human society. Like the local saints of Christian Italy (who were so often their lineal successors) they were the intermediaries to whom men turned when confronted by the hazards and seeming irrationalities of the world around them.

By comparison with this heritage from an older, simpler past the mystery religions were relatively recent. Classical Greece had had its Mysteries, but in the forms in which the Mystery religions made themselves most powerfully felt at Pompeii and elsewhere in contemporary Italy, they represent a fund of oriental religious experience to which the classical world fell heir as the result of Alexander the Great's conquest of the ancient East. More recent again, though derived ultimately from the same eastern sources, was the institution of the cult of the emperor as the symbol and formal embodiment of the well-being of the Roman state.

Few if any classical sites can equal Pompeii for the light which they throw on religion at its popular, grass-roots level. The household shrines (*lararia*) which are such a prominent feature of the houses (No. 220) represent religion at its simplest and least

articulate and yet, because it was obviously so much a part of everyday life, also at its most real. Traditional Roman religion was concerned with success, not sin: as Cicero remarks, 'Jupiter is called the Best and Greatest (*Optimus Maximus*) not because he makes us just or sober or wise, but because he makes us healthy, rich and prosperous.' At every level of society religion was a matter of observance, not doctrine.

Lararium in the atrium of the House of the Menander.

By Cicero's time the public face of religion was entirely in the hands of colleges of priests, prominent citizens who were elected or appointed to perform the proper ceremonials and rituals on behalf of the community they represented. Domestically the father of the family fulfilled the same office on behalf of the household under his care, offering daily prayers and gifts at the *lararium*, within which were displayed the figures of the traditional household gods, the *Lares* and the *Penates*, and of such other divinities as the family might hold in especial honour. Here too were performed the rituals associated with important family events, such as a boy's coming of age. These simple rituals were a part of daily life which no prudent Roman would have willingly neglected.

Yet another aspect of primitive religion that lived on into historic times was an emphasis on fruitfulness and reproduction, an idea which was closely associated in popular belief with that

Terracotta wall plaques with a phallus.

Priapus painted on the vestibule wall of the House of the Vettii.

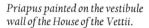

of good and evil fortune as active forces which had to be no less actively fostered or diverted. The Italian peasant who hangs a pair of horns at his roof tree, or who makes a gesture with his hand to ward off the evil eye, is acting out traditions that go right back to the patterns of belief natural to a primitive agricultural society, in which survival and fruitfulness are virtually synonymous. Many of the oldest Latin gods, such as Faunus, Silvanus and Flora, had been concerned with aspects of agricultural or pastoral plenty; objects such as wreaths of fruit or horns of plenty (*cornucopiae*) were among the enduring commonplaces of religious symbolism; and the *phallus* (the extended male reproductive organ) is apt to turn up in (to modern eyes) the most disconcerting contexts: on a plaque at a street corner, on the statue of a minor rustic divinity, in the entrance lobby of a wealthy villa. The owner of the House of the Vettii, one of the wealthiest houses of the last period of the city's history, saw nothing incongruous in displaying in the entrance a figure of Priapus with a gigantic male organ being weighed in a pair of scales, as a symbol and safeguard of the prosperity of his house. Fruitfulness was an accepted and important fact of life.

Man's devotion to the little gods, even when they bore great names, is easy enough to understand. But what of the great Olympian gods – Zeus, Aphrodite, Apollo, Poseidon and their fellows – whose quarrels and whose amatory exploits fill the pages of classical literature, and who figure so prominently on the walls of Pompeii? The Romans freely identified them with the gods of their own pantheon. But could any intelligent society take them seriously as divinities? Or were they little more than literary and artistic conventions, comparable to Milton's nymphs and shepherds or the Venuses of Botticelli and Correggio?

There is no simple, all-embracing answer. The old, anthropomorphic religion of the Greek Olympian gods was in truth long dead, killed finally by the collapse of the institutions which had given it life and buried for ever beneath the elaborate edifice of mythology which literature and art had built up around it. But despite the massive Hellenization of Roman educated society, and the consequent transference to many of the old Italian gods of the attributes and characteristics of their Greek counterparts, so far as the traditional religion of Italy was concerned these were superficial changes. Jupiter might be portrayed in the guise of Zeus, but it was as the time-honoured guardian divinity of Rome, whose temple on the Capitol was at once the symbol and the enduring guarantee of Roman prosperity, that he continued to head the Roman pantheon. When in 80 BC a colony of Roman citizens was established at Pompeii, one of the first acts of the new regime was to convert the existing temple of Jupiter (Zeus) at the head of the Forum into a temple of Jupiter Optimus Maximus Capitolinus. This was not just a token of Roman political dominion: in terms of traditional Roman belief, it was the obvious and natural way of ensuring the continued welfare of Pompeii within the larger polity of Rome, of which Pompeii had now become a part.

What had changed was not the substance of traditional Roman religion, but the outward symbols by which its meaning could be expressed, whether in art or in literature. When Augustus built a state temple in honour of his own chosen guardian divinity, Apollo, or of the divinity who personified the military might of Rome, Mars the Avenger, it was as natural to have the cult statue carved in terms of contemporary Hellenizing taste as it was for Donatello or Carpaccio to portray St George as a youthful knight in contemporary armour. We meet the same phenomenon all the way down the social scale. Trimalchio, the parvenu millionaire of Petronius's *Satyricon*, had himself portrayed on the walls of his house as protected and sustained by Mercury, the god of commerce; and at Pompeii we have an actual illustration of just such a situation. On the two doorposts of a dyer's establishment in the Via dell'Abbondanza are shown, respectively, Mercury and Venus, of whom the latter was doubly appropriate, both as the patron of a business that dealt in feminine adornment and as the patron goddess of Pompeii. Mercury is shown in the traditional guise of the Greek Hermes, staff and money-bag in hand, stepping from

Temple of Jupiter Capitolinus at the northern end of the Forum.

Aphrodite-Isis riding in an elephant quadriga.

Mercury, patron god of commerce.

his temple to bring his blessings to the house; Venus, on the other hand, appears in one of her more exotic manifestations, as Aphrodite-Isis, riding in triumph in a chariot drawn by four elephants and escorted by the personification of the city bearing horns of plenty. The familiar images of the old gods, and of some of the newer gods too, had become a conventional language in which anybody might express his own individual hopes and interests; and it was because of the very familiarity of those images that they were able to convey their meaning.

With the mystery religions we enter a very different world of ideas. Whereas traditional religion had been a matter of influencing the higher powers through a discreet mixture of propitiation, flattery and ritual observance, the mystery religions all in varying degrees envisaged the possibility of man's entering into some more direct relationship with the sources of divine power, and thus of obtaining special favour in either this world or the next, or both. To achieve this state one underwent some form of initiation, at which a 'mystery' was revealed, and through which one became a member of an inner communion, with all its privileges and its obligations.

In the classical world, as elsewhere, the basis for such a relationship had existed since long before the dawn of written history. In any agricultural society one of the earliest subjects of religious speculation was almost bound to be the cycle of the seasons and of the death and rebirth of the crops upon which man's whole existence depended: the notion of the seasonal death or rebirth of some divine embodiment of these events is one of the commonplaces of primitive religion everywhere. In Greece the central figure in this annual drama was Demeter, goddess of crops and in particular of corn, whose daughter,

1. Temple.
2. Main altar.
3. Building with water tank.
4. Meeting hall.
5. Initiation chamber.
6. Priests' lodging.

A. Statue of Venus.
B. Statue of Isis (no. 202).
C. Herm of Norbanus Sorex.
D. Statue of Dionysus
E. Shrine of Harpocrates.

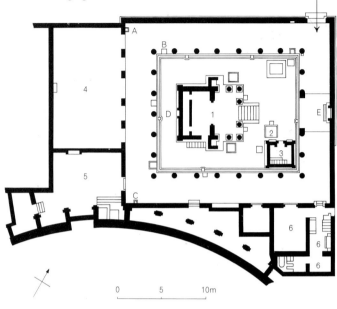

Kore or Persephone, was abducted by the god of the underworld, whence through the intervention of Zeus she was each year restored for a spell of life in this world. The centre of the cult of Demeter was Eleusis in Attica, where each year at the appropriate seasons the story was enacted symbolically in the famous Mysteries. The archaeological evidence at Eleusis appears to indicate continuity since Mycenean times; and the story (and by clear implication the Mysteries themselves) had already taken near-definitive shape by the time it first appears in literature in the Homeric *Hymn to Demeter*, composed probably around 600 BC.

At what stage and in what measure the notion developed that the individual initiate himself underwent some form of divine rebirth and an assurance of a blessed afterlife it is very hard to determine. To ourselves, the heirs to a Christian culture within which the concept of individual redemption is central, it is not easy to envisage the attitudes of mind of a world where such a concept was alien; but the weight of evidence is that at Eleusis it was in fact quite a late-comer, probably introduced by assimilation with the ideas of the other mystery cults. The Eleusinian story plays only a very modest part in the funerary art of Rome, which is our richest single source for the strength and nature of such beliefs in later antiquity. Instead, we are confronted by the stories and the symbols of the mystery cults of Asia Minor, Syria and Egypt: the Great Mother (Cybele) and Attis, Dionysus

Isis-Fortuna from the cookshop IX, 7, 21/22. Naples Museum.

(in one of his several aspects), Sabazios, Aphrodite-Astarte and Adonis, Isis, Mithras, and a host of lesser divinities.

The content and moral tone of these religions varied greatly, and Christian apologists both in antiquity and since have been at pains to emphasize the differences between Christianity and the mystery religions. There were indeed substantial differences, but there were also a great many resemblances. Jesus's reply to his disciples when they asked him why he taught in parables: 'Because it is given unto you to know the mysteries of the kingdom of Heaven, but to them it is not given' (*Matthew* xiii. 11); or St Paul's, 'Behold, I show you a mystery . . . the trumpet shall sound and the dead shall be raised incorruptible' (*I Corinthians* xv. 51) – these were words that would have been immediately intelligible to the followers of many other cults. Sacramental rites, including initiation and ritual meals; a theology based on the death and resurrection of a member of the divine family; belief in the readiness of divinity to intervene on behalf of those human individuals who were ready to accept divine authority, a belief often coupled with an emphasis on purity and morality rather than on the performance of ritual acts – in a great many respects Christianity and the mystery religions followed parallel paths.

The most obvious and significant difference was that Christianity, the child of Judaism, held itself rigidly apart from all other creeds, whereas most of the mystery religions happily gathered in all and sundry as manifestations of one and the same divine spirit. One of the most moving passages in classical literature is where Lucius, the hero of Apuleius's second-century AD romance, the *Metamorphosis*, calls in his trouble upon the Queen of Heaven (Isis), 'whether thou art Ceres . . . or Venus . . . or Diana . . . or Proserpine . . . by whatever form of divinity, by whatever ritual, in whatever shape it is right to call upon thee.' In her reply Isis acknowledges these and many other forms of her godhead, adding that 'It is the Egyptians who call me by my true name, Isis.' Here, out of the welter of ancient cults, we see the emergence of the concept of a single, oecumenical, all-embracing divinity. Christianity chose a simpler, more direct road to monotheism. But in the event, as it matured, even Christianity had to develop such doctrines as the Trinity, the special status of the Mother of God, and the communion of the saints. Old beliefs have their own ways of creeping back. As the heirs to a Christian culture, we ourselves have no difficulty in understanding the contemporary appeal of the mystery religions.

It was no doubt to her readiness to merge with the established forms of traditional religion that Isis owed something of her popularity at Pompeii. In the household shrines (*lararia*) it is exceptional for Isis and her co-divinities to usurp altogether the place of the traditional household gods, but they do very commonly occupy a place side by side with them. Isis in particular, in the guise of the Roman Fortuna, is found watching over every aspect of daily life. In a cookshop in Region IX (insula 7, 21/22) the owner, not content with the traditional *lararium* in front, had a second shrine painted on the wall leading to the lavatory, in which we see the two serpents characteristic of such shrines, a gracious Isis-Fortuna – and the figure of a man relieving himself. At its most elementary, Roman popular religion could indeed be severely practical.

For a truer assessment of the significance of the mystery religions, we do of course have to look to their more organized manifestations, and here there can be no possible doubt that of the mystery religions current in Italy in the period before AD 79 the most popular and widely practised was that of Isis and her consort Serapis (the Egyptian Osiris). Although the existing buildings of the Iseum at Pompeii all date from the period between AD 62 and 79, they followed closely the lines of a predecessor which was already established there before the foundation of the colony in 80 BC. It took the form of an enclosed precinct, within which the temple, a rather exotic, stuccoed and

Watercolour drawing of the precinct wall of the Temple of Isis, made at the time of excavation. Society of Antiquaries, London.

gaily painted version of a small classical temple, stood on a high platform, facing eastwards down the axis of a peristyle court-yard towards a shrine in honour of the third member of the divine family, the child god Harpocrates (the Egyptian Horus). In the south-east corner of the courtyard there was a smaller building, with access to a subterranean vaulted chamber in which there was a tank, thought to have contained holy water from the Nile. Opening off the south portico, behind this build-ing, there was a lodging for the resident priest, and at the far, west end, behind the temple, two rooms that had evidently been added at some later date, at the expense of the Samnite-period *gymnasium*. The larger of these was elaborately deco-rated and served probably as a place of reunion and, very possibly, for the service of the ritual meals which constituted an important part of the cult. The smaller, entered by a small separate door, seems to have been used at night (in it were found eighty-four small lamps), and it may well have been the scene of the dramatic initiation ceremonies which played an important part in this and other mystery cults.

At the moment of excavation in 1764–65 the walls of these buildings were still covered with paintings (the illustration below is one of many sad reminders of how much was lost in that early work) and although the cult statues had been removed, the altars and most of the temple vessels and fittings

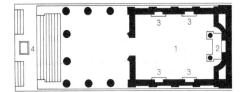

Temple of Dionysus, at S. Abbondio, near Pompeii.

1. *Temple.*
2. *Altar.*
3. *Ritual banqueting couches.*

Temple of Fortuna Augusta.

1. *Temple.*
2. *Cult statue.*
3. *Statue niches.*
4. *Altar.*

were still in place. The central mysteries of Isiac spiritual ex-perience are probably lost for ever. But the Isiac religion was also one of elaborate ceremonial observance; and here for once, in the temple at Pompeii, classical literature and the archeo-logical remains converge to give us a vivid glimpse of the daily rituals of one of the most powerful precursors and rivals of early Christianity.

Campania's mercantile connections and the large numbers of resident slaves and freedmen of Greek or Asiatic origin together made it fertile ground for the introduction of non-Italian reli-gions, and there are in fact at Pompeii scattered traces of many such (for example, Cybele and Sabazius, see No. 200). But the only one to have taken a hold at all comparable to the cult of Isis was that of Dionysus (Bacchus) who, though long an adopted member of the classical Greek pantheon, was in origin a stranger from the lands to the north and east of the Aegean (Thrace and Phrygia) and one who had far too many disturbing overtones ever to be fully absorbed within it. Visitors to the 'Thracian Gold' exhibition will recall the opulent drinking services of the Thracian devotees. But although Dionysus is best known as the god of the grape and of wine, he did in fact rep-resent a very wide variety of religious experience, ranging from the uninhibited, ecstatic possession which is so vividly portrayed in Euripides's *Bacchae* to the sort of fine-drawn mystic experi-ence to which so much later Roman art bears witness. His was a complex religious personality, and an aspect of it that bulks very large in art is its intimate association with the origins of Greek drama. It was in the Theatre of Dionysus, on the slopes of the Acropolis at Athens, that the plays of Aeschylus, Sophocles and Euripides were first performed, and the repertory of later classical art of all periods is filled with motifs that derive from this association.

In the absence of any substantial body of doctrinal or liturgi-cal Dionysiac writing, the precise meaning of any particular archaeological manifestation can often only be a matter of in-formed guesswork, but it does seem that at Pompeii one would have encountered several distinct layers of Dionysiac belief and practice. One was that of domestic religion. In a town whose prosperity was so closely linked with the wine trade, it is hardly surprising that many individuals should, like the owner of the House of the Centenary (IX, 8, 3), have chosen to put themselves under the personal protection of the god of wine. Another aspect of Dionysiac worship, based presumably on the rituals inherited from Greece, was that practised by the community of believers which established the small temple found and ex-cavated outside the walls at S. Abbondio. At yet another level of sophistication were the rites and rituals of which the walls of the Villa of the Mysteries offer so tantalizing a glimpse. Here the

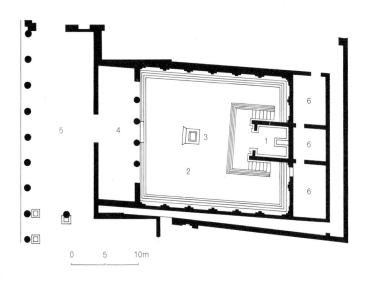

Temple of Vespasian.

1. Temple.
2. Courtyard.
3. Altar.
4. Vestibule.
5. Forum portico.
6. Sacristies and storerooms.

Altar carved with a scene of sacrifice (no. 3 on plan).

worship of Dionysus was plainly a 'mystery', based upon one of the primaeval aspects of his personality, as a god of vegetation, of seasonal death and rebirth, and of reproduction. Common to all these layers of observance and belief was a symbolic language which was remarkably durable and pervasive. Grapes and vine scrolls, pine cones, ivy leaves, satyrs and maenads, panthers, theatrical masks, certain forms of drinking vessels: these are among the commonplaces of Pompeian art, so common indeed that they often seem to have been used as almost purely decorative motifs, with very little reference to their symbolic meaning.

What of Jews and Christians? Of St Paul, voyaging from Malta to Rome in AD 62, it is recorded that '. . . on the second day we came to Puteoli. There we found brethren, and were invited to stay with them seven days' (Acts 28.13–14). Members of this harbour-town Jewish community could well have had connections in Pompeii, and it is just possible that among them there might have been Christian sympathizers. But that is really as much as one can say. If there were, they have left (and indeed at this early date they could have left) no tangible trace that we can recognize. The romantically minded will do better to rest content with the pages of Bulwer Lytton.

The third strand in the religious life of Pompeii in its later years was that of the Imperial cult. The notion of the ruler as a divine being may seem strange to modern thinking, but it was one very widely held in antiquity, and it was one with which the Hellenistic monarchs had found it both prudent and profitable to come to terms. For a society within which the formal observances of state religion were a necessary condition of the welfare of the community, it was indeed a logical function of kingship to have a direct line to the sources of divine authority, and in the eastern provinces Roman rulers, from Caesar onwards, accepted divine honours as a matter of course. Italy, with its long republican traditions, was not yet ripe for the overt, direct worship of the reigning emperor; but it was very ready to accept the sort of polite fictions of which Augustus was master. By getting

divine honours conferred upon the dead Caesar, he became himself the son of, and successor to, a god; and within a generation cults in honour of his *genius*, his *numen*, and other similar personifications of his position as head of the Roman state were springing up all over Italy. At Pompeii the building shortly before 2 BC of an official temple in honour of the Divine Providence (*Fortuna*) of Augustus is typical, and there is an inscription (*CIL* x. 896) which records the building of a second shrine, dedicated in this case, it seems, to Augustus himself.

The establishment of these cults was clearly in the first instance a demonstration of loyalty, which might reasonably be expected to yield a dividend of Imperial favour; and it is significant in this respect that one of the very few new buildings put up in Pompeii in the difficult times following the earthquake of AD 62 was a small temple beside the Forum in honour of Vespasian and the new Flavian dynasty. But they also served another purpose. Whereas the major priesthoods were, in effect, elected magistracies and were held by such prominent citizens as Marcus Holconius Rufus (page 39) and his brother, Celer, who were among the first priests (*sacerdotes*) of the Augustan cult, the day-to-day administration of the cult could be put in the hands of freedmen (and in one instance also of trusted slaves), at first as clients of the wealthy families, but before long as well-to-do citizens in their own right, thus providing a healthy outlet for the social ambitions of a new and rapidly growing class in the body politic – and a means of tapping their new-won wealth for the benefit of the community. The freedmen *Augustales* occupied a position of status and privilege second only to that of the municipal senate, the *ordo decurionum*. The *ministri Augusti* (No. 206) and the *ministri Fortunae Augustae* (No. 205) were smaller fry. Even so their appointment (and it must be remembered that of the three men named in No. 206 two were still slaves) throws a vivid light on Rome's extraordinary ability to attract and absorb the talents and loyalties of a potentially troublesome minority.

Entertainment, sport and leisure

The public provision for exercise and entertainment at Pompeii faithfully reflects the city's mixed Greek and Italic heritage. At one end of the scale we have the public exercise grounds (*palaestrae*) which were the direct successors to the Greek *gymnasia*, that is to say places where a young man might pursue the physical excellence which was such an important part of his education. At the other extreme we have the Amphitheatre, an arena for brutal spectator sports, which took formal architectural shape in Campania, but which embodied far older Italic traditions to which Greece was a stranger; and in between the two we have such buildings as the theatres and the bath buildings, which represent Greek traditions modified to suit Italic and Roman ways.

The old Samnite-period *palaestra*, beside the Theatre, was in all but name a Greek *gymnasium* – a rectangular courtyard surrounded by elegant Doric porticoes, with a row of rooms opening off one short side. At some later date one end of it was annexed to allow for an extension of the Temple of Isis, but by this time its place had been taken by the vast new *palaestra*, undated but almost certainly an Augustan building, which lay immediately to the west of the Amphitheatre. This was a huge rectangular open space, three acres in extent and enclosed on three sides by porticoes. It was shaded by orderly rows of large plane trees and in the centre there was a swimming pool (*natatio*), the whole complex forming a magnificent public setting for such athletic sports as running, jumping, throwing the discus, wrestling and swimming. There was a *palaestra* of comparable proportions at Herculaneum but, before the time of Nero, nothing of the sort in Rome. This was a specifically Campanian innovation.

Another, and in Roman terms more orthodox, development from the old Greek *gymnasium* was its incorporation within the newly-evolving type of the Roman bath building – 'Roman' because it was the Romans who completed its development and carried it with them to the remotest corners of the Empire. But we now know that both the technology of the Roman bath building and the social habits of which it was an expression first took shape in Campania. The first public bath building in Rome was not built before 19 BC, whereas there were already two in Samnite Pompeii, a century earlier. Recent excavations within the Stabian Baths have documented in detail the gradual transformation of what had been a typical Greek establishment (as represented, for example, at Olympia), with small individual 'hip bath' cubicles, into a fully-fledged Roman bath, with chambers of varying temperatures heated by the passage of hot air beneath the floors and up through the flues in the walls, and equipped with hot-water and cold-water plunges – in effect what today we would call a Turkish bath, but with certain

Hot room (*calidarium*) in the Forum Baths, Pompeii.

Terracotta telamons flanking cupboard niches in the walls of the warm room (*tepidarium*), Forum Baths.

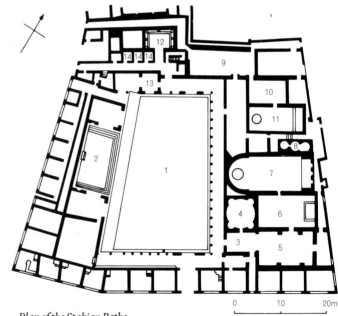

Plan of the Stabian Baths.

1. Palaestra.
2. Swimming pool (*natatio*).
3. Entrance hall.
4. Cold bath (*frigidarium*; formerly a hot sweating room, *laconicum*).
5. Undressing room (*apodyterium*).
6. Warm room (*tepidarium*).
7. Hot room (*calidarium*).
8. Furnaces.
9. Women's *apodyterium*
10. Women's *tepidarium*.
11. Women's *calidarium*.
12. Latrine.
13. Bath supervisor's office.
14. Individual 'hip bath' cubicles.

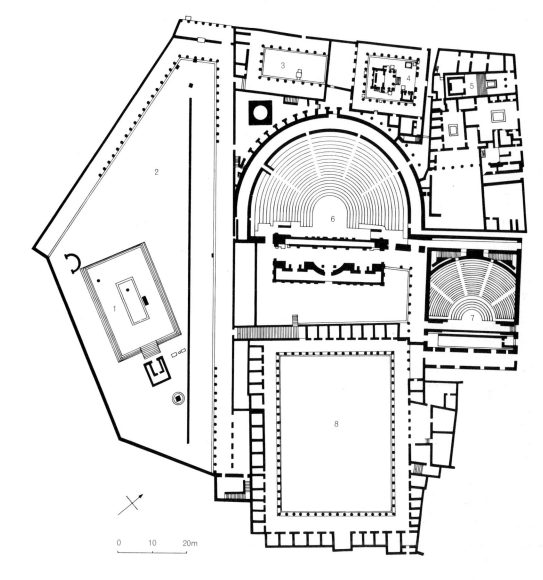

Theatre complex

1. *Temple of Hercules (Doric Temple).*
2. *Triangular Forum.*
3. *Samnite palaestra.*
4. *Temple of Isis.*
5. *Temple of Zeus Meilichios.*
6. *Large theatre.*
7. *Covered theatre (Odeum)*
8. *Gladiators' barracks.*

0   10   20m

additional facilities. One of these was the addition of a *palaestra* for the taking of exercise before bathing. As the inscription which records the modernization of the Stabian Baths soon after 80 BC records (No. 229), there was already a *palaestra* in the old Samnite Baths, and it was to remain an important part of the establishment down to AD 79.

The theatres of Pompeii (see plan, above) represent a comparable merging of Greek, Italic and Roman traditions, once again with Campania playing a prominent part in shaping the merger. As regards both the forms of classical drama and the highly specialized buildings that grew up to house them, the classical theatre was, of course, a purely Greek invention. It evolved steadily over the centuries; but it retained an extraordinarily durable hard core of continuity, as one sees very clearly, for example, in the visual conventions of the Roman theatre, which were still steeped in Dionysiac symbolic imagery – an association that goes right back to the very origins of Greek

drama, in the dances and sacred rituals connected with the cult of Dionysus. The original Samnite-period theatre at Pompeii had been a Greek-style building terraced into the slopes overlooking the Stabian Gate. Later it was almost totally remodelled in the Roman manner, by building up the seating and by reshaping the relation of seating to stage and the form of the stage building itself; but one can still get a very good idea of what the earlier building would have looked like from the recently excavated second century BC theatre at Pietrabbondante (*Bovianum Vetus*), a sanctuary deep in the mountain country of western Samnium. This, it must be remembered, was a century or so earlier than the first permanent theatre in Rome itself, the Theatre of Pompey, built in 55 BC. Beside the large open-air theatre at Pompeii was later added a smaller, covered theatre (*theatrum tectum*) or Odeum. This was built soon after 80 BC by the same pair of chief magistrates as built the Amphitheatre. Except for the subsequent addition of marble paving in the *orchaestra* and

Large Theatre.

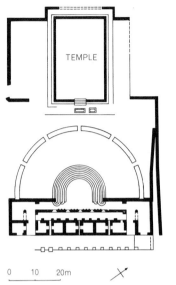

Phylax players.

0   10   20m

the facing with marble of the front of the stage building (originally decorated with Second Style painting) the remains in this case are still those of the original building. It had an unsupported roof span of 20.6 m, a good indication of the technical skills of the Campanian architects of the Sullan period.

What sort of performances would these theatres have staged?

For the more serious cultural occasions there was the Covered Theatre, occasions such as concerts, lectures, readings of verse, or the displays of visiting rhetoricians in which antiquity took such a perverse pleasure. The Large Theatre was, by contrast, a place of popular entertainment, and Rome was not the only society to discover that patronage based on popular taste does not make for a very high level of theatre. It is not improbable that in its more serious moments the Large Theatre may have staged the comedies of Plautus and Terence, perhaps even the tragedies of Pacuvius (who came from south Italy and bore an Oscan name) and Accius. But in the long run the Roman dramatists of the second century BC were to prove more important for the history of Latin literature than for the creation of a flourishing dramatic tradition. A single anecdote will serve to show what they were up against. Even in his own lifetime Terence, who died in 159 BC, saw the first performance of one of his plays ruined by the rival attractions of a rope dancer and a boxer, and, at the second attempt, by rumours of a gladiatorial combat. By the first century BC tragedy had become an almost exclusively literary form, written for declamation or private performance; and although comedy was more robust (the texts of some of the plays of Plautus have survived because they were performed) it too was fast losing ground to simpler, more popular forms of entertainment.

It is difficult to present a coherent picture of this popular entertainment, for several reasons. One is that, being non-literary or at best sub-literary, it has left all too few traces in the written record. Another is that at this level of performance the element of improvisation tended to be high and the demarcation lines correspondingly fluid. If we accept the distinctions made by classical writers, at least three well-known types of entertainment were certainly presented in the Theatre at Pompeii: the Atellan Farce, the Mime, and the Pantomime.

The Atellan Farce would have found a ready audience. Named after Atella, near the modern Aversa, between Naples and Capua, it was a Campanian speciality, played in Oscan. Like the later Italian *Commedia dell'Arte*, or (to take a modern analogy) like many strip cartoons, it portrayed scenes of small-town life, revolving around the incongruous adventures and buffoonery of a few stock characters – Maccus the greedy clown, Pappus the gaffer, and a few others. Rendered in Latin, it had a brief semi-literary vogue in late Republican Rome, but it was really popular, grass-roots entertainment, bawdy, topical and wholly lacking in sophistication.

Of all the forms of Roman theatrical entertainment, the Mime was at once the most elementary and the most enduring. Such formal shape as it assumed was derived from many sources, including no doubt the Atellan Farce and (another, slightly earlier Campanian speciality) the *phlyax* players of the fourth and third centuries BC, who seem to have specialized in ribald burlesques of mythological subjects; but above all from the companies of strolling performers, the forebears of 'I Pagliacci', who for centuries past had been dancing, singing, juggling, and playing their way from town to town, wherever they could drum up an audience. By Roman times at any rate, they seemed to have abandoned the masks of Greek theatrical

Amphitheatre.

tradition, since the lead player, the *archimimus*, evidently relied heavily on facial expression. Like the Atellan Farce, the Mime had a brief literary vogue in late Republican Rome; but it was really, and it remained, a sub-literary form, deriving its vitality and lasting popularity precisely from its impromptu adaptability to the changing demands of local taste and of contemporary fashion.

The most sophisticated of the popular art forms was the Pantomime, which was introduced to Rome in 22 BC from the eastern Mediterranean, and which soon achieved enormous popularity. To modern ears the name calls up visions of the old-fashioned Christmas pantomime, but the classical pantomime was in fact something totally different, far more closely resembling modern ballet, involving the acting out of some traditional story in wordless gesture. The main difference was that almost the entire action was in the hands of a single player, the *pantomimus* (literally, 'one who imitates all things'), supported by a chorus and musicians. A top-ranking *pantomimus* was the pop star of his day, the idol of the public and often the intimate of emperors. A typical career was that of L. Aurelius Pylades, 'the first *pantomimus* of his time', who had been born a slave and, after a successful acting career, was freed by the emperors Marcus Aurelius and Lucius Verus (AD 161–166). He retired to Puteoli where, as a wealthy gentleman of leisure, he became a prominent local benefactor. At Pompeii, as the *graffiti* make clear, the ratings of rival *pantomimi* were followed eagerly and the visit of a successful *pantomimus* was a major event.

The level of theatrical performance at Pompeii may not have been very exalted, but the Theatre did undoubtedly play a lively part in local life. This is brought vividly home to us by a bronze bust, on a herm, which dates from about the turn of the first centuries BC and AD and which is now in Naples Museum (inv. no. 4991; incription *CIL* X. 1, 814). It was found in the Temple of Isis and it commemorates one Caius Norbanus Sorex, described as a player of second parts, a descendant (probably the grandson) of the well-known *archimimus* of the same name who had been a personal friend of the dictator Sulla. 'To play second parts' was, in Roman terms, 'to play second fiddle'; the Pompeian Norbanus Sorex was no David Garrick. Moreover, in the eyes of the law acting was one of the dishonourable professions, whose members were disqualified from holding public office. And yet here we have one of a pair of honorary herm-portraits (the shaft of the other was found in the Eumachia Building) set up in a popular public temple with the formal approval of the town council (*ex decurionum decreto*), by the *magistri* of the *pagus Augustus Felix suburbanus*, a body which one might loosely translate as the parish council of one of the country sub-districts

outside the walls of Pompeii – not perhaps a very large pond, but in it a Norbanus Sorex could be quite a large fish and, by implication, a substantial public benefactor. Once again we are reminded that Pompeii was not Rome, and that, whatever the law might say, a successful local actor could be an honoured member of the community.

The amphitheatre was an Italian creation, in which Campania, with its hybrid Hellenized Italic culture, played a leading part. Rather surprisingly, Rome itself did not have a permanent arena until 29 BC, and even then it was built of timber on masonry footings, not unlike the seating for the open-air opera in the Baths of Caracalla in present-day Rome. Before 29 BC displays of gladiators or of exotic beasts had had to take place under makeshift conditions in such open spaces as the Roman Forum or the Circus Maximus. This was a costly business, and it could be dangerous, as when the elephants displayed by Pompey in 55 BC took fright and stampeded. Keeping performers and mobs of excited spectators apart is no new problem in popular spectator sport. The problem was resolved, and it was resolved in Campania, by the creation of the *amphitheatrum* (literally 'a place for viewing from all sides') consisting of an oval arena separated by a barrier from rising tiers of stone benches. The Amphitheatre at Pompeii, built soon after the foundation of the colony in 80 BC, lacks the grandeur and sophisticated planning of the later giants at Capua and Puteoli, or the Colosseum in Rome. But it has an honoured place in architectural history. It is the earliest surviving example of an architectural form that is still in worldwide use today. It is also one of the first public buildings in Roman Italy to have used the arcade as a monumental feature in its own right. Campania at this time was way out in front as a centre of lively architectural invention.

Marble relief from a tomb outside the Stabian Gate.

Although the Amphitheatre could be used for any form of large spectacle, in practice what the crowd expected was blood, in the form either of gladiatorial combats or of performances involving the pitting of ferocious wild beasts against human victims or against each other. The provision of 'games' (*ludi*) was a ready passport to popular favour, and one of the formal requirements of public office at Pompeii was the expenditure of a large sum either on public building or on public entertainment (see No. 229). The human performers were either condemned criminals exposed to some form of sophisticated butchery, or else trained gladiators, who might be either the unwilling victims of circumstance (slaves, prisoners of war, lesser criminals) or else tough, voluntary professionals. They were organized into schools (*familiae*) under private or public ownership (in Rome itself they very soon passed into Imperial hands), one of the earliest and most famous of such schools being that at Capua from which Spartacus and seventy-seven other gladiators made their historic escape in 73 BC. The possession of an amphitheatre was a valuable civic asset, bringing in spectators from all the nearby towns. The disastrous Amphitheatre riot of AD 59 was sparked off by the presence of large numbers of fans from Nuceria, a neighbouring city which, in the best Italian tradition, was also Pompeii's deadly rival. It was natural that Pompeii, with its fine arena, should set up its own gladiatorial establishment. This was installed after the earthquake of AD 62 in what had been a large porticoed foyer behind the Theatre (see plan, page 63). By AD 79 it was already partly occupied, and in it were found some of the fine armour and weapons now in the Naples Museum.

Every gladiator was a specialist, belonging to one of a number of conventional categories, which were clearly distinguished by their armour and weapons, and which bore conventional names. These names appear regularly in the literature and in the advertisements, and at any given time and place the fans would certainly have known exactly what to expect (and how to lay their bets) when a *myrmillo* from such-and-such a training school, with twenty-five wins to his credit, was matched against a less experienced but well spoken of *Thrax* from such another school. We today cannot follow all the nuances; and when one recalls how even in so conservative a game as cricket the positioning of players in the field and the naming of those positions have changed quite substantially in the last fifty years, it is hardly surprising that the evidence from antiquity is not always consistent. Most of the main types seem to have been first established by the introduction of prisoners of war wearing their native armour and weapons, beginning with the 'Samnites' in the third century BC, and followed by the 'Gauls' and 'Thracians' and, possibly introduced by Julius Caesar from Britain, gladiators fighting from chariots (*essedarii*). Broadly speaking, they may be divided into the group of heavily-armed fighters which evolved from the original 'Samnites'; a somewhat more mobile, less heavily-armed group of which the 'Thracian' was typical; and a number of more specialized types, of which the most colourful was the *retiarus*, or net-thrower, who was very lightly armoured (alone among gladiators he fought bare-headed) and who was armed only with a net, a fisherman's trident and a dagger, relying entirely on his own greater speed and mobility. He was normally matched against a *myrmillo* (so named from the representation of a fish, the *morimylos*, which he wore on his helmet) or a *secutor* ('chaser').

The games followed an established ritual. After a public banquet the evening before, in which all the contestants participated, they started off with a procession (*pompa*), which was heralded by trumpets and horns, and which included the sponsor of the games and all the fighters, dressed in splendid costumes and wearing armour, which they would later change for their actual fighting equipment. After a series of rather tame preliminaries (mock fights, fights with wooden weapons, etc.) the serious business of the day began with a war trumpet (*tuba*) sounding for the first pair of gladiators, who proceeded to fight to the death, although there was a reasonable chance of a good loser being allowed to live to fight another day. About midday there was a slack period, filled with more mock fighting, assorted displays and the executions of criminals, after which the afternoon would be devoted to *venationes*, in which wild animals were pitted against each other or against trained animal-fighters (*bestiarii*). Throughout the day there was a more or less continuous accompaniment from trumpets, horns, pipes, drums, water organs and, possibly, from voices. The whole performance is vividly portrayed in a marble triple frieze found outside the Stabian Gate (see illus.), probably from a large tomb: in the upper register, the procession; in the middle, on a larger scale as befits the major attraction, five scenes of gladiatorial combat; and below, incidents from the *venationes*.

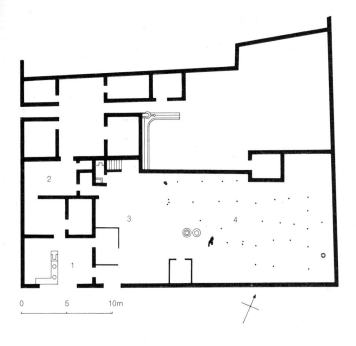

Caupona of Euxinus (I, 11, 10).

1. Bar.
2. Kitchen and latrine.
3. Open air dining/drinking area.
4. Vineyard.

A bar counter on the Via dell' Abbondanza.

To conclude this section about leisure activities, a few words about eating customs.

The Roman's single main meal of the day (*cena*) was taken in the evening after the afternoon bath. In polite society one dined on a couch (see Nos. 259–262) reclining on one's left elbow. The average dining room took its name (*triclinium*) from the fact that it held three couches (*klinai*, or *lecti*), though a wealthy house might have several *triclinia* for different seasons, including one for *al fresco* dining in the garden; and for a really large dinner party several might be used at once – carefully graded socially, if we are to believe the contemporary satirical writers. The couches faced inwards upon three sides of a square, within which stood the tables and from which the food and drink were served. Three courses were customary, each consisting of several different servings, and wine (normally but not invariably mixed with water, and in some contexts served hot) was drunk both with and after the meal. The details varied greatly according to the taste of the host and the degree of formality. Frequently the meal was accompanied or followed by some form of entertainment such as music, dancing, acrobatics or, if the host had literary pretensions, readings from poetry. Petronius's *Satyricon*, for all its element of parody, offers a brilliant picture of the sort of dinner which might have been served by a wealthy vulgarian in mid-first century Pompeii.

For the man in the street and for visitors there were numerous bars and eating houses (*cauponae*), many of which also provided lodging, with or without female company. The Canpona of Euxinus will serve as an example. It was one of a number situated near the Amphitheatre to cater for the crowds of visitors who came from all the neighbouring towns whenever there was a show. On the facade was a painted inn-sign, with a figure of a Phoenix and two peacocks and the words *Phoenix felix et tu* ('You too will enjoy the Happy Phoenix'), and below it were two electoral posters painted up on the orders of the innkeeper, Euxinus, whose name and address are attested also by the inscriptions on three wine amphoras found in the bar: *Pompeiis ad amphitheatr(um) Euxino coponi* ('to Euxinus the innkeeper, near the amphitheatre, Pompeii'). The premises were large: on the street corner a bar, with a typical L-shaped counter, a store, large jars for keeping food hot, and traces of a wooden rack for storing wine amphoras; behind the bar three other rooms, a storeroom and a lavatory; and on it to the right a large open courtyard, which did double duty as a vineyard and, as in many a *trattoria* today, a place for open-air drinking and dining and, no doubt, gaming (see No. 227). At the far end of the garden was a painted *lararium*, and stairs led to some upper rooms, and there was more accommodation in the adjoining house.

The *graffiti* found on the walls were characteristic, including representations of Dionysus and Priapus and tags of verse. One of these ran:

'Blondie bad me hate the dark ones. If I can I will. If I cannot, all unwilling I will love them still'.

Painting

The standard classification of Pompeian wall painting into four successive 'Styles' was first enunciated by August Mau in 1882, and it still provides the best framework for any outline survey of the two hundred-odd years of painting presented on the walls of Pompeii itself and of the neighbouring towns and country villas.

The First, or 'Masonry', Style followed closely the conventions of the decoratively jointed stone masonry of which it was a gaily coloured representation. Very similar work has been recorded from sites as far afield as Macedonia, Asia Minor and Israel, and by the second century BC it was evidently already a commonplace of both public and domestic interior decoration throughout the Hellenistic world. At Pompeii it was already giving place to the Second Style when the interior of the Capitolium was decorated shortly after the foundation of the Roman colony in 80 BC, and very soon after that it was generally replaced by the Second Style. The House of Sallust (see illustration) is one of the relatively few examples that survive in good condition. Relying as it did for its effect upon the patterns of the painted surfaces, which imitated in stucco the cornices and plinths, blocks and slabs of real ornamental masonry, it was essentially a style that emphasized the real solid qualities of the walls which it adorned.

The Second, or 'Architectural', Style began to come in soon after 80 BC, reflecting the widening cultural perspectives created both by the foundation of the Roman colony and by Italy's ever-increasing involvement with the established centres of the arts in the eastern Mediterranean. The element common to all its very varied manifestations was a development of the wall surfaces in seeming depth, usually within a framework of simulated architecture: where the First Style had emphasized the tangible solidity of the wall, the Second Style did all it could to play down that solidity and to create an illusion of receding space. In its earlier stages (Style IIA), before the middle of the first century BC, this took the form simply of making the main wall surface appear to be set back behind a framing order of painted Corinthian columns, which looked as if they stood upon a projecting plinth and supported a projecting cornice (see illustration). This was a direct two-dimensional imitation of a real architectural device already current in the earliest concrete-vaulted architecture of Campania and of Latium, and the resulting simulation of reality by every known trick of illusionistic perspective and lighting was to remain characteristic of the Second Style in all its manifestations.

At first the wall surfaces 'behind' the framing architectural colonnade continued to be treated much as in the previous period. But quite soon (for example, in the secondary rooms of the Villa of the Mysteries, c. 60–50 BC) this began to be accompanied by an opening-out of the upper part of the wall, as if the lower part were merely a screen over the top of which one could glimpse the open sky framed by receding architectural vistas. This search for visual escape from the sense of enclosure imposed by the inherited traditions of a compact, inward-facing urban architecture was to remain one of the dominant trends of Roman domestic architecture throughout the Pompeian period. The best known of all Pompeian paintings of this period, the Hall of the Dionysiac Mysteries (No. 204) in the Villa of the Mysteries, is in this respect an exception, Second Style in date but not in its composition. Not only does it omit the columns of the architectural framework but it also portrays the figures of the frieze itself as if they were acting out their parts in front of a neutral background rather than moving into and out of it. It is only in the small bedchambers (cubicula) that one finds the characteristic glimpses of open spaces beyond the wall (see illustration). In this respect the great figured frieze of this Villa, like the Aldobrandini Wedding frieze in the Vatican Museums, is an intruder for which the precedents must be sought outside Italy in the Hellenistic world. Within less than a generation, however, this alien tradition had been captured and assimilated, and it is thus that we find it, displayed within a conventional Second Style architectural framework, on the walls of the Villa of Publius Fannius Synistor at Boscoreale on the slopes of Vesuvius. Despite its numerous and continued borrowings from, and links with, the larger Hellenistic world, the Second Style was evidently already an established Italian phenomenon, created for the houses and villas of wealthy Romans in the

Tablinum wall in the House of Sallust. First Style.

Cubiculum in the House of the Silver Wedding. Second Style (IIA).

Cubiculum in the Villa of the Mysteries. Later Second Style (IIB).

Cubiculum in the House of the Epigrams (from a drawing). Late Second Style (IIB).

capital and in Campania, and faithfully reflected on the walls of the well-to-do citizens of Pompeii.

In the third quarter of the first century BC the Second Style (Style IIB) took a turn which was to affect the whole subsequent history of wall painting at Pompeii. The painted architectural framework, which had at first faithfully conformed to the simple rectangular shapes of the rooms which it adorned, began to take on a life of its own, with each individual wall treated as a separate compositional unit, symmetrically balanced about the central bay within the larger symmetry of the rooms' three main walls. Both the painted architectural foreground and the wall surfaces which it framed lent themselves admirably to such treatment. Among the many recurrent schemes one may note the development of the whole wall as an elaborately three-dimensional architectural facade articulated about three large doors, as in the Villa of P. Fannius Synistor at Boscoreale: the portrayal of a porticoed courtyard enclosing some central feature such as a circular *tempietto* (*tholos*) glimpsed between the columns and curtains of an ornately baroque columnar screen as in the large painted *triclinium* at Oplontis (No. 338), or, prominently displayed within the central bay, a large representation of a panel picture, usually depicting some mythological subject (see illustration).

Scholars have expended much erudition and ingenuity in tracing the sources of these compositions: in contemporary stage design, for example; in the fantasy architecture which graced the courts of the Hellenistic monarchs (and particularly that of the Ptolemies of Egypt); and in the elaborately contrived landscape architecture of the villas of Campania itself. That there was any single, all-embracing source is in fact doubtful: this was the expression of an aspect of late Hellenistic taste which no doubt found many outlets. But, making every allowance for an element of painterly exaggeration, it does seem clear that a great deal of what we see portrayed on the walls of Pompeii was rooted in real three-dimensional fantasy architecture. When, in one of the rare surviving passages of classical literature that indulges in contemporary art-criticism, the architectural historian Vitruvius, writing about 25 BC, roundly condemns this style for its 'unreality', it is clear from the context that the reality with which he contrasted it was the sober functionalism of traditional classical architecture. Not for him the heady baroque fantasies favoured by the avant-garde decorators of Rome and central Italy.

Two other famous surviving Second Style paintings must be mentioned because of their importance for what follows. One is the frieze illustrating scenes from Homer's *Odyssey* within the setting of a continuous landscape. Found on the Esquiline in Rome, it is now in the Vatican Museums. Scholars are divided as to the extent to which the 'Odyssey Landscapes' reflect lost Hellenistic originals, but there can be no doubt about the degree to which this tradition of naturalistic landscape with figures had already taken root on Italian soil. In this case the landscape is shown as if glimpsed between the columns of a typical columnar order. In the Garden Room from the Villa of Livia, wife of

*Tablinum wall in the House of
M. Lucretius Fronto. Late Third
Style.*

were still there on the walls of the older houses for all to see.

The dominant characteristic of the Third Style was its renunciation of the search for an illusion of three-dimensional depth and its concentration instead upon the purely decorative possibilities inherent in the formal schemes which it had inherited from the previous period. It retained the rigid horizontal symmetry of the later Second Style, with its two flanking panels leading the eye in towards the panel picture framed by the central *aedicula;* but although the formal vocabulary of the latter was still largely that of Second Style fantasy architecture, it was increasingly an architecture without substance, little more than a frame for the picture which had become the focus of the whole composition. At the same time there was a steadily increasing emphasis upon the fields of colour and upon the patterns presented by the surrounding wall surfaces. Slender candelabra, trailing tendrils, arabesques of delicate foliage, abstract geometrical motifs – all these were used with an elaborate inner logic to create a formal unity covering the whole wall surface (see illustration). A good example of this can be seen in the Villa of the Mysteries, in the black *tablinum.*

Vertically too there was the same movement away from the illusion of real architecture characteristic of the Second Style towards two-dimensional schemes of balanced pattern. The plinth, the middle register of the wall, and what had been the zone opening out above this middle register, became three rigidly distinct horizontal bands of composition, linked by little more than the shared tripartite symmetry of the overall design. The gable of the central *aedicula* was flattened and compressed downwards into the middle zone, to the upper and lower borders of which added emphasis was given by the introduction of secondary bands of small, elongated horizontal panels; the plinth became an independent strip of colour set along the base of the wall and with its own independent ornament, while along the upper register were ranged groups of delicate, architectural fantasies, as far removed in spirit from the illusionistic Second Style fantasy architecture of which they were the offspring as the former had been from the 'real' architecture with which Vitruvius so contemptuously contrasts them.

A third and very important component of the Third Style was its use of colour to emphasize the formal divisions, and in particular the vertical divisions, of the design. A typical colour scheme is that of the *oecus* of the House of the Menander, with its black dado, its green middle zone punctuated by black vertical members, and its white upper zone. To such wall schemes must be added the sober white or black and white of the mosaic or marble floors and the patterned polychrome tracery of the stucco vaulting. These were carefully studied, often sophisti-

Augustus, at Prima Porta just outside Rome (see illustration), even this formal restraint is lacking: the four walls simply flow outwards, portraying in loving detail the trees and shrubs, the birds and flowers of a formal garden laid out beyond a low fence. In this respect the Second Style could go no further.

If we have lingered over the Second Style, of which relatively few Pompeian examples were to survive another century of rebuilding and redecorating (and of which it is, in consequence, very hard to convey any real impression from the few fragments available for exhibition), it is because this was the great creative period of Roman wall painting. This was when the basis of most of the subsequent repertory was established. It is common to speak of the Third and Fourth Styles as if they represented an orderly sequence of development. Development there certainly was, but much of it was achieved in terms of a repertory of inherited patterns and motifs, and it was punctuated by frequent references back to the recent past, the products of which

House of the Red Walls (VIII, 5, 37). Early Fourth Style.

House of the Centenary, detail of wall in the white dining room. Early Fourth Style.

House of 'Loreius Tiburtinus' (II, 2, 2–5).

House of the Apollo (VI, 7, 23).

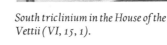

South triclinium in the House of the Vettii (VI, 15, 1).

cated effects. To modern eyes much of the colouring may seem rather overpowering, but there was nothing indiscriminate about its application.

In so far as it is possible to draw an arbitrary dividing line between two stages of a single, developing artistic phenomenon, the line between the Second and Third Styles appears to fall around 15 BC, and the Third Style may reasonably be regarded as a direct reflection of the rather formal classicism which characterizes the official art that was just then taking shape at the court of Augustus. The earliest and finest Third Style paintings in Rome itself come from just such a milieu, a villa in Trastevere (near the present Villa Farnesina) which was probably the residence of M. Vipsanius Agrippa, the colleague

and designated heir of Augustus, after his marriage in 19 BC to Augustus's daughter, Julia. If that is correct, the link with Pompeii is clear. The child of the marriage was Agrippa Postumus, born shortly after his father's death in 12 BC; and it was in a villa belonging to this son, found in 1902 at Boscotrecase on the slopes of Vesuvius, two miles from Pompeii, and reburied by the eruption of 1906, that a number of paintings were found, so close in style and content to those of the Villa Farnesina that they may well have been painted by one of the artists who had worked there (see Nos. 129, 131 and illustration). This sort of thing, though we can rarely document it so precisely, must in fact have been common practice in the wealthy patrician villas of the Bay of Naples; and when one sees how many such villas

71

there were within a ten-mile radius of Pompeii (see page 16), it is easy to understand how, in style if not always in quality, the walls of this small provincial city came to reflect so faithfully and so rapidly the art of Rome itself.

The latest manifestations of the Third Style proper date from the middle of the first century AD (an unusually well-preserved example is the *tablinum* of the house of M. Lucretius Fronto (v, 4, 9; see illustration)) and once again it was changes of taste at court that ushered in the fourth and last phase of Pompeian wall painting, in the years immediately preceding the earthquake of AD 62. This is conventionally known as the Fourth Style, but it might in fact better be described as a chronological phase, embodying a number of concurrent stylistic trends, some of which reflect the extravagant innovations of taste introduced into the art of the capital by Nero, while others hark back to the recent past of Pompeii itself.

Space only permits us to illustrate a few of the more striking aspects of this Fourth Style. At one extreme we find rooms like those in the House of the Red Walls (VIII, 5, 37) and in the House of the Centenary (IX, 8, 6; see illustration), in which the walls are treated as a single sheet of colour, upon which is overlaid a delicate patterned tracery; there is a marked tendency to reduce the size of the panel pictures, or even to omit them altogether. A favourite conceit within this *genre* is to balance a 'White Room' against a 'Black Room', as in the House of the Centenary and in the recently excavated House of Julius Polybius (IX, 13, 19–26). At the other extreme we find a reversion to the illusionistic architecture of the Second Style, this time, however, treated as a continuous architectural backdrop to the main action of the composition, which is portrayed as if taking place on a stage. Good examples of this are in the House of Pinarius Cerealis (III, 4, 4) and in the House of Apollo (VI, 7, 23). Between these two extremes lie a large number of rooms which are formally no more than an ultimate phase of the Third Style, more or less combined with elements derived from the Second Style or from other types of Fourth Style practice. A room such as the south *triclinium* of the House of the Vettii (see illus.) quite obviously incorporates elements derived from both the preceding styles.

Because this was the sort of painting current at the time of the city's destruction it bulks large in the surviving remains, its wider artistic significance is less. For one thing, the last years of Pompeii were a time of marked economic and social decline, a decline that was inevitably reflected in the levels of patronage and, in consequence, of artistic standards. For another, wall painting as an important art form was on the way out, to be replaced by marble panelling and, in really wealthy circles, wall mosaic. In this respect the eruption was nicely timed. Another few years, and there would have been little left of the older, finer Pompeii.

And what of the mythological panel pictures which were the most prominent features of so many Pompeian walls and which, torn from their context, have for so long dominated the modern image of the Roman painter's art? Very early on in the excavations it was realized that they were in some sense 'Old Master Copies', based on well-known Greek originals, and for a very long time it was almost exclusively as evidence of these lost originals that they captured the imagination of scholars. It is only quite recently that they have begun to be studied in their own right as paintings which, though presented in terms of certain inherited conventions, are in many cases as Roman as the walls which they adorned.

That they represent free variations upon the themes established by the originals, and not merely straight copies of them, is apparent the moment one compares the different versions of one of the more familiar myths. There are, for example, ten versions of the story of Theseus and the Minotaur derived from at least three different originals. The competence varies greatly; and those who wish to demonstrate the artistic superiority of the lost originals have no difficulty in finding telling examples: this was after all the work of house decorators doing their best to furnish their clients with a 'Greek' art which was not their own, but which social convention demanded. But a more fruitful line of enquiry is that of the extent to which these panel pictures reflect developments in contemporary Roman painting. Here their real quality emerges; and there can be little doubt that one of the most significant of such developments lay in the field of landscape painting, and in particular of the sort of landscape with figures of which Second Style 'Odyssey Landscapes', referred to above, afford such an eloquent foretaste.

Although many of the standard motifs of Second Style landscape paintings and stuccoes – isolated trees, towers, rustic shrines, altars, columns, rocky outcrops – do seem to derive from a pre-existing Hellenistic tradition of painting or stuccowork, few today would question that a painting such as the 'Rescue of Andromeda' in the House of the Priest Amandus (I, 7, 7) represents a fresh and specifically Italian version of that tradition (see illustration). This painting occupies the centre of the left-hand wall of a *triclinium* which was redecorated in a version of the Third Style that is variously attributed to the middle of the first century AD or to the years just before AD 79. Comparable figured landscapes, portraying respectively the Fall of Icarus and the story of Polyphemus and Galatea, occupy two of the other walls, while the fourth wall displays a painting of Hercules in the Garden of the Hesperides, which is a reasonably competent, if to modern eyes rather dull, copy of a Greek original (see illustration). The differences between this last

'Rescue of Andromeda'.

House of the Priest Amandus,
triclinium. 'Hercules in
Hesperides'.

picture and the other three leap to the eye. In it the figures are isolated against a neutral background very much in the manner of the figures of a carved classical relief; and the orange tree, illustrated because it is an essential feature of the story, stands in the same plane, without the slightest attempt to convey any illusion of an actual garden setting. This was the classical Greek tradition. The other three pictures are quite different in mood, composition and treatment. It is the landscape that dominates, with its all-encompassing sense of real space; and the conventions used in its portrayal foreshadow to a startling degree those of later Roman narrative art. This is truly Roman painting. Ironically, but predictably, it was the 'Greek' picture that got the post of honour. The educated Roman, hypnotized by the prevailing taste for Greek art, was notoriously blind to his own country's very real artistic achievements.

Much the same qualities emerge in the smaller decorative panels and other accessories which figure so largely on the walls of the Third and Fourth Styles. Still lifes (Nos. 254, 256), architectural landscapes (Nos. 8, 11, 12), the Egyptianizing, or Nilotic, scenes which constitute the Roman equivalent of *chinoiserie*: painted in the broad, impressionistic technique of which Roman painters were the masters, they have an assurance and a directness which cannot fail to appeal to modern taste. This too was an art which had achieved a distinctively Roman personality.

One final question before we leave these mythological pictures. Was there any logic behind the choice of scenes? Did they carry a message, or were they simply the stereotypes of phil-hellenic artistic fashion?

That many of the individual scenes carried widely accepted overtones of religious or philosophical interpretation, there can be no doubt. Used in combination with each other and with the secondary motifs by which they were regularly surrounded (a

great many of which had themselves entered the artistic repertory in the context of religious symbolism) they constituted a visual language which could be used to convey a remarkably clear and explicit message. Thus, the paintings from the villa of Publius Fannius Synistor at Boscoreale (see No. 121) have been very plausibly interpreted as showing that the owner was an initiate into the mysteries of Aphrodite (Venus) and Adonis. In such a context the language of symbolism could be as subtle as it was eloquent, because it was addressed to people who understood what it was saying. At a more generalized level of communication, the mythological pictures are commonly used in what appear to be significant pairs, or trios, and some of these too may have been chosen because they illustrated the stories of the divinities to whose protection and good will the owner of the house aspired. Others again (for example, the Trojan cycle in Ala 4 of the House of the Menander) may simply reflect the owner's literary or artistic tastes, although here too it would have been quite easy to read into them overtones of moral or philosophical meaning.

It does not on the other hand follow (as is sometimes claimed) that all of the mythological paintings at Pompeii carried a deliberate message. It is implicit in the language of symbolism that the more widely it is used, the more the precision of its meaning tends to get blunted. The terms become so familiar that they need a context to give them precise meaning, and in such a situation meaning tends increasingly to lie in the eye of the beholder. The workshops of Pompeii were not laboratories for the portrayal of belief. Under sophisticated patronage they could be so used; and at a more commonplace level any householder might select the current models that best suited his own personal tastes and convictions. But they remained essentially workshops, repositories of a body of established models, patterns and skills; and what they produced was determined by the

Wild beasts on the garden wall of the House of the Epigrams (V, 1, 18).

Large landscapes on the garden wall of the House of the Small Fountain (VI, 8, 23).

fashions of contemporary taste, which to many citizens must have been largely a matter of keeping up with the Joneses. In the matter of giving more esoteric meanings to these paintings one has to take each case on its own merits.

We have dealt at some length with the formal painting which, by the very fact of its survival in such quantity, constitutes Pompeii's unique contribution to the history of classical art, and which, because it operated within a very precise range of conventions, does need some such explanation to be intelligible. By the same token we can be very brief in presenting the other facet of Pompeian painting, namely the popular art which adorns the gardens, domestic shrines, bars and shopfronts. Simple, unsophisticated, direct, it tells its own story.

Much of this popular art was concerned with the portrayal of the well-known things of daily life: the shop of a baker (see page 54) or a potter (No. 292), fullers or felt-makers at work (see page 53), a ship (No. 252), scenes of tavern life (No. 227) or of daily life in the Forum (see illustration, page 75). Occasionally it gives us a glimpse of larger contemporary events, as in the well-known scene of the amphitheatre riot of AD 59 (see illustration, page 35); but for the most part it was the work of simple craftsmen giving direct expression to what they saw around them. Even so, it was curiously selective: it was rarely used without some practical purpose. There are no scenes of bathing, while the amphitheatre, that immensely popular institution, figures only indirectly in the scenes of hunting and of wild beasts which are common in the garden paintings of so many of the houses – for example, in the House of Ceius (I, 6, 15) and in the House of the Epigrams (V, 1, 18; see illustration). For the portrayal of gladiatorial combats, other than in funerary art (where it has a specific contextual meaning), one has to turn to the ubiquitous *graffiti* (see page 66).

It is at this level of meaning that one can most intelligibly draw a rational distinction between the spheres of formal and of popular Pompeian art. Although, as we have seen, the former could be used in sophisticated hands to express the religious, philosophical or literary preferences of an individual patron, it was in itself no more than a repertory of motifs and styles of which the common denominator was the norms imposed by contemporary artistic taste. Popular art, on the other hand, like

the popular religion of which it was so often an expression, tended to operate at a far simpler, more direct level of human experience. Nothing could be more stridently 'popular' than the painted household shrines (*lararia*) with their great curling serpent figures (No. 210); and many of the street-front paintings were placed directly under the protection of the owner's patron divinity (see illustration, page 57): advertisements of his activities, it may be, but also at the same time tangible insurances against the changes and chances of a capricious providence. This was a grass-roots art, shaped not only by its use of everyday themes but also by its expression of everyday attitudes of mind.

As in most such classifications, the distinctions between formal and popular Pompeian art tend to get a bit ragged at the edges. One sees this very clearly in many of the gardens. Here, side by side with formal Third and Fourth Style rooms are rooms and garden walls treated in a wide variety of other styles. Many of the subjects are borrowed from the small, secondary panels of the house itself – landscapes, scenes of hunting, animal landscapes, occasional mythological figures – but they tend to be treated in a far more relaxed manner, and often on a very much larger scale; typical examples are the huge landscapes in the House of the Small Fountain (VI, 8, 23–24; see illustration), the very large animal frieze on the garden wall of the House of M. Lucretius Fronto (IV, 2, 1), and the birth of Venus in the House of the Venus (II, 3, 31). Occasionally the influence was in the other direction, the garden influencing the house. Miniature garden panels such as No. 91 and No. 92 patently derive ultimately from such famous originals as the early Third Style garden room of the Villa of Livia at Prima Porta, while plants such as those in No. 97 were freely copied on the dadoes of formal Fourth Style compositions, as for example in the House of the Silver Wedding (V, 2, Mau E). There was a marked tendency for the garden, its fountains and its plants to invade the paintings of the adjoining walls. At the same time the influence of wall mosaics was just beginning to make itself felt. The last phase of Pompeian art was one of transition towards a future which Pompeii itself was never to see. In it what had been 'popular' art was rapidly acquiring a fresh, more monumental dimension.

Sculpture

The early history of Roman sculpture in Campania is largely shaped by the fact that by the first century BC there were few wealthy or influential Romans who did not possess luxurious country residences on the Bay of Naples. These were the people who, under the late Republic, were busy amassing private collections of sculpture inspired by the huge galleries of Greek loot on display in the temples and public buildings at Rome. Original works were naturally in short supply and contemporary Greek workshops in the old sculptural centres of the eastern Mediterranean were quick to take advantage of the growing demand for replicas and adaptations of old masterpieces. The letters of Cicero (who had two, if not three, properties in Campania, one near Pompeii) provide us with an entertaining picture of the lengths to which an educated Roman would go in order to furnish his country retreats with suitable statuary. The amazing array assembled by Lucius Calpurnius Piso Caesoninus, a rich but not exceptionally wealthy Roman, in his villa near Herculaneum (see page 79) vividly demonstrates the size and quality of one of these early collections. Most of the eighty-three pieces were acquired between 60 and 40 BC, the products of various workshops. Among the many close copies and freer interpretations, which reveal Caesoninus' preference, in common with most of his contemporaries, for Archaic and Classical Greek originals, was a series of eighteen busts, herms and statues of Greek philosophers, orators and poets, and an impressive group of portraits of Hellenistic kings and generals. There were only two portraits of Romans, both of them historical personalities whose identities are in dispute, but no portraits of the family itself. Despite their relative prosperity the wealthy citizens of Pompeii could not compete on this level, but small-scale echoes are found in such bronzes as the Dancing Faun from the House of the Faun (Naples Museum, inv. 5002), the statue of Perseus from House v, 3, 10 (Naples Museum, inv. 126170), the statue of an ephebe adapted to a lamp-holder from a fourth century BC original and found in the House of Cornelius Teges (I, 7, 10; Naples Museum, inv. 143753), to which may now be added a similar conceit from the House of Fabius Rufus.

It was not until the political stability which accompanied the re-establishment of central authority by Augustus that the erection of public municipal statues in honour of members of the Imperial family and of prominent local citizens became part of the everyday life of a small town like Pompeii. Once launched, the fashion caught on rapidly. But for the earthquake of 62 and the salvage operations which followed the eruption, a visitor to the Forum would have been confronted by a forest of statues. Three very large bronze statues, probably of members of the Imperial house, occupied most of the space at the southern end, and among the eighteen equestrian statues which stood on bases marshalled along the front of the western portico, in front of the Temple of Jupiter and elsewhere, must have been that recorded on the tombstone of the wealthy *garum* manufacturer and chief magistrate of Pompeii, Aulus Umbricius Scaurus. (*CIL* x. 1024). Perhaps his is among those portrayed in a scene of the Forum from the Villa of Julia Felix (Naples Museum, inv. 9068, see illustration). About fifty other standing figures wearing the toga, the majority probably in marble, commemorated the services of other local worthies. In the surrounding public buildings and temples, here and elsewhere in the town, were numerous other opportunities to indulge this new craze. Among the few survivals are the herm portrait of Norbanus Sorex (Naples Museum, inv. 4991, see page 65) in the Temple of Isis (of which a duplicate stood in the Eumachia Building) and those of such conspicuous benefactors and donors of public buildings as Eumachia herself (Naples Museum, inv. 6232), Marcus Tullius (Naples Museum, inv. 6231) and Marcus Holconius Rufus (Naples Museum, inv. 6233) who were responsible for the fullers' hall, the Temple of Fortuna Augusta and the rebuilding of the Large Theatre respectively.

It is at this period that portrait statues of family members begin to join the other sculptures in the Villa at Herculaneum, and portraits appear on semi-public display in private houses at Pompeii. Fine examples of these are the bronze busts of a man and a woman placed in an *ala* of the atrium in the House of the Citharist (Naples Museum, inv. 4992, see overleaf, and No. 26) and the series of portraits on herm shafts found placed

Equestrian statues in the Forum. Naples Museum.

Bronze portrait bust. Naples
Museum inv. 4992.

Bronze portrait bust. Naples
Museum inv. '19'.

Marble head of a woman from a
statue. Naples Museum inv.
120424.

at the entrance to the *tablinum* in several of the larger houses. The most famous is that of the banker, L. Caecilius Felix (better but mistakenly known as Caecilius Jucundus, see illustration, page 39), but there are also good-quality marble examples portraying successful businessmen who were well known in the town: Vesonius Primus from House VI, 14, 20 (Pompeii Antiquarium, inv. 407–4), Cornelius Rufus from VIII, 4, 15 (Pompeii Antiquarium, inv. 403–4) and the portrait of an old man (see No. 32). Styles and techniques are so closely related to those found in public statuary that presumably, and not surprisingly, they were produced by the same workshops.

Such 'display' portraits must be distinguished from the purely private aspects of family portraiture which already had a long history behind them. Among these are the stylized funerary statues of which No. 33, executed by a local craftsman in local materials, offers a good example. The series begins about the time the Sullan colony was established and continues until the eruption. Another aspect is exemplified by the shrine of the *imagines maiorum* in the House of the Menander (see illustration). These are little more than puppet heads carved in the traditional materials of wood or wax, taken to represent the probably generalized and purely symbolic portraits which formed part of the ancestral cult. That this was still a living portrait form and not an extraordinary survival from a much earlier period is shown by the still unpublished wooden heads, on a larger scale, from Herculaneum, the best preserved of which appears to represent a woman of Augustan or later date. There was obviously an element of the population who, whatever it may have thought of the developing, strongly Hellenized style in vogue for public statuary, preferred to uphold, in a funerary context at least, the established conventions of an older tradition. Once again we see the 'popular' forms and those more sophisticated trends influenced by the larger world existing happily side by side.

One of the saddest losses is that of all but a few fragments of the cult figures of the temples, among which must have been some of the earliest and finest pieces of sculpture that the town possessed. All the statues of divinities that have survived are secondary dedications within the temple precincts (see Nos. 95, 202) or from private houses, such as the Venus from a blue-painted shrine in the garden peristyle of House 1, 2, 17 (Naples Museum, inv. 6412) and the Artemis, No. 94, all copyist works of varying quality and almost all produced in the early Empire.

With garden decoration we are again in the familiar world of Hellenistic imagery, and here one cannot help being struck by the extraordinary dominance of Dionysiac themes. These included all the rustic members of Dionysus's company and of course brought in all the characters of ancient theatre. It looks as though there was a very strongly established convention in this field which the suppliers and their clients were content to follow. The only major exceptions appear to be the various animal figures allowed as appropriate to fountains.

There is nothing in the surviving works at any level to support the idea that Pompeii had its own school of sculpture. Undoubtedly a number of local jobbing workshops produced much of the simpler sculpted ornament on public fountains, well-heads, less extravagant tombs and the odd figured group in local tufa like the naively conceived gladiator and Priapus commissioned by a tavern-keeper (Pompeii Antiquarium, inv. 11739). Some experienced craftsmen must have been charged with the daily maintenance and occasional repairs required by the growing quantities of municipal and official statuary. One or two workshops specializing in funerary sculpture of the traditional type – a type found all over Campania – could have supplied the needs of the town in this context. But most of the major commissions, if not imported as finished works from Rome or Greece, would have been executed by the workshops based at Puteoli, where a steadily growing body of evidence attests the considerable activities of marble workers and sculptors.

The other arts

Tombs outside the Nuceria Gate.

'Imagines maiorum',
House of the Menander.

In a society which made no distinction between fine arts and craftsmanship, the 'minor arts' were bound to play an important role. Although some of the pieces here exhibited were heirlooms or luxury pieces imported from other parts of the Roman world, the majority were made locally in Campania, which is known to have been an important centre for the production of metalwork and glass, and which was almost certainly largely self-supporting in such things as jewellery, the engraving of seals and gems, stuccowork and mosaic.

In the second and first centuries BC the long-established Campanian bronze industry, centred on Capua but with workshops probably in many of the neighbouring towns, was exporting all over the Roman world, and although by the first century AD it was losing ground to new centres established in northern Italy, Gaul and probably elsewhere in the provinces, in AD 79 it was still a flourishing industry. Its products await detailed study, but it is clear that they went in very large quantities to the European market, both in the provinces and beyond the frontiers. Although it was famed particularly for its large wine-vessels (*situlae*) and other fine bronze tableware, it was certainly producing bronzework of many other kinds, including household furniture of all sorts, heating and lighting equipment, small-scale statuary and statuettes. Several Pompeian families had connections with the Capuan industry, among them the Hordionii and the Nigidii, one of whom, M. Nigidius Vaccula, presented a large bronze brazier to the Stabian Baths and a bronze bench to the Forum Baths. Small workshops established in the town to undertake repairs may also have produced some of the simpler domestic utensils. Two *graffiti* mention coppersmiths (*fabri aerarii: CIL* IV, 3702 and 4256) and a bronze strainer found at Boscoreale is inscribed *pertudit Pompeis Felicio* ('pierced by Felicio at Pompeii'). In 1899 a partially excavated site outside the Vesuvius Gate produced quantities of scrap bronze, two plaster models of heads, a statuette of an ephebe brought in for repair and a number of little bronze-workers' anvils. The coppersmith seen at work in the relief No. 287 was evidently producing fresh work as well as undertaking repairs, and he was surely resident in Pompeii. Priscus the engraver (*caelator*) who greeted Campanus the gem-cutter in a *graffito* on the wall of the Palaestra (*Priscus caelator Campano gemmario fel(iciter)*) (*CIL* IV, Suppl. 8502), could have worked either in bronze or in silver (see illustration above).

The Roman passion for collecting silver plate was first fostered by the enormous wealth of treasure brought back by the victorious generals of the early second century BC from the Greek cities of southern Italy and from Greece itself and the East. At first it was available only to the very rich, who bought the booty sold at public auction; but silversmiths were soon

*Mosaic emblema of a nilotic
landscape, House of the Menander.*

*Display of silver plate painted on
the wall of the tomb of Vestorius Priscus.*

established in Rome, producing plate in ever-increasing quantities, until by AD 79 we find even quite modest households possessing one or two pieces. Sets of eating silver (*argentum escarium*) and drinking silver (*argentum potorium*), together with one or two show pieces that were treasured as family heirlooms, were proudly displayed on special tables, such as that painted in loving detail on the precinct wall of the tomb of the young aedile, C. Vestorius Priscus, outside the Vesuvius Gate at Pompeii (see illustration).

Individual pieces from such services had been found in Pompeian houses ever since the excavation began; but a great many of the larger collections had doubtless been recovered after the eruption, and it was not until 1895 that a complete set of silver plate, 109 pieces in all, was found in a *villa rustica* at Boscoreale, two miles north-west of Pompeii. It had been deposited in a vat in the wine-press room (see plan, page 53), together with gold jewellery and over one thousand gold coins, and beside it lay the skeleton of a woman. The collection had been made very largely in the early years of the first century AD, but it also included a dish over three hundred years old (No. 336) and there were some later purchases. As well as drinking cups and eating dishes there were also some display pieces (e.g. No. 335) and toilet mirrors (e.g. No. 337).

In 1930 this hoard was matched by the discovery of a similar treasure in an underground room of the House of the Menander (see plan, page 100), where it had been stored for safe keeping in a large wooden chest, reinforced with bronze, each piece carefully wrapped in a cloth and neatly arranged in series. It comprised 118 pieces, weighing a total of just under 53 lb (24 kg). Alongside it was found the family jewellery, which included the *bulla*, No. 48, and a number of gold and silver coins, carefully chosen (as is customary in such stores of reserve coinage) from issues which, because of their gold or silver content, were secure against the inflation which was already steadily eroding the value of ordinary contemporary coinage. Most of the vessels were probably produced by the workshops in Rome, but there were silversmiths from southern Italy and Greece resident in Neapolis and Puteoli who could as easily have supplied the more

strongly Hellenistic forms. The carefully executed repairs made to some of the silverware found would certainly have been done locally.

Goldsmiths and gem-cutters were among the small craftsmen of Pompeii. The *aurifices* declared themselves as supporters of an electoral candidate, and Campanus, a *gemmarius*, is hailed by the metal-engraver (*caelator*) Priscus. A dealer or cutter of gemstones, Pinarius Cerealis, lived in a house (III, 4b) on the Via dell'Abbondanza, in which were found some engraving tools and a box containing 114 cut and partially worked carnelians, sardonyx, amethysts and agates.

Most of the fine glass found in Pompeii probably came from Puteoli, where glass-blowing was a major industry. No glass furnaces have yet been found at Pompeii itself, but these would in any case have tended to be located outside the residential districts in areas as yet only very summarily explored. There are, moreover, several rather simple forms – a particular type of plain beaker, for example, and a special form of squat, handled wine jug (*askos*) – which appear to be peculiar to Pompeii. It seems likely that, like jobbing bronze-workers, small potters and lamp-makers, there were also glass-workers catering for the simple everyday needs of the town.

Among the other craftsmen active at Pompeii, there were a great many painters, mosaicists and stuccoists. The almost total absence of any reference to them in the inscriptions and in the *graffiti* does, however, suggest that, as at many other periods of history, such men tended to travel wherever their skills were required, and that most of them were based elsewhere in Campania. There was also a measure of centralized workshop production for some of the finest pieces, such as the mosaic *emblemata* which constituted the highly-prized centrepieces of many of the best pavements (as in the House of the Menander, see illus.) and which were made in specially transportable trays. The same would have applied to the painted *pinakes* which, being on wood, have almost all perished. In both cases one thinks naturally of Neapolis, that great local centre of conservative Greek culture, the Roman-period archaeology of which is probably lost to us for ever.

Herculaneum

Herculaneum lay on the coast, on a spur projecting from the foot of Vesuvius, about five miles east of Neapolis (Naples) and ten miles west of Pompeii. The ancient coastline is today so overlaid by later deposits that it calls for a strong effort of the imagination to picture Herculaneum as it is described by the first century BC historian Sisenna, namely as a small city set on a headland between two inlets which served as harbours. Dionysius of Halicarnassus refers to the excellence of these harbours, and Strabo refers to it as an unusually healthy place. To judge from the few references in ancient literature (and archaeology has as yet barely touched the earlier levels) its early history was very similar to that of Pompeii. Founded probably as a fortified Greek trading post, it passed with Pompeii under Samnite rule. During the Social War it was occupied by Sulla's troops in 89 BC, but there is no evidence to indicate that, like Pompeii, it was refounded as a Roman colony. Instead, at about this time it seems to have acquired the status of a municipality (*municipium*), a status which involved the establishment of municipal institutions closely akin to those of a *colonia*, but without any expropriations of property or the introduction of fresh citizens from outside. Though badly damaged in the earthquake of AD 62, Herculaneum made a more rapid recovery than Pompeii. Within the area excavated much is rebuilt or redecorated, but there is little unfinished work. In broad essentials the two cities continued to have much in common, enough certainly to justify the use of exhibits from Herculaneum wherever, for one reason or another, comparable material is not available from Pompeii.

There were, however, also significant differences, of which two in particular deserve mention here. One is that whereas Pompeii, thanks to its position at the mouth of the river Sarno, became a prosperous local port and market town, Herculaneum developed on more exclusively residential lines. Some local commerce it did of course have: the line of the main coast road ran straight across the town, of which it was the principal transverse street, and the harbour was the natural outlet for the vineyards of the southern slopes of Vesuvius. But one has only to walk through the streets of the excavated quarter to sense the difference of atmosphere: almost exclusively residential, with shops and bars grouped along two of the main streets and very little trace of local industry. Herculaneum's role was that of a miniature Brighton, profiting from its salubrious climate and from the proximity of many wealthy villas. One of these, the Villa of the Papyri, the property of L. Calpurnius Piso Caesoninus, the father-in-law of Caesar, lay just outside the west gate. Here, eighteenth-century tunnelling brought to light a unique series of late Hellenistic bronze sculptures and a library of more than a thousand papyrus rolls, most of them – such are the ironies of archaeological survival – the works of minor Epicurean philosophers. The area of the city so far uncovered, running southwards from the main cross-street towards the south-eastern part of the sea frontage of the promontory, is laid out on a street grid of Greek type. Among the public buildings excavated, or explored by tunnelled galleries in the eighteenth-century manner, are a small but richly adorned theatre; a building opening off the main street which may or may not prove to have been a basilica; two public bath buildings, one within the town and akin to the Stabian baths and a more modern building outside the walls; and on the east side of the town a large *palaestra* similar to that near the Amphitheatre at Pompeii. Still to be located, but known from inscriptions, are a market building (*macellum*), a temple of Isis, and a temple of Magna Mater, the predecessor of which had been destroyed by the earthquake (*terrae motu conlapsam*) and was restored in AD 76 through the bounty of the emperor Vespasian.

A second and to ourselves very important distinction between Pompeii and Herculaneum is the very different manner in which they were hit by the final catastrophe, a circumstance which has materially affected the nature and condition of the surviving remains. Whereas Pompeii was slowly but inexorably engulfed by layer upon layer of airborne, sulphurous debris, at Herculaneum the destruction took place in two sharply distinguishable stages. The initial bombardment of incandescent pebbles and rocks resulting from the first explosion may well have been more intense than at Pompeii; it will be recalled (see page 36) that a few hours later Pliny the Elder was already unable to put ashore here and had to coast down to Stabiae. But

Herculaneum.

there was not much ash, and most of the inhabitants seem to have been able to make good their escape up the road to Naples. Relatively few bodies have been found within the city. Then came the second stage, in which the town was engulfed by a horrendous avalanche of liquid mud, swept down the mountainside by the torrential rains that frequently accompany an eruption, and channelled towards Herculaneum by the valleys of which the city's two harbours were the mouths. A wall of mud flooded through the streets and into the houses, bringing down the roofs of some and filling up others. When the area became once more accessible, the coastline had changed beyond all recognition. The city lay buried beneath a mantle of deposit in places as much as sixty-five feet deep, which was rapidly hardening into the solid rock through which well-diggers in the early eighteenth century chanced upon the Roman theatre, and upon which the houses of the modern Resina now stand.

This sequence of events had several important consequences. One is that whatever was not destroyed by the first impact of fire and mud was securely sealed against all intrusion until modern times. At Pompeii few of the public buildings or the wealthier houses escaped the post-eruption attentions of their owners or of looters. They could be located because many of the taller landmarks were still visible, and although it was dangerous work (and some of the bodies found are certainly those of looters rather than of eruption victims), there were rich prizes to be won. The Forum area was stripped of its bronze statuary and much of its marble and fine building stone, and private houses were ransacked for their treasure chests and other valuables. At Herculaneum all that was not removed during the first few hours of the eruption was preserved for posterity. Sadly, the eighteenth-century treasure hunters destroyed far more than they recovered, but even so we have a unique body of public statuary found as and where it was used in antiquity. Another consequence was the preservation not merely of the impressions of organic objects, but also in many cases of the actual carbonized remains of the objects themselves, such things as furnishings and woodwork, doors and screens, foodstuffs, or the papyrus rolls referred to above. Such objects are, alas, too fragile to travel, but they have added very materially to our knowledge of many aspects of daily life in antiquity which in normal circumstances are irrevocably lost.

Bronze Isis-Fortuna (190). Bronze Apollo (214).

right
Aphrodite with Priapus (218).

overleaf
Painted frieze from the Hall of the Mysteries (204)
Scenes VII and VIII; Scene IX.

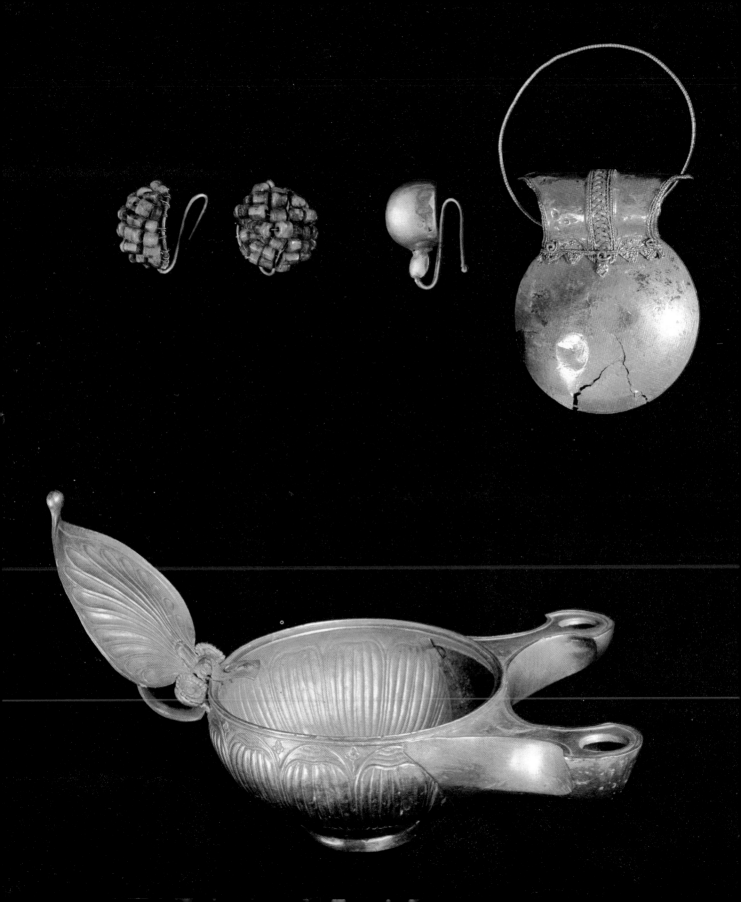

left
Earrings in gold and emeralds (53, 54). Gold *bulla* (48).
Gold lamp (169).

Silver hand mirror with Leda and the Swan (337).
Silver *phiale* (335).

overleaf
Painted wall at Oplontis detail (338).

Catalogue

Seventeen coins illustrating events and personalities in the history of Campania and of Pompeii.

The first contacts with Rome

a. Romano-Campanian didrachm, struck at Rome about 269–266 BC, for use in southern Italy, where the didrachm (two Greek drachmas) was the standard unit of precious metal currency.
Obv. Youthful head of Hercules.
Rev. The statue of the wolf suckling Romulus and Remus, which was set up in Rome in 296 BC.
BMCRR, Romano-Campanian 30. Sydenham, no. 6. Crawford no. 20.1.

b. Anonymous Semilibral Sextans, struck at Rome about 217–215 BC, for use in southern Italy. The standard, representing a reduction in weight, seems to have been introduced after the disastrous defeat of the Roman army by Hannibal at Lake Trasimene.
Obv. The she-wolf suckling Romulus and Remus.
Rev. An eagle with a flower in its beak, a reference to the eagle which brought food to the twins.
BMCRR, Romano-Campanian 121. Sydenham, no. 95. Crawford no. 39.3.

The Social War, 90–89 BC

c. Denarius of the Italic Confederacy, minted somewhere in the north-east of the confederacy territory.
Obv. Head of Italia.
Rev. An oath-taking ceremony.
BMCRR, Social War 23. Sydenham, no. 619 or 620.

d. Denarius of the Italic Confederacy, possibly struck in Samnium.
Obv. Head of Italia, legend in Oscan script.
Rev. Soldier trampling on a Roman standard and a bull, symbolizing Italia.
BMCRR, Social War 5. Sydenham, no. 627.

e. Posthumous portrait of Sulla (founder of the Roman colony at Pompeii) on a denarius, struck at Rome in 54 BC by Q. Pompeius Rufus, his grandchild by his daughter, who was in that year the official in charge of the mint. On the other face Rufus showed his paternal grandfather, also named Q. Pompeius Rufus, who had been consul with Sulla in 88 BC.
BMCRR 3884. Sydenham, no. 908. Crawford no. 434.1 and p. 734.

f. Portrait of Julius Caesar on a denarius struck at Rome in 44 BC by the moneyer L. Aemilius Buca. In that year the senate voted to place Caesar's portrait on the coinage – the first time a living person had been so represented.
Obv. Head of Caesar and legend CAESAR DICT. PERPETVO ('Caesar, dictator for life').
Rev. A *fasces* (without an axe), symbolizing *Libertas* (!); a *caduceus*, a globe and clasped hands, symbols respectively of *Felicitas* (prosperity), *Pax* and *Concordia*.
BMCRR 4157. Sydenham, no. 1063. Crawford no. 480.6.

g. Posthumous portrait of Agrippa on a copper *as* issued by Tiberius (AD 14–37), whose first wife, Vipsania, was Agrippa's daughter. Agrippa, the victorious admiral at the battle of Actium in 31 BC and the designated heir to Augustus, died in 12 BC. Shortly before his death he started building the villa at Boscotrecase, inherited by his son Agrippa Postumus.
Obv. Agrippa wearing a crown embodying the prows of the defeated galleys.
Rev. Neptune.
BMCRE I, Tiberius 162.

The first Roman Emperors: the Julio-Claudian dynasty

h. Augustus (27 BC – AD 14). Copper *as*, issued in 7 BC. Augustus owned many properties in Campania, notably on Capri. His nephew Marcellus (d. 23 BC), was official patron of the colony between 25 and 23 BC. For Augustus, see also No. 45.
Obv. Wreathed head of Augustus.
Rev. The name of one of the moneyers of this year around a large S.C., indicating that this base metal coinage was issued on the authority of the Senate (*senatus consultu*).
BMCRE I, Augustus 41★ (inv. 1934 10.18.1).

i. Tiberius (AD 14–37). Bronze sestertius. Tiberius spent the last eleven years of his life in semi-retirement on Capri. His son and heir-apparent, Drusus (d. AD 23) was honorary chief magistrate of Pompeii (*duovir quinquennalis*) in AD 20 or 21.

Obv. Seated figure of Tiberius and an inscription recording his munificence to the cities of Asia Minor after an earthquake in AD 17.

Rev. The titles of Tiberius around a large S.C. (as in 8 above).

BMCRE I, Tiberius 72.

j. Gaius, usually known as 'Caligula' (AD 37–41), great-nephew and heir of Tiberius. Bronze sestertius. In AD 33 or 34, before his accession, Caligula had been honorary *duovir* of Pompeii, and as emperor, in AD 40, he was *duovir quinquennalis*.

Obv. Bare head of Caligula.

Rev. The three sisters of Caligula, personified as *Concordia*, *Securitas* and *Fortuna*.

BMCRE I, Caligula 36.

k. Claudius (AD 41–54), nephew of Tiberius. Sestertius.

Obv. Head of Claudius.

Rev. The name and titles of Claudius's father (Nero Claudius Drusus, brother of Tiberius) framing a representation of a triumphal arch commemorating his victories over the Germans in 12–9 BC.

BMCRE I, Claudius 121.

l. Nero (AD 54–68), son of Agrippina the Younger, the sister of Gaius (Caligula) and niece of Tiberius. Sestertius, issued after the coinage reforms of AD 64. It was during Nero's reign that Pompeii incurred the displeasure of the central government as a result of the amphitheatre riot of AD 59, a probable reason for the surprising lack of official aid after the earthquake of AD 62.

Obv. Head of Nero.

Rev. The goddess Roma.

BMCRE I, Nero 116.

The Year of the Four Emperors. After the
suicide of Nero on 9 June 69 and the extinction
of Julio-Claudian dynasty, there was a
period of anarchy with three short-lived
emperors, a period brought to an end by the
victory of Vespasian, founder of the new
Flavian dynasty.

m. Galba (9 June 68–15 January 69).
Sestertius.
Obv. Head of Galba.
Rev. The deified Livia, wife of Augustus, who
had helped Galba early in his career.
BMCRE I, Galba 54.

n. Otho (15 January–25 April 69).
Denarius. Otho had been an earlier husband
of Poppaea Sabina, Nero's second wife, who
may well have been the owner of the villa at
Oplontis.
Obv. Head of Otho.
Rev. Figure of Peace and the legend PAX
ORBIS TERRARVM.
BMCRE I, Otho 3.

o. Vitellius (2 January – 20(?) December 69).
Sestertius.
Obv. Head of Vitellius.
Rev. Figure of Peace.
BMCRE I, Vitellius 57.

The Flavian Dynasty

p. Vespasian (AD 69–79). Sestertius.
Pompeii, in erecting a temple to him
(page 61) was clearly anxious to secure the
favour of the new dynasty, and there are
records of an official land-commissioner's
activities on the city's behalf. See also No. 5.
Obv. Head of Vespasian.
Rev. Vespasian, accompanied by the goddess
Roma, raises a kneeling personification of the
city of Rome. Legend: ROMA RESVRGENS.
BMCRE II, Vespasian 566.

q. Titus (AD 79–81). Sestertius, issued in
AD 73. Although in August AD 79 Titus had
been emperor (*Augustus*) for barely two
months, he had been officially associated
with his father's rule since 1 July 71. See
also No. 4.
Obv. Head of Titus.
Rev. Titus on horseback spears a fallen foe.
The oblong shield is that of a Gaul or
German, and the coin probably refers to the
annexation in that year of some territories
between the Rhine and the Danube.
BMCRE II, Vespasian 653.

2

Oscan dedicatory inscription.
Length 43 cm; height 29 cm.
British Museum, inv. 1867.5–8.76.
Found built into the inner arch of the Nola Gate.

V. Popidius V. med. túv. aamanaffed isidu profatted, of which the Latin equivalent would be *V(ibius) Popidius V(ibi filius) med(dic) tu(ticus) (=publicus) faciendum curavit, idem probavit.*
'Vibius Popidius, son of Vibius, chief magistrate, had charge of this work and approved it.'

The Meddix Tuticus was chief magistrate of the Samnite town, the equivalent of one of the later *duoviri*. Vibius Popidius, a member of what continued to be one of the leading families of Roman Pompeii, was evidently in this instance operating in his official capacity on behalf of the township. One notes the identity of the Italic and Roman forms of nomenclature and the use of close equivalents of what were to become the stock formulae of official Latin epigraphy.
J. Svetaieff, *Inscriptiones Italiae Inferioris Dialecticae* (Moscow 1886) 51, no. 44.
E. Vetter, *Handbuch der Italischen Dialekte* (Heidelberg 1953) I, no. 14.

3

Portrait head of the emperor Augustus.
Greek island marble, possibly from Paros.
Height 38.5 cm.
British Museum, inv. 1879.7–12.9.
Findspot unknown.

The over life-size head, carved to be inserted into a statue body, shows Augustus aged about thirty-six, at the time when he became emperor. The type, known in over fifty replicas from all over the Empire, was probably based on an official portrait created soon after his victory at Actium in 31 BC.

There were at least three statues of Augustus in Pompeii, one of them very large, set up in the Forum and its surrounding public buildings. None of them has survived.
BMC Sculpture III, no.1879.

4

Portrait head of the emperor Vespasian.
Fine-grained white marble.
Height 40.5 cm.
British Museum, inv. 1850.
Found in the excavations of Sir Thomas Reade at Carthage in 1835–36.

Carved to be set on a colossal togate statue, the head shows Vespasian aged about sixty, at the beginning of his reign (AD 69–79).

No portrait statue of Vespasian has been found at Pompeii, but the temple dedicated to his cult on the eastern side of the Forum (see page 61) must undoubtedly have contained one.
BMC Sculpture III no. 1890. M. Wegner (ed.), *Das römische Herrscherbild. Die Flavier* (Berlin 1966) 10f. and 76.

5

Portrait head of the emperor Titus.
Greek marble, from Naxos (?).
Height 29 cm.
British Museum, inv. 1909.6–10.1.
Acquired in London, said to come from Utica, in Tunisia.

The head, broken from an over life-size statue, was probably made by a Greek sculptor in the eastern Mediterranean in about AD 70, when Titus was heir apparent. His father, Vespasian, died on 24 June 79, two months before the eruption, and it was on Titus's administration that the burden of bringing relief to the area fell.
M. Wegner (ed.), *Das römische Herrscherbild. Die Flavier*, (Berlin 1966), 27 and 28.

2

3

4

6
Pair of villa landscapes.
Width 53 cm; height 22 cm.
Naples Museum, inv. 9406.
From Pompeii.

Two separate views of villa facades probably from the lateral panels of a Third Style scheme (see illustration p. 70), now mounted as a pair. The left-hand view shows a straight porticoed facade upraised on a platform with a tall columnar central porch; in front of the portico is a garden with a large axial enclosure and at either end, rising from a lower level, is a double portico, of two orders, facing outwards. Above and beyond the right-hand portico is the facade of a temple-like building facing inwards; there may have been other buildings or trees in the damaged upper left-hand part. The right-hand view shows a central gabled porch at the junction of two gable-ended inward-facing porticoes, enclosing on three sides a trapezoidal space concentric to which is an enclosure with posts at the angles. Above and behind rise a number of other buildings including a circular *tempietto* (*tholos*) and

another colonnade. The perspective of these scenes is syntactic, and some of the detail (e.g. the half-gables of the flanking porticoes on the left-hand panel) is without parallel in surviving contemporary architecture, but it is generally accepted that such facades were a feature of the wealthy *villae marittimae*.
Peters 115f.

7
Painting of a villa beside the sea.
Diameter 25 cm.
Naples Museum, inv. 9511.
From Stabiae.

Roundel portraying the two-storied columnar facade of a *villa marittima*. The centre of the facade curves inwards, towards a tower-like circular feature. In front is a platform with two projecting jetties, human figures and statues. Beyond are other buildings, trees, and a rocky crag on which are trees and what appears to be a group of statuary. The roundel and its companion pieces (Naples Museum, inv. 9408, 9409) would have occupied the centres of large panels in a Fourth Style scheme, comparable to those in the first room off the peristyle in the House of 'Loreius Tiburtinus' (II, 2, 2–5; Schefold, *WP* 51).
Rostowzew, 'Architekturlandschaft' 75(b).
Peters 157.

6

7

5

8

Painting of a villa beside the sea.
Length 39.5 cm; height 17 cm.
Naples Museum, inv. 9480.
From Stabiae.

The seaward frontage of an elaborate *villa marittima*; in the foreground is a platform with arches and steps down to the water, and in the background are other buildings, gardens, and a rocky eminence crowned by a temple. On the platform are sketched figures, at the bottom right-hand corner part of a boat and, behind it, a statue posed on a rock.

Probably from the centre of a panel in a Third Style wall, as in the *tablinum* of the House of M. Lucretius Fronto (see page 70) or possibly used like the landscapes or still lifes in the wall schemes of the courtyard of the Temple of Isis (see illustration page 59).
Rostowzew, 'Architekturlandschaft' 75, no. 3.
Peters 159f.

9

Sacro-idyllic landscape.
Width 30 cm; height 26 cm.
Naples Museum, inv. 9447.
From Herculaneum.

Highly impressionistic view of a rustic sanctuary, a small, circular, tower-like structure, a rocky crag, and trees. On the left a figure is carrying a basin; on the right another figure stoops before a herm. In the centre, in shadowy outline, is a statue on a pedestal.

Presumably from the field of a Fourth Style lateral panel, as in the atrium of the House of Fabius Amandio (I, 7, 2–3).

10

Painting of a sanctuary beside the sea.
Width 62 cm; height 52 cm.
Naples Museum, inv. 9482
From Pompeii (see below)

Painted in light colours on a black ground, this fragment portrays a sanctuary, set on a rocky island or promontory, and in the foreground two boats. The details of the sanctuary are conventional: a central,

circular shrine, or *tholos*, flanked by porticoes and a re-entrant facade wall, in front of which, facing on to the water, is an open platform, on which are several groups of figures, including a woman and a dog. On the enclosure wall is a statue, and beyond it are trees and buildings perched on rocks. In the left margin are traces of a frame and part of an ornamental column.

The scene probably formed part of a much larger panel set between columns as on the Third Style wall, found at Pompeii on 23 August 1758 (*Pitture di Ercolano* II, p. 273, pl. L) which shows above, in the background, a similar sanctuary; in the middle is a boat, and below, in the foreground, another island sanctuary and a fisherman.
Rostowzew, 'Architekturlandschaft' 52.
Peters 117f.

11

Architectural landscape with figures.
Length 36 cm; height 37 cm.
Naples Museum, inv. 9475.
Found in 1776 in the Temple of Isis.

One of a series of idealized landscapes, found on the walls of the portico enclosing the main precinct, which occupied the centres of large monochrome panels within the composition (as illustrated on p. 59), alternating in this position with representations of priests and of other ceremonial attendants of the goddess (see also No. 187). They follow the familiar 'sacro-idyllic' conventions, but most of them include elements that would have been recognizably Egyptian in intention: in this instance the tall tower with curving 'horns', which may be compared with the altar portrayed in No. 201, and which may represent a tomb.
Elia, *Mon Pitt* 12. Rostowzew 'Architektürlandschaft' 79, no. 3.

8

10

12

Seascape with boats and buildings.
Width 33 cm; height 23 cm.
Naples Museum, inv. 9463.
From Pompeii

A small, highly impressionistic landscape, including a central *tholos* on a rocky islet with a jetty and two fishermen, a porticoed facade with trees beyond it, and two boats. The scene is viewed as if across a palisaded fence and appears to come from one of the complex architectural framing members of a Fourth Style scheme, as Nos. 149, 151.
Rostowzew, 'Architekturlandschaft' 85, note 2.

13

Landscape panel within a stucco cornice.
Length 2.10 m; height 52 cm.
Naples Museum, inv. 9496.
From the *exedra* off the west side of the middle peristyle of the House of the Citharist (1, 4, 5).

A long, narrow, idealized landscape and seascape, set within a stucco cornice of which the left end is missing. At the left end of the field, on a fortified rocky promontory, can be seen a small temple and, at the foot of the slope, a large seated statue on a tall pedestal, accompanied by the inevitable tree. The unusual building with three receding storeys is thought to represent a *belvedere*. Beyond it and at the right end are two rather similar buildings with landing stages and porticoed facades enclosing gardens and other buildings, free representations of *villae marittimae*. In the right foreground stands a

large urn on a pedestal. This picture blends into a single romantic landscape elements that are derived from a variety of sources, among them being some that are derived from the Hellenistic Nilotic landscapes and from the sacro-idyllic repertory, and others from the contemporary architecture of the Campanian *villae marittimae*.
Rostowzew, 'Architekturlandschaft' 91, no. 4.
Peters 165f.

9

11

12

13

14

Inscribed slab recording the building of the colonnade round the Forum.
Limestone.
Height 45.5 cm; width 44 cm.
Naples Museum, inv. 3825.
Found in 1814 in the Forum, near the entrance to the Basilica.

14

V(ibius) Popidius Ep(idii) f(ilius) q(uaestor) porticus faciendas coeravit.
'Vibius Popidius, son of Epidius, quaestor, had charge of the building of this portico'.

The inscription, which dates from the last period before the foundation of the Sullan colony in 80 BC, records the construction of a portico, built of tufa, around the central open area of the Forum. This Samnite portico, which marked an important step in the monumentalization of the city centre, was in process of being replaced at the time of the earthquake and the eruption. The official in charge, Vibius Popidius, was at the time a *quaestor*, one of the junior magistrates of the Samnite town. He belonged to a very prominent indigenous Pompeian family, the Popidii, who are known to have provided at least two chief magistrates *(meddices)* of the pre-Roman period (see No. 2).
CIL x 794; *ILS* 5538.

15

Inscribed slab recording the rebuilding of the Temple of Isis.
Marble, recomposed from 37 pieces.
Length 2.35 m; height 49.5 cm.
Naples Museum, inv. 3765.
Found in 1765 fallen from its position over the entrance from the street to the Temple.

N(umerius) Popidius N(umerii) f(ilius) Celsinus aedem Isidis terrae motu conlapsam a fundamento p(ecunia) s(ua) restituit. Hunc decuriones ob liberalitatem cum esset annorum sexs ordini suo gratis adlegerunt.
'Numerius Popidius Celsinus, son of Numerius, at his own expense rebuilt from its foundations the Temple of Isis, which had been totally destroyed by earthquake. In recognition of his generosity the city council elected him to their number without any further fee, although he was only six years old.'

The ostensible donor was the son of a wealthy freedman of the Popidius family, Numerius Popidius Ampliatus, who was himself debarred from election to the council of decurions because he had been born a slave. There was normally a lower age limit for the decurionate (often twenty-five years), but exceptions could be made, and in this instance the usual admission fee was also waived. Within the sanctuary the father, Ampliatus, was able to dedicate in his own name a statue of Dionysus (here, as often, identified with Osiris); and Celsinus, together with his mother, Corelia Celsa, and a brother, is named as donor of the pavement in the larger of the two rooms beyond the temple.
CIL x. 846. *ILS* 6367.

16, 17

Plaster casts of two marble reliefs showing scenes of the earthquake of AD 62.
Lengths 86 cm; heights 13 cm and 17 cm.
Originals from the House of L. Caecilius Jucundus (v, 1 26).

The reliefs formed part of the household shrine *(lararium)*. Though carved in a strikingly 'popular' style they afford valuable evidence for the appearance of buildings which were still in ruins at the time of the eruption seventeen years later.

The first relief shows the collapse of the Capitolium at the northern end of the Forum (see plan, page 44), its steps flanked by a pair of equestrian statues. On the left is the monumental arch, of which the core still stands, and on the right an altar to Tellus (Earth), which was demolished when the Forum paving was repaired, leaving only traces of its foundations. Around the altar are shown vessels and instruments for the sacrifice of a bull.

The scene on the second relief would have been visible from Caecilius's house. It shows the Vesuvius Gate collapsing, and beside it the main distribution tower for the city's water supply *(castellum aquae)*. Although the structure of the latter withstood the tremors, it was still out of action in AD 79. Two mules pulling a cart narrowly escape the falling gate, and on the far right, apparently just outside the walls, is a rustic altar beside a tree, presumably a familiar landmark.
Maiuri *L'ultima fase* 1ff.

N POPIDIVS N F CELSINVS
AEDEM ISIDIS TERRAE MOTV CONLAPSAM
A FVNDAMENTO P S RESTITVIT HVNC DECVRIONES OB LIBERALITATEM
CVM ESSET ANNORVM SEXS ORDINI SVO GRATIS ADLEGERVNT

15

16, 17

18
Mosaic representing a skeleton carrying two askoi.
Height 91 cm; width 70 cm.
Naples Museum, inv. 9978.
From one of the sites in the Vesuvius area.

The skeleton, set within a rectangular frame and carried out in black and white mosaic, holds a pair of wine jugs (*askoi*; see Nos. 266 and 267). A product of the *memento mori* conventions fostered by Epicurean philosophy, it probably adorned the centre of a *triclinium*. Unlike the coloured floor mosaics, which derive from Hellenistic models, these black and white mosaics were a specifically Italian creation. Often naive, but always direct and lively, they are the artistic equivalent of the 'popular' strain in contemporary painting.

19
Model of the site of Pompeii.
Scale 1 : 250.

The model shows the present state of the excavations of the town, where about two-fifths remains to be uncovered. Little excavation has taken place outside the walls, and any attempts to investigate the immediate surroundings are greatly hampered by the huge mounds of debris from earlier excavations. A great deal more detailed survey work is needed before it will be possible to establish exactly where the ancient coastline and the port of Pompeii lay in relation to the town itself (see map, page 16).

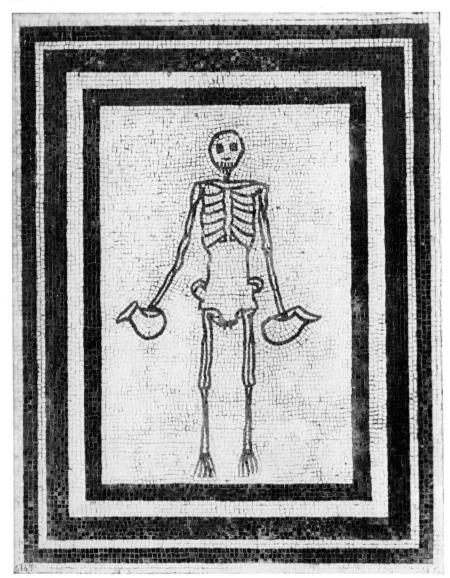

18

21

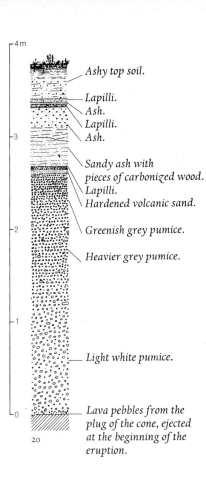

Ashy top soil.

Lapilli.
Ash.
Lapilli.
Ash.

*Sandy ash with
pieces of carbonized wood.*
Lapilli.
Hardened volcanic sand.

Greenish grey pumice.

Heavier grey pumice.

Light white pumice.

*Lava pebbles from the
plug of the cone, ejected
at the beginning of the
eruption.*

20

20

**Section through the volcanic and later
debris covering the site at Pompeii.**

The successive layers of lava pebbles, pumice
stones, ash and dust which fell on Pompeii
vary considerably in depth from point to
point within the town, but the general
sequence bears out the evidence of Pliny's
account of the eruption (see page 36). One of
the clearest, least complicated sections
through the deposit was recorded on the
level, open ground of the Grand Palaestra
beside the Amphitheatre, excavated in
1938–39. The deposits associated with the
eruption of AD 79 were here, on average just
under twelve feet (3.50 m) deep.

21

Plaster cast of a watchdog.
Height 50 cm.
Original in Pompeii, Antiquarium.
From the House of Vesonius Primus
(VI, 14, 20).

The unfortunate dog, wearing his
bronze-studded collar, was left chained up,
and suffocated beneath the ash and cinders
which then hardened round the corpse,
forming an impression which, with the
disintegration of the organic remains,
became a perfect hollow mould. It was the
archaeologist Fiorelli who first realized that
by filling such hollow moulds with plaster
one could obtain faithful replicas of objects
such as bodies, wooden doors, furniture and
foodstuffs.

22

Plaster cast of the body of a young woman.
Length 1.50 m.
Original in Pompeii, Antiquarium.

Like almost all the other human victims of
the eruption, this young woman died of
suffocation from the fumes of the falling ash
and cinders, which she had vainly tried to
keep from her nose and mouth by pulling her
tunic up over her face.

22

23
Painted portrait of a man and his wife.
Height 65 cm; width 58 cm.
Naples Museum, inv. 9058.
From House VII, 2, 6, on the back wall of a
small *exedra* opening off the Atrium.

The man, with a short curly beard and
moustache, wears a toga and carries a
papyrus scroll with a red seal. His wife
wears a red tunic and mantle, and her hair is
dressed in a fashion popular about the
middle of the first century AD. In her right
hand she holds to her lips a *stylus* (see No. 284)
for writing on the two-leaved wooden tablet
spread with wax (*diptych*, see also No. 258)
which she holds in her left. Although this
pose might be thought to indicate that the
subject had literary tastes, it is found in other
contemporary portraits of young women and
is probably no more than a fashionable
painter's convention. Both in style and in
treatment there is a striking resemblance to
the Egyptian mummy portraits of the
Roman period (as for example in the
National Gallery, London, no. 2914).
    The painting belongs to the last years of
the town, when the house and the adjoining
workshop area at the corner of the insula
may have belonged to an owner who was
involved in baking or patisserie. The name

long but erroneously associated with this
family portrait is that of Paquius Proculus,
whose name appeared on an election poster
painted on the front of the house.
Subsequent attempts to identify the owner
of the house have been ingenious rather than
convincing.
M. della Corte, *JRS* XVI (1926) 146–154.
E. Drerup, *Die Datierung der Mumienporträts*
(Paderborn 1933) pl. 4.

24
**Wall painting: portrait of a woman in
profile.**
Height 52 cm; width 39 cm.
Naples Museum, inv. 9077.
From Herculaneum or Stabiae.

Framed portrait from the centre of the left-
hand lateral panel of a Third Style wall. Old
drawings of it show bands of ribbons hanging
loosely down from the hair over the
shoulders, and the loss of this overpainting
accounts for the seeming disproportion of the
neck. The same drawings indicate that the
hair-band was shown as being made of some
precious metal, and that from it sprang
delicate sprays of flowers probably executed
in pearls and emeralds on gold wire stems.
The portrait itself is obviously imitating a

23

cameo, and it has been suggested that it represents Cleopatra.
Pitture di Ercolano IV (1765) 109f, fig. 113. R. Herbig, *Nugae Pompeianorum (Bilderhefte des D.A.I. Rom*, I, 1962) 19f.

25
Wall painting: figure of a girl.
Height 56 cm; width 38.5 cm.
Naples Museum, inv. 8946.
From Pompeii.

The girl sits beside or leans against a column, gazing down at something held in her hands, of which only part is preserved. In her hair she wears an ivy wreath. Although she is probably intended to represent a figure sacrificing or in attendance upon some religious occasion, the head has all the appearance of having been drawn from life.

The fragment comes probably from a Fourth Style architectural composition similar to those in the cubiculum of the House of Pinarius Cerealis or in the House of Apollo (see page 71).
Elia 215, fig. 30.

26
Bronze portrait bust of a woman.
Height 37 cm.
Naples Museum, inv. 4990.
From the House of the Citharist (1, 4, 5).

Found in the *ala* of the atrium, together with a similar bronze bust of a man (Naples Museum, inv. 4992; see page 76). There is some evidence to suggest that this house, once one of the finest in Pompeii, belonged to the influential local family of the Popidii, and this pair of busts, probably of a man and wife, may well in that case represent members of that family. The analogies for both portraits, including the hairstyles, indicate a date in the early first century AD. There is another portrait head from Pompeii of what is almost certainly the same woman, in marble, slightly over life-size (Naples Museum, inv. 120424, see p. 76). The findspot of this is not recorded, but it clearly comes from a public statue, confirming the suggestion that she belonged to one of the ruling families of the city.

The head was cast in two parts, the looped braid at the nape of the neck being cast separately, and all the finer detail of the hair and eyebrows was worked in with a chisel after casting. A striking and rare feature is the preservation of the original right eye (the left eye is partly restored). The eye sockets were left open in casting and were afterwards filled with a very fine white cement, into which were set the lens-shaped pupils, made of a brown, semi-precious stone. The bulging of the eyes is due to the swelling of the cement under the damp conditions of burial.
Kluge-Hartleben II, 22f. De Franciscis 49f.

26

24

25

27

Bust of a middle-aged man, perhaps a member of the Popidius family.
Rather large-grained, translucent white marble, perhaps from Paros.
Height 39 cm.
Naples Museum, inv. 6028.
Found together with No. 29 in the House of the Citharist (1, 4, 5).

The break across the left shoulder is ancient and was repaired in antiquity with a bronze dowel. The surface of the marble is weathered, suggesting that the bust may have stood originally in a tomb and have been brought to the house for safety after the earthquake of AD 62. There are traces of red paint on the hair at the back of the head.

As in the case of No. 29 there have been numerous attempts to identify this as the portrait of some Roman public figure (Pompey, Crassus, Horace, Agrippa, Sejanus, and others), but on balance it is far more likely to be a family portrait connected with the house in which it was found. The form of the bust and the treatment of the hair and facial details indicate a date about the middle of the first century AD. The workmanship suggests a sculptor from the eastern Mediterranean, based presumably at Puteoli and working for local Campanian patrons.
Fiorelli, *Scavi* 164, no. 147. F. Poulsen, *RM* 29 (1914) 59. De Franciscis 49.

28

Bronze portrait of a young man on a herm shaft.
Height overall 1.73 m; height of bust 37.5 cm.
Naples Museum, inv. 5584.
Probably one of the two bronze busts found in the Basilica at Pompeii in 1813.

The surface of the bronze is heavily corroded and a large fragment is missing from the chest. The pupils of the inlaid eyes have been lost, but the white cement of the right eyeball survives complete, while that on the left is only preserved on the inner corner. Because of the damaged surface it is difficult to assess the original qualities of the workmanship, but it appears that the modelling was rather hard and lifeless by comparison with No. 26, and that less care was taken in engraving the short strands of hair after casting. The herm shaft, which is ancient, may not belong; it is made in lava and stands on a base of tufa.

The head bears a marked resemblance to the other bronze bust (Naples Museum, inv. '19') considered to have been found with it and also, at least in the unusual quoif of hair over the brow, to the marble portrait of a young man (No. 29) which was found in the House of the Citharist and perhaps represents a member of the Popidius family. The special connection that the Popidii had with the Basilica (see No. 14) may be seen as further evidence to support such an identification.
Fiorelli, *PAH* 1, part 3, 225. De Franciscis 43f.

29

Head of a young man, perhaps a member of the Popidius family.
Fine-grained white marble, probably from Phrygia in Asia Minor.
Height 36.5 cm.
Naples Museum, inv. 6025.
From the House of the Citharist (1, 4, 5), found together with No. 27 on 19 October 1868 in the stable block, having perhaps fallen from an upper room.

Rough surfaces on the shoulders mark the lines of drapery folds that have been dressed off, indicating that this was probably retrieved from a statue and adapted to a bust after the earthquake of AD 62. When found, the nose and ears were damaged and have been restored in plaster, but the repair to the lower lip was made in antiquity, in Italian marble. The hair was probably painted a reddish brown, and the slightly roughened surfaces of the eyeballs may have had the iris and pupil rendered in red and black in the manner usual at this period. The unusually smooth, transparent quality of the flesh

27

28

surfaces is due to the fine marble, which also permitted the sculptor a greater subtlety and sensitivity of modelling than usual.

The portrait is that of a young man born about the end of the first century BC, with a quoif of hair over his brow which closely resembles that found on No. 28 and in Naples Museum, inv. '19' (see p. 76). Scholars have variously identified him with a number of Roman worthies, including the young Marcus Brutus, Agrippa Postumus or other descendants of Agrippa, Domitius Ahenobarbus, Drusus, son of Germanicus, and there is indeed a close resemblance to a head, of unknown provenance, in the Capitoline Museum in Rome (Stuart-Jones, *Catalogue* plate 88). But there is also a marked family resemblance to the male bronze from the atrium of the same house (inv. 4992; see page 76) and to the bronze head from the Basilica, and it seems far more likely that this is a member of the local family to whom this house belonged, usually identified as the Popidii.
Fiorelli, *Scavi* 164, no. 148. F. Poulsen, *Ikonografische Miscellen* (Copenhagen 1921) 57ff. L. Curtius, *RM* 47 (1932) 228f. De Franciscis 47.

30
Epitaph of Titus Terentius Felix, a city magistrate.
Marble.
Width 53 cm; height 38.5 cm.
Naples Museum, inv. 3879.
Found in 1763 just outside the Herculaneum Gate, where there is now a reproduction.

T(ito) Terentio T(iti)f(ilio) Men(enia tribu) Felici maiori aedil(i). Huic publice locus datus et HS ∞ ∞. Fabia Probi f(ilia) Sabina uxor.
'To Titus Terentius Felix senior, son of Titus, of the tribe Menenia, aedile. The site (of this monument) was presented to him by the city together with the sum of 2000 sesterces. It was erected by his wife, Fabia Sabina, daughter of Probus.'

Terentius Felix may have died as a relatively young man, possibly while holding the junior magistracy of the aedileship, which would account for the contribution from public funds towards the cost of his monument. He appears as first witness to one of the documents of Lucius Caecilius Jucundus in the period preceding the earthquake of AD 62. The Terentii were an old Italic family long established in Campania. His wife too came from an old family, the Fabii, most of the known Pompeian representatives of which were freedmen engaged in the wine trade. Another Titus Terentius (Felix junior?), who

may well have been his son, was a candidate for the aedileship in the last period of the city.
CIL x. 1019. Castrén, no. 402,9. Andreau 209, 321.

29

30

31
Bronze portrait bust of a young man.
Height 42.5 cm.
Naples Museum, inv. 5617.
From Pompeii.

The surface of the bronze appears severely
cleaned and the eyes given a modern inlay of
silver and copper to replace the ancient
cement and glass. Although the work is
technically competent, and great care went
into the secondary working of detail in the
hair and eyebrows after casting, the portrait
lacks the character and individuality of most
of the other Pompeian bronzes, having more
in common with the rather cold academicism
of many of the Herculaneum portrait busts
(e.g. Naples Museum, inv. 5632). It has often
been identified as a youthful portrait of the
Emperor Tiberius (born 42 BC, died AD 37),
but there is little to support this
identification beyond the arrangement of the
locks of hair over his brow. The form of the
bust indicates, rather, a somewhat later date,
about the middle of the first century AD.
De Franciscis, 42f. fig. 34. L. Polacco, *Il Volto di
Tiberio* (Rome 1955) 184, no. 6.

32
Portrait bust of an old man.
Pentelic marble.
Height 37.8 cm.
Naples Museum, inv. 6169.
From Pompeii.

The gaunt face, with its hooked nose and
projecting ears, a type one can still see among
Neapolitans today, is uncompromisingly
realistic. It is a good example of a long-lived
and popular style of Roman portrait
sculpture whose origins can be sought in the
various trends current in the late Republic,
but which prevailed far into the first
century AD. The carving of the eyes and hair
and the treatment of the flesh surfaces show
that it was probably made in the first quarter
of the first century AD.

Although its original location is not
recorded, the cutting of the bust shows that it
was mounted on a herm shaft, perhaps to
stand beside the entrance to the *tablinum* in a
Pompeian house.
B. Schweitzer, *Die Bildniskunst der römischen
Republik* (Leipzig, 1948) 115 and 119.
A. N. Zadoks-Josephus Jitta, *Ancestral
Portraiture in Rome* (Amsterdam 1932) 54
and 67. De Franciscis 40f.

33
Male portrait head.
Grey coarse-grained limestone.
Height 24 cm.
Pompeii, Antiquarium P.76/147.

The head is broken off from a life-sized
statue, which has apparently not been found,
but which probably stood in a tomb outside
the walls of Pompeii. It is worked in a hard,
linear style characteristic of the local central
Italian tradition (see page 76) and in marked
contrast to the contemporary 'Roman'
portraiture represented by Nos. 26, 31.
The hair is treated as a formal pattern and the
ears almost as abstract designs; facial details
like the wrinkles on the brow and the lines in
the jowls are equally reduced to a severe
symmetry. The faint half-smile of the lips
appears all the more expressive as a result.

31

32

33

34
Terracotta statuette of a tipsy old woman.
Height 39.5 cm.
Naples Museum, inv. 124844.
From House VI, 15, 5.

The subject, well known in later Hellenistic
sculpture, pottery and terracotta, may be
derived from a statue by Myron that was set
up at Smyrna (Izmir) in Asia Minor. The
almost toothless old woman is shown seated,
with hair and clothing dishevelled,
grumbling to herself and clutching the
bottom half of a wine amphora, of which the
top half lies beside her foot. The figure is
hollow and is adapted to serve as a jug. On the
back is a filling hole at the nape of the neck
and the remains of a handle. Her mouth was
the spout. Mid-first century AD.
    This piece was found in the fountain niche
at the far side of the garden peristyle,
together with two glazed terracotta
statuettes, a marble statuette of a nymph,
and another terracotta figurine of similar size
representing an elephant carrying a tower
(Naples Museum, inv. 124845).
NSc 1897, 23f. Levi 197, no. 849.

35
Terracotta doll.
Height 17.5 cm.
Naples Museum, inv. 123971.
From Pompeii.

Schematic female figure, with tall conical
body and a tiny knob-like head, perhaps a
simple child's toy. The details of her dress are
added in red paint.
Levi no. 870.

35

34

36–40

Five terracotta figurines.

Heights from 17 cm to 18 cm.

Naples Museum, inv. 20741, 20750, 20752, 20753, 20766.

Found in Pompeii in August 1853, at the point of intersection between the Via delle Sonatrice and the Via dell'Abbondanza, 2.10 m. above street level and 8.60 m from the front of the statue base of Holconius Rufus, together with 43 other terracottas of various types.

These five figurines were evidently part of the stock of a dealer in such wares. One of them is declaiming (20766), the others holding scrolls, and the realistic detail of all of them, coupled with an element of caricature, suggests they may portray actors in Mime. Although the significance of such figurines is not known for certain, it is possible that they were among the small gifts distributed at the New Year festival of the Saturnalia, given as mementoes of past shows or perhaps as hints of shows to come. See also Nos. 43, 299–302.

PAH II, 575, Von Rohden 54f and pl. 44.1; 44.2; 44.4. Levi nos. 863, 862, 864. Winter II, 439, 1b; 2; 9.

41

Caricature bust in terracotta.

Height 11.5 cm; width of body 9.5 cm.

Naples Museum, inv. 20579.

Probably the piece that was found on 1 June 1755 in the Villa of Julia Felix, in one of the small niches on the eastern side of the garden.

It is hard to determine whether this piece is complete as it stands, or whether it was part of a larger object, such as the jugs in the shape of grotesque figures (see von Rohden pl. XXXVI). A very similar figure in the British Museum (inv. 1873, 5–29.10), wearing a *bulla* on a red-painted necklace, is identified as a character from Roman mime.

Von Rohden 53, pl. XLI, 4. Levi no. 867.

36–40

41

42
Terracotta mask.
Height 14 cm.
Naples Museum, inv. 116712.
Found in the Atrium of House no. 24 on the
Via Stabiana, 7 August 1867.

Replica of a theatrical mask, provided with
two small holes at the top, for suspension. It
is suggested that the furrowed brow, hooked
nose, and enormous open mouth portray
Maccus, the stock figure in Atellan farce
(see page 64), whose leading
characteristic seems to have been excess of
every sort.
Levi no. 874.

42

43
Statuette of an actor, in amber.
Height 8.4 cm.
Naples Museum, inv. 25813.
From Pompeii.

Probably a character from Roman mime,
wearing an ample cloak, the figure belongs
to a series of amber carvings on the same
theme of which Naples Museum has two
others and the British Museum five, said to be
from Nola. They were produced in
Aquileia, in northern Italy, about the middle
of the first century AD. Amber was highly
prized by the Romans from the early first
century AD, when the trade routes to the
source of supplies in the Baltic began to
operate, as an amulet and for its alleged
medicinal qualities as well as for carving.
Roman women often carried a piece in their
hands in summer, and amber carvings of
animals, fruit and ears of corn were given as
New Year's presents.
Fiorelli, *Scavi* 157, no. 56 (20 Feb. 1863).
Siviero no. 568.
D. E. Strong, *Catalogue of the Carved Amber in
the Department of Greek and Roman Antiquities*
(British Museum 1966) pp. 5, 35, 91 and
nos. 109–113.

43

44
Forequarters of a bronze griffin.
Height 15.5 cm.
Naples Museum, inv. 115392.
From the debris of earlier excavations on the
Via della Marina, Herculaneum,
15 July 1872.

Bronze finial from the tip of the pole of a
four-horsed chariot *(quadriga)*. The group,
comprising chariot and driver, probably a
portrait of an emperor, stood outside the sea
wall at Herculaneum, where many
fragments of it were recovered in the earliest
tunnelling at the site. Some are preserved in
the Naples Museum, but a great many
others went into the melting pot.
E. Gabrici, 'La Quadriga di Ercolano',
BdA I, fasc. 6 (1907) 1–12.

44

45

Small bronze bust of the emperor Augustus.
Height (excluding the modern base) 13.4 cm.
Naples Museum, inv. 5473.
From Herculaneum, 26 October 1752.

Hollow cast. The first Roman emperor is
portrayed in a variant of his most popular
official portrait type, best known from the
statue found in the Villa of Livia at Prima
Porta (Vatican, Braccio Nuovo 14). Made after
his death, probably in the reign of Tiberius or
Claudius, the little bust was possibly
dedicated in a shrine of the Imperial cult
somewhere near the Theatre.
P. Zanker, *Studien zu den Augustus-Porträts.*
I. *Der Actium-Typus* (Göttingen 1973) 32 no. 20.

45

46

46

Bronze statue of Lucius Mammius Maximus
Height 2.12 m.
Naples Museum, inv. 5591.
From Herculaneum, found in the Theatre on
24 December 1743.

The statue, which honours a wealthy
benefactor of Herculaneum (see No. 47)
was found, together with its marble
pedestal and bronze dedicatory inscription,
on the highest level of the auditorium of the
Theatre. It is hollow cast in a rich copper
bronze. The head and neck, the left hand,
the right forearm, part of the drapery and
the two feet were cast separately. The
casting is technically very accomplished, and
the surfaces have been very carefully worked
over, to remove traces of the processes of
casting and assembly and to make good
minor blemishes. The head is a portrait and
was certainly modelled by a different
sculptor, probably from a different
workshop and working to order.
  Bronze public statuary was common in
antiquity, but the vast majority has since
disappeared into the melting pot. Large
bronze statues such as this are very rare
survivals, and it is in marble sculpture that
one has to look for parallels. Stylistically the
head of Mammius closely resembles the
portrait statue of Fundilius, an actor, found
at Nemi and now in Copenhagen. The
arrangement of the toga, too, closely
resembles that on the Fundilius statue and on
another piece found in the theatre at Caere

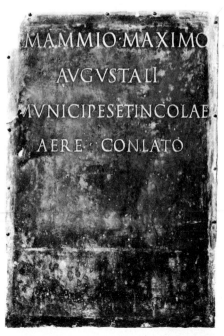

47

(Cerveteri), a mode which appears to date from the years immediately following the middle of the first century. This fits well with the likely date of Mammius himself. Venuti, *Heraclea*, 75. Kluge-Hartleben II 65ff. Goethert *RM* 54 (1939) 240f.

47
Bronze dedicatory inscription.
Height 70 cm; width 45 cm.
Naples Museum, inv. 3748.
Found at Herculaneum, attached to the marble base of No. 46.

L. Mammio Maximo Augustali municipes et incolae aere conlato.

'To Lucius Mammius Maximus, Augustalis, (this statue is erected) by the citizens and other residents, by public subscription.'

The name of L. Mammius Maximus figures on a number of other inscriptions at Herculaneum, three of which (*CIL* x. 1, 1413, 1417, 1418) record dedications to Livia, who was deified by the emperor Claudius, to Antonia, his mother, and to Agrippina, his niece and the mother of Nero; a fourth (*CIL* x. 1. 1451) recording an unspecified donation to the city, and a fifth (*CIL* x. 1, 1450) his construction or restoration of a market building (*macellum*) and his giving of a public banquet on the occasion of its dedication. The Mammii (sometimes spelt Mamii) were an old Samnite family, represented also at Pompeii, where they were one of the first non-colonist families to achieve public office after 80 BC, at Capua, at Aquinum and in the mountains of Samnium. It was a relative or connection of this family, L. Annius Mammianus Rufus, who built the theatre at Herculaneum, probably under Augustus (*CIL* x. 1, 1443–1445). As an Augustalis Mammius Maximus was almost certainly a freedman, which would accord with his failure to mention his father's name. Born the slave of a powerful, land-owning family, it was doubtless with the family's support that as a freedman, like Petronius's Trimalchio, he achieved great wealth and, by his lavish use of it, achieved high civic honour.
CIL x. 1, 1452. *ILS* 6352. For the Mammii, see Castrén 188, no. 237.

46

48

Gold bulla.
Length 6.5 cm; weight 14.08 grammes.
Naples Museum, inv. 145490.
From the House of the Menander (I, 10, 4).

The *bulla* was a small bag-shaped amulet,
worn around the neck, a practice which the
Romans derived from the Etruscans, among
whom it seems to have been worn as an
ornament by both sexes. Among the Romans
the gold *bulla* (sometimes known as
Etruscum aureum) took on a more restricted
significance, being worn from infancy by the
sons of citizens as a visible token of free birth.
On coming of age and formally assuming the
dress of manhood (the *toga virilis*) it was
customary to lay the *bulla* ceremoniously
aside in the household *lararium* (see No. 220).
At a later date its use was permitted also to
the sons of freedmen.

This example is shaped in the form of a
miniature pouch, with a lens-shaped body
made of two plain convex discs, riveted to an
elaborately ornamented flap, through which
passed the small suspension ring of beaded
gold wire. The decoration of the flap is
symmetrical about a central braid, made up
of two ribbons, each of three strands of gold
wire, plaited and framed between two pairs

of counter-twisted wire which are arranged
so as to convey the impression of a minute
chain of heart-shaped links. This frame is
continued round the plain fields to right and
left of the central braid. Along the junction
of the flap and the body are pendant
triangles of gold beading.

This handsome piece was found in the
House of the Menander, together with
several other pieces of fine jewellery, in the
same wooden chest as the famous set of
silver plate (see page 78).
Maiuri, *Menandro* 381, no. 127. Breglia no. 918.
Siviero no. 340.

49

Gold finger ring with a sardonyx cameo.
Diameter 2 cm.
Naples Museum, inv. 25181.
From Pompeii.

The stone is a true cameo, portraying, in
light-coloured relief against a dark ground,
the theatre mask of an old man with a beard,
presumably a representation of one of the
stock figures of Comedy, a bad-tempered old
miser. Late first century BC or early first
century AD.

This ring was worn by Charles III, King of
Naples, who initiated the excavations at
Pompeii. It was donated by him to the
Museum when he left to become King of
Spain.
Breglia no. 599. Siviero no. 436.

50

Gold signet ring with sardonyx intaglio.
Diameter 2 cm.
British Museum, inv. WT. 1387.
Probably from the Naples area.

The oval bezel is set with a tiny sardonyx
incised with the figure of a running wild goat.
First century BC or first century AD.
BMC Rings no. 415.

51

Finger ring in the form of a snake.
Diameter 2.4 cm.
British Museum, inv. 1867. 5–8. 422.
Probably from Campania.

The ring is in the form of a snake coiled
round the finger with its head pointing down
it. The eyes were set with small pieces of
emerald (one of which survives) and the
scales were indicated with cross-hatching.

There are many variants of this theme in
Roman jewellery of the first century BC and
first century AD, in armbands (No. 56) as well
as in finger rings. A number of such rings
have been found at Pompeii. (For a very
similar ring, see Naples Museum,
inv. 113744.)
BMC Rings no. 933. Cf. Greglia no. 680.
Siviero no. 214.

48

52
Pair of cluster earrings.
Gold, pearls and green plasma.
Length 2.8 cm and 3.0 cm.
Naples Museum, inv. 25266 and 25267.
From one of the sites in the Vesuvius area.

The centre of each flower-like cluster consists
of an oval cabouchon of green plasma set
in a gold frame edged with gold beads.
Radiating from it are sixteen petals,
consisting alternately of shaped gold sheet
and of irregularly-shaped pearls set on pegs
of gold wire. A globule of mother-of-pearl
hung from the bottom-most gold petal.
A large gold hook is soldered to the back.
First century BC to first century AD.
Breglia nos. 226, 227. Siviero no. 307.

53
Pair of earrings.
Gold and emeralds.
Diameter 2.2 cm.
British Museum, inv. WT. 1405.
Probably from the Naples area.

To a circular gold frame is fastened a convex
grid of gold wires threaded with emeralds
used in their natural hexagonal form. The
hook is soldered to the back of the frame.
A similar pair of earrings was found in the
treasure from the House of the Menander.
BMC Jewellery nos. 2622–3. Higgins 184.

54
Pair of gold earrings.
Length 2.5 cm.
British Museum, inv. 1866. 5–4. 95–6.
Findspot unknown, but compare Naples
Museum, inv. 24827 from Pompeii (Siviero
no. 253).

Similar to No. 55 in basic form, but the gold
wire hooks are soldered to the small gold
boss at the bottom of each earring.
BMC Jewellery no. 2616–7. Higgins 184.

55
Pair of gold earrings.
Length 2 cm.
Musée de Mariemont, inv. B.358.
From a villa at Boscoreale, 1908.

Hollow, hemispherical bosses of sheet gold,
backed with slightly concave plates, to each
of which is soldered a length of thick gold
wire, which also forms the hook. They are the
counterparts of armbands such as No. 62.
Over eighty examples have been found in the
Vesuvian towns.
Mariemont R. 110.

56
Gold armband in the form of a snake.
Diameter 8 cm; length 11 cm.
Naples Museum, inv. 24824.
Probably found at Pompeii.

One of a pair of such armbands, each shaped
from a flat ribbon of gold on which the scales
were indicated with a V-shaped punch; the
head was cast separately, and the eyes were
originally set with green vitreous paste.
First century BC to first century AD.
*MB*7 (Rome 1831) pl. XLVI. Breglia no. 827.
Siviero no. 202.

49

50

51

52

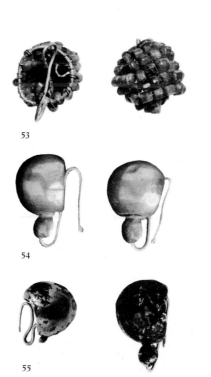
53

54

55

56

57
Gold bracelet in the form of a snake.
Diameter 6.7 cm.
British Museum, inv. F. 2780.
From Italy.

Shaped from thick gold wire. The head is
carefully modelled and cross-hatching has
been added to indicate the scales. Very
similar bracelets have been found at
Pompeii (Naples Museum, inv. 24874–5).
First century AD.
BMC Jewellery no. 2780.

58
Open-ended gold bracelet.
Diameter 8 cm.
Musée de Mariemont, inv. B. 352.
From one of the villas at Boscoreale, 1908.

Hollow tube of gold to the ends of which have
been soldered two snakes' heads; incised
scales decorate the body. The form is also
found in miniature as a finger ring, both in
gold and in silver (Naples Museum inv. 20540
and *BMC Rings* no. 1135). It had passed out of
favour by the end of the first century AD.
Mariemont R. 104.

59
Gold bracelet.
Diameter 6.2 cm.
British Museum, inv. 1879. 1–15, 21.
From Pompeii.

A sheet of gold rolled into a tube and then
bent round into a circle; a plain version of
No. 60.
BMC Jewellery no. 2830.

60
Gold bracelet set with an emerald.
Diameter 7.8 cm.
Musée de Mariemont, inv. B. 354.
From one of the villas at Boscoreale, 1908.

Similar to No. 59; slightly flattened and
expanded at one point so as to take an oval
gold frame in which is set an emerald.
Mariemont, R. 106.

61
Gold armband.
Diameter 8.3 cm.
Naples Museum, inv. 109587.
From House I, 2, 3.

Two lengths of thick gold wire loosely
intertwined to form eight large loops,
soldered together at the crossings; over one
of these is an applied gold ornament.
First century BC to first century AD.
Breglia no. 868. Siviero no. 238.

62
Flexible gold armband.
Length 23.5 cm.
Musée de Mariemont, inv. B. 357.
From a villa at Boscoreale, 1908.

Composed of eleven pairs of hollow
hemispherical bosses in sheet gold, each pair
fused by a collar of gold beads and joined to
its neighbours by little loops of gold wire.
These armlets appeared suddenly in the first
century AD, with earrings to match (Nos. 54,
55), and remained very popular until the
second century. At least seven examples are
known from Pompeii.
Mariemont R. 109. Higgins 184, 187.

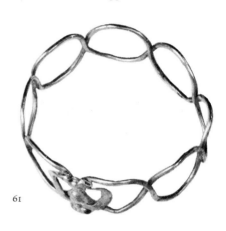

61

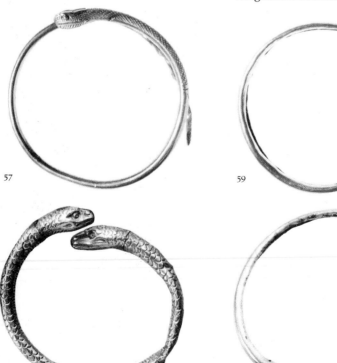

57

58

59

60

62

63

Part of a necklace of gold ivy leaves.
Length 53 cm.
Naples Museum, inv. 111114.
From Pompeii, 9 June 1877.

The necklace consisted originally of two
concentric bands of ivy leaves stamped out of
sheet gold and linked to each other by tiny
loops of gold wire; the loops are masked by
small gold bosses. The 48 leaves of this piece
converge symmetrically upon a large convex
gold disc. Its companion piece (Naples, inv.
111113) contained 46 leaves, but was
otherwise identical. The clasp which joined
the two bands behind the neck is missing.
The form, rare in Roman jewellery, probably
derives from the Hellenistic world. First
century BC to first century AD.
Breglia no. 478. Siviero no. 166.

64

Gold pendant chain.
Length 35 cm.
Musée de Mariemont, inv. B. 355.
From a villa at Boscoreale, 1908

A heavy chain composed of 22 figure-of-eight
loops of beaded gold wire. Linked around the
central point of the chain is a beaded ring
from which the now-missing pendant hung.
The clasp is a simple hook. First century AD.
Mariemont, R. 107.

65

Gold pendant and chain.
Length of chain 35 cm; height of pendant
3 cm.
Musée de Mariemont, inv. B. 356.
From a villa at Boscoreale, 1908.

Chain composed of looped figures-of-eight of
gold wire. From a hook in the centre hangs
a tiny pendant figure of a winged Eros
drawing his bow.
Mariemont, R. 108.

66

Gold amulet.
Diameter 1.7 cm.
Musée de Mariemont, inv. B. 360.
From a villa at Boscoreale, 1908.

A thin disc of sheet gold edged with three
rows of gold beads and provided with a ring
to suspend it from a chain. It is stamped with
a phallus in relief to ward off evil spirits.
Mariemont, R. 112.

67

Pendant chain in gold and emeralds.
Length 33.5 cm.
Musée de Mariemont, inv. B. 359.
From a villa at Boscoreale, 1908.

The chain is made up of emeralds in gold
bezel settings alternating with small convex
gold discs. At the central point there is a ring
attachment for a pendant. Chains made up of
precious stones set in gold were a common
feature of Hellenistic jewellery, but their use
in combination with elements of pure gold
was a Roman variant, introduced in the later
first century AD.
Mariemont, R. 111. Higgins 186.

63

64

65

66

67

68
Silver hand mirror.
Diameter 10.5 cm; length of handle 11 cm.
Naples Museum, 76/243.
From one of the sites in the Vesuvius area.

The reflecting disc of the mirror has a cusped
border. The back bears a simple decoration
of engraved concentric circles. The looped
form of the handle is unusual.
For similar forms, see Mau-Kelsey 378–9,
fig. 213. Strong 157.

69
Silver hand mirror.
Diameter 11 cm; length of handle 9.3 cm.
Naples Museum, inv. 25716.
From Pompeii.

A very common form of hand mirror. The
back is decorated with concentric circles and a
border of palmettes edged with two rows of
beaded dots. The baluster handle is one of the
two most usual types, the other being in the
shape of a club of Hercules.
Strong 157.

70
Fragment of a bone hair comb.
Width 6.1 cm; surviving length 8 cm.
Naples Museum, inv. 119990.
From a *cubiculum* off the atrium in House IX,
6, 5.

Combs in antiquity, made of ivory or bone,
were normally of this shape, with teeth down
both long sides. As in many modern combs
the teeth are spaced differently, about seven
to the centimetre on one side and about
fourteen on the other. Similar combs have
been found in some numbers at Pompeii,
among them one which is painted with a
design of two ducks in red, black and white.
Mau-Kelsey 371.

68

69

71

Six hairpins with variously decorated finials.

a. Bust of a female divinity. Ivory. Length 13.2 cm. Naples Museum, inv. 77441. From Pompeii.
b. Aphrodite (Venus) tying her hair. **Ivory.** Length 9.8 cm. Naples Museum, inv. 121730. From the corridor beside the *tablinum* in the House of the Cenaculum (v, 2, Mau D).
c. Hand with fingers spread. Ivory. Length 11.6 cm. Naples Museum, old inv. 9326. From Pompeii.
d. Male herm wearing a mantle *(himation)*. Bone. Length 18.2 cm. Naples Museum, old inv. 9272. From Pompeii.

e. Hand with fingers together. Ivory. Length 10.3 cm. Naples Museum, old inv. 9327. From Pompeii.
f. Pudicitia, personification of modesty and chastity. Bone. Length 10.8 cm. Naples Museum, old inv. 9270. From Pompeii.

Many Roman hairstyles involved the use of tight curls, made with hot tongs, and some of these pins would have been toilet instruments, used for arranging the hair rather than as ornaments or for fastening the hair in place.
Mau-Kelsey 372, fig. 203.

72

Mosaic portrait of a woman.
Height 25.5 cm; width 20.5 cm.
Naples Museum, inv. 124666.
From a small *cubiculum* in House VI, 15, 14.

Portrait, probably from life, of a young woman. Her hair is parted centrally and tied behind with a ribbon. She wears earrings of pearls set in gold, a pearl necklace with a gold clasp set with precious stones, and a dark, low-necked dress which shows through a gold-embroidered transparent veil. Dress and jewellery suggest a woman of rank.

This is a studio piece (*emblema*) made with very small tesserae, shaped and toned, set within a shallow, tray-like limestone frame. It was found in the centre of an *opus sectile* pavement made up of hexagons, lozenges, and triangles of blue-grey, white, and red marble, dating from the last period before AD 79. In this context it was almost certainly reused. The mosaic itself can hardly be later than the end of the first century BC.
A. Sogliano, *NSc* 1898, 171ff. A. Mau, *RM* 16, (1901) 283f. Pernice VI, 88 and 178–9.

70

71 a b c d e f

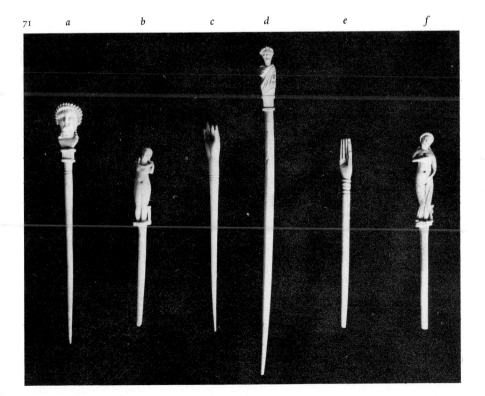

72

73

Bronze head of a horse, with traces of gilding.
Height 51 cm.
Naples Museum, inv. 115390.
Found in the Theatre at Herculaneum, January 1739.

At least six equestrian statues in gilded bronze decorated the seating area (*cavea*) of the Theatre at Herculaneum and were brought to the surface piecemeal in the course of the first tunnelled excavations. This head belonged to one that was probably set up in the last ten years before the eruption. Many fragments of the same statue and of the others still exist in the Naples Museum, but some of the larger pieces were judged to be 'good for nothing' and, since the heads of the riders were missing, it was agreed 'to make two great medallions with the mouldings of Brass, about 2 yards high, with the Pourtraits of the King and Queen of Naples'.

The horse was probably shown rearing slightly on its hind legs, tightly reined in by its rider. The arrangement of the straps of the bridle is unusual, paralleled only in a much later bronze horse's head from Ausgburg, and the decoration on them, with cup-like bosses between small studs, is found elsewhere only on a fragment of another bronze horse, now in Baltimore.

Technically the work is of very high quality, of a thinness at least twice as fine as most bronze-casters would attempt today – a factor which must have contributed to the crushing and dismemberment of these pieces to which the accounts of their discovery bear witness. The metal, as in most bronzework of this period, has a high lead content. This greatly helped the application of a layer of fine gold leaf over the whole surface. The gold was beaten on over a thin layer of mercury which had been fused with the bronze after casting, thereby securing a molecular amalgamation of the two, and the layer was further compacted by burnishing it with a smooth, semi-precious stone, such as an agate or a chalcedony. The head and neck were cast separately from the body of the horse the joint being hidden and strengthened by means of a bronze collar. The figure of the rider would also have been cast separately.
Venuti, *Heraclea* 54. Kluge-Hartleben II, 78 and 80f. H. von Roques de Maumont, *Antike Reiterstandbilder* (Berlin 1958) 84f. For technical details see *BdA* series 4, XLV (1960) 42ff.

74

74
Large Neo-Attic vase (crater).
Pentelic marble.
Height 82 cm; diameter at the rim 65 cm.
Naples Museum, inv. 6778.
From Stabiae.

Both the form and much of the decoration of
this vase derive closely from metalwork
prototypes, commonly reproduced also in
South Italian bronzeware (see No. 137) and in
the fine South Italian pottery. The figured
decoration is Dionysiac in inspiration. On one
side is Dionysus himself, portrayed in the
Archaic manner, holding a jug and a *thyrsus*
and leading personifications of Summer and
Autumn; on the other side are Spring and
Winter with a Satyr. At the junctions of the
tall volute handles with the body are Silenus
heads.

Some of the best Athenian craftsmen of the
later first century BC were engaged in
producing large marble vases of this sort.
They were normally used as garden
ornaments.

75
Dionysiac herm in coloured marbles.
Height 87 cm.
Naples Museum, inv. 126252.
From Pompeii.

The head is that of an elderly Silenus, one of
the drinking companions of Dionysus, shown
wreathed with ivy berries. The slightly
tapering shaft stands on two bare human
feet, carved out of the same block of white
Italian marble as the base, which in its turn is
veneered with profiled mouldings and a
deeply cusped facing slab. A narrow
rectangular pillar runs up the back of the
herm. The head, shaft and pillar are of
coloured marbles imported from Imperial
quarries overseas: the head, of yellow
Numidian marble, *giallo antico*, from
Simitthu (the modern Chemtou) in
north-western Tunisia; the shaft and base
mouldings, of purple and cream variegated
marble from Skyros, an island in the north
Aegean; the pillar of green and white
marble, *cipollino*, from Euboea off the eastern
coast of Greece.

A herm of this sort was probably used as a
table support (cf. No. 127) in a peristyle or
garden.

75

76
Bronze figure of a he-goat.
Height 55.5 cm; length 55 cm.
Naples Museum, inv. 4903.
Found under the floor of a Roman building at
Nuceria (Nocera).

The body of the goat is hollow cast, the legs,
tail, ears and horns were apparently joined
on as separate castings. The long hairs down
the neck and back, and the hairs of the beard,
were part of the original casting but were
given more precise detailing with a chisel
edge when cold. Although there is no sign of a
water pipe, the figure probably decorated a
fountain, possibly as part of a group like
No. 83. First century AD.
  This is one of the few surviving finds from
Pompeii's neighbour and rival, Nuceria.
M. Ruggiero, *Scavi di Antichità nelle provincie
di Terraferma dell'antico regno di Napoli dal
1743–1876*, vol. II (Naples 1878) 446.

77
Oscillum in the form of a theatre mask.
Italian marble.
Height 36 cm.
Naples Museum, inv. 6613.
From Pompeii.

Oscilla hung between the columns of a
peristyle garden; see also Nos. 78, 82, 87, 90.
The mask, that of a heroine in Greek tragedy,
is distinguished by sloping brows, wavy hair,
and a low *onkos*. First century AD.
MB7 (Rome 1843) pl. VIII. Bieber, *Theater*,
fig. 567. Webster, *Tragedy and Satyr Play* 85,
NS 5.

78
Theatre mask in high relief.
Italian marble.
Height 31 cm.
Naples Museum, inv. 6611.
From Pompeii.

Though possibly made to be hung as an
oscillum, this mask was probably set in a wall,
as in the garden of the House of Neptune and
Amphitrite at Herculaneum. With its tall,
rounded peak and hair falling in corkscrew
curls, this would appear to be a mask from
Tragedy. The fillet (ribbon) across the brow,
with two dangling ends, and the wreath of
ivy leaves and berries suggest specifically
Dionysiac associations.
MB7 (Rome 1843) pl. VIII.

77

76

79

Rectangular panel with theatre masks in relief.
Pentelic marble.
Height 25.5 cm; width 33 cm.
Naples Museum, inv. 6619.
From Pompeii.

The panel, which is carved on both faces, probably stood on a small column in a Pompeian garden similar to that of the House of the Gilded Cupids (see page 49). In high relief on one side are masks belonging to stock characters in Greek New Comedy: on the right, the scheming, impudent, leading slave; and on the left the delicately brought-up youth (*hapalos*), suitor for the hand of the daughter of the old man whose mask lies below. Beyond the youth, in low relief, is the mask of a Satyr, and on the other face of the panel, again in low relief, those of an elderly Silenus *(papposilenos)* and of a young Satyr.
Bieber, *Theater* 155. Webster, New Comedy 194, NS 17.

80

Rectangular panel with theatre masks in relief.
Pentelic marble.
Height 29.5 cm; width 40 cm.
Naples Museum, inv. 6633.
From Pompeii.

The panel is carved on both sides and, like No. 79, was probably mounted on a low column. In high relief on the front are masks from Greek New Comedy – a delicate youth,

a curly-bearded old man (top right) and a leading slave (bottom left). In the background is a temple front in low relief. A large fragment missing from the bottom right-hand corner may have contained a fourth mask, of an angry youth, as on a similar relief from Ostia. On the reverse of the panel, facing one another in low relief, are two masks of Tragedy, laid on rocks, both with high *onkoi*. One is accompanied by a

sword, and probably represents a hero, the other is a woman, with a large kerchief covering her hair-piece and side-locks.
MB 8 (Naples 1844) pl. XLVII. Bieber, *Theater* 155f. Webster, *New Comedy* 195, NS 22, *Tragedy* 92, NS 8.

79

78

80

81
Bronze fountain figure of a raven.
Height 26 cm; length 58 cm.
Naples Museum, inv. 4891.
From a villa at Stabiae, not found in position.

Hollow cast, the wings cast separately and added. The water pipe led in under the tail and out through the mouth. The raven was one of the many attributes of Apollo, many of whose sanctuaries were built around springs.
Kapossy, *Brunnenfiguren* 52. Ruggiero, *Stabia*, p. viii, villa no. 1. *MB* 8 (Rome 1844) pl. LIII.

82

82
Circular oscillum.
Italian marble.
Diameter 34 cm.
Naples Museum, inv. 6647.
From the peristyle garden of the House of the Black Wall (VII, 4, 59).

An *oscillum* was an ornament freely suspended by a chain from the architrave between the columns of a peristyle. On one side of this example is carved in low relief a figure of the youthful Hercules, a lion skin about his shoulders and carrying a club and bow; in front of him runs a boar, the sacrificial animal proper to his cult. On the other side an elderly Pan plays his pipes beside a tree, from which hangs a goatskin bag of fruit.
F. G. Welcker, *Alte Denkmäler* II (Göttingen 1848), 132, no. 40. *MemErc* III (1843) 238.

83
Bronze fountain group: two hounds attacking a boar.
Height 50 cm; maximum width 1.22 m.
Naples Museum, inv. 4899, 4900, 4901.
From the House of the Citharist (I, 4, 5).

The group, which derives from Hellenistic animal sculpture, stood between bronze figures of a snake, a deer and a lion on the semi-circular fountain basin in the middle peristyle. Water gushed into the pool from a pipe in the boar's mouth; also, it seems, from the mouth of the hound on the right, which is trying to bite the boar's leg. The front paws of the hound on the left were fixed to the side of the boar by rivets. Tails and ears were cast separately, and great care went into the working of such secondary details as the boar's hide. The group is among the liveliest pieces of sculpture found at Pompeii.
Kapossy, *Brunnenfiguren* 48.

83

84

Rectangular panel with theatre masks in relief.
White Italian marble.
Height 29.5 cm; width 39.5 cm.
Naples Museum, inv. 6631.
From Pompeii.

The panel, carved on both sides, was probably set up in a garden (as No. 78). In relief on the front, and resting on a rocky shelf, are masks which derive from those used in the Greek Satyr Play: on the left Dionysus, and on the right a Maenad. Both are treated in the Archaic style. An unusual feature is that, instead of the large drill holes normally used for the pupils of such masks, the eyes are here blank and were presumably painted. On the reverse, in very low relief, are the masks of a Silenus and a Satyr.
Bieber, *Theater* 158.

85

Fountain figure: boy with dolphin.
Italian marble.
Height 49 cm.
Naples Museum, inv. 6112.
From the peristyle of House IX, 2, 27.

The boy sits on a small base, his right hand on the dolphin's head, his left holding the tail, watching the water pouring from the dolphin's mouth. The hair and eyebrows were painted red, and red paint was used also to indicate the eyelashes and the iris, with the pupil marked by a black dot. The figure belongs to a large series of small children and Erotes, riding dolphins or clutching amphorae, shells, dolphins, frogs, hares, ducks, or doves, variously adapted as fountain jets. It was made in Campania, about the middle of the first century AD.
Fiorelli, *Scavi* 165, no. 159. Kapossy, *Brunnenfiguren* 42.

86

Herm of Hercules.
Yellow marble *(giallo antico)*, from Tunisia.
Height 80 cm.
Naples Museum, inv. 6383.
From Herculaneum.

Hercules is portrayed as bearded and wearing a large lion-skin wrapped around him like a cloak, a type that seems to date back to Greek sculpture of the fourth century BC. The head, body and base are carved separately in three different qualities of the same stone. Close parallels are found in other coloured stones: one from Sparta in red Laconian marble *(rosso antico)* and another, also from Herculaneum but adapted as a table support, in a black and red marble *(africano)* from western Turkey.
cf. Daremberg and Saglio s.v. *Hercules* fig. 3802.

81

84

85

86

87
Pelta-shaped oscillum.
Italian marble.
Height 22.5 cm; width 37 cm.
Naples Museum, inv. 6664.
From Pompeii.

An angular version of the *pelta*, the traditional shield of the Amazons. The central projection, from which it hung is carved as a palmette, and the outer ends of the crescent as griffin's heads. Rather simply carved in low relief within the field are a bird eating cherries and, on the opposite face, a basket of fruit.

88
Bronze fountain figure of a bull.
Length 51 cm; height 39 cm.
Naples Museum, inv. 4890.
From the Atrium of the House of the Bull (v, 1, 7).

Hollow cast, with the short horns, ears and tail added separately, the bull is shown as a young and powerful animal. Though perhaps a purely ornamental piece, it would have had associations with several well-known divinities, including Zeus (see No. 132), Poseidon and Dionysus. The figure stood on the edge of the *impluvium* basin in the centre of the Atrium, water spouting from the jet in his mouth. Though interior fountains had been a feature of the large Campanian country villas since the first century BC (e.g. the Villa of the Papyri at Herculaneum), their appearance in the town houses of Pompeii is a late phenomenon.
Niccolini III, pl. 21. Kapossy, *Brunnenfiguren* 53.

89
Archaising female herm.
White Italian marble.
Height 96 cm.
Naples Museum, inv. 126251.
From Pompeii.

The figure of a woman, possibly a Muse, in the Archaic Greek manner, has been adapted to the form of a herm. She wears a fillet in her hair and her long tunic, tied with a knotted girdle below her breasts, is carved in shallow relief on the three flat sides of the herm shaft. The eyes are hollowed out for inlay.

The shaft is socketed into a heavy block of lava, and a pillar of travertine runs up the back of the herm to a point slightly above the head. The herm was probably used as a table support in a garden or in a peristyle corridor.

87

88

89

90
Oscillum in the form of a theatre mask.
Italian marble.
Height 29 cm.
Naples Museum, inv. 6618.
From Pompeii.

The *oscillum*, one of a pair, is in the form of a
theatrical mask of a youth from Greek New
Comedy, distinguished by a roll of
corkscrew curls and hanging corkscrew
locks. At the top there are the remains of the
bronze rod by which it was hung from the
architrave of the peristyle. First century AD.
MB7 (Rome 1843) pl. VIII. Webster, *New
Comedy* (1969) 194, NS 16.

91
Wall painting of a garden.
Length 1.25 m; height 35.5 cm.
Pompeii Antiquarium, inv. 1200-4.
From the western portico of the Villa
Imperiale, near the Porta Marina.

Part of the dado of the Third Style
decoration of the back wall of the portico.
The garden, a rectangular enclosure with
low trelliswork walls, is shown as if viewed
obliquely from above. The facade is
symmetrical about a wide central opening
flanked by a pair of tall pillars, bearing
vases, which frame a square pool with a
central fountain figure, set on a pedestal;
two identical pillars mark the outer corners
of the facade, and midway between the
right-hand and left-hand pairs of pillars are
two square, openwork pavilions. The side
walls of the enclosure are plain. The rear wall
echoes the scheme of the facade, with a
central *aedicula* flanked by two
trellis-vaulted arbours. The vegetation
within the garden is indicated
schematically by a line of trees
immediately behind the front wall.
cf. P. Grimal, *Les jardins romains*
(Paris 1969) 265f.

90

91

92

Wall painting of a garden.
Length 1.37 cm; height 32 cm.
Naples Museum, inv. 9964.
From Herculaneum.

This scene, probably from the dado of a wall of the late Third or Fourth Style, shows one side of a garden enclosure, the trellised fence of which is laid out symmetrically about three semi-circular *exedrae*. Midway between the latter are two passageways arched over the trelliswork, while at the two ends of the composition there are two rectangular openwork arbours planted with vines. Fountain basins set on pedestals stand at the entrances to the passages, and at four points along the fence taller, trellised posts support large, slender, bronze-coloured vases. Five long-legged, stork-like birds complete the scene.

Most of the elements of this sort of fenced garden are already present in the Garden Room paintings from the Villa of Livia at Prima Porta (see page 70) and they recur in varying combinations in many Pompeian paintings (see No. 91). The type was evidently firmly established in painting. This does not, of course, preclude the use of similarly fenced formal gardens in the *villae marittimae* of Campania. Real gardening and painted representations of gardens are two aspects of a common tradition.
Pitture di Ercolano I, 239. *MB* 9 (Rome 1845) 576, pl. LXXXVI. P. Grimal, *Les jardins romains* (Paris 1969) 267.

93

Wall painting, part of a garden.
Height 80 cm; width 80 cm.
Naples Museum, inv. 9705.
From Pompeii.

This painting and its companion pieces (Naples Museum, inv. 8723, 8762 and '9710') come probably from the walls of a small garden enclosure (*viridarium*) or covered garden room. A large fluted fountain bowl stands in the re-entrant recess of a wooden fence, on the rail of which a bird is perched, trying to drink from the fountain jet. Beyond the fence is dark foliage, of trees or bushes, and in the foreground are the faded traces of low, iris-like plants.
H. Roux Aîné, *Herculaneum et Pompéi* V (Paris 1875) 98, pl. 52.

93

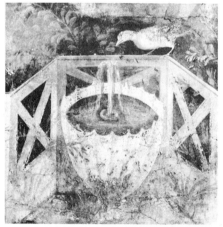

94

Statue of Artemis in the Archaic manner.
Pentelic marble.
Height 1.08 m.
Naples Museum, inv. 6008.
Found on 19 July 1760 in one of the houses of VIII, 2 or 3 (VIII, 3, 14?).

The goddess is represented striding purposefully forward, bow in hand (the bow itself being of bronze or wood); she may also have held some object in her left hand. The manner of the face and drapery is consciously derived from Archaic Greek sculpture, but such features as the movement of the body (involving liberal use of marble struts), the carving of the hair, the smoothly polished flesh surfaces, and the execution of the drapery (with considerable use of the drill, and with the surfaces left as worked with a fine, flat chisel), all point to it being the work of Athenian workshops at the turn of the first centuries BC/AD, or slightly later. Such archaizing work was in great demand in Rome (see also No. 95), and there were many copyist workshops both in Greece and in Italy busy turning out work of this sort.

The statue was found in the garden of the same house as Nos. 210, 312, 313. It stood on a base veneered with coloured marbles, within a shrine that was approached by steps and preceded by a pair of herm shafts in *cipollino* marble. When found, it still retained many traces of colour: yellow (gilded?) hair; eyes with red-brown irises and black pupils; black eyelashes and eyebrows; diadem pink with yellow rosettes; quiver pink with white decoration; pink and yellow, finely detailed border on the drapery; sandals with pink, yellow and blue straps; and on the plinth traces of black.
PAH I, 114. F. Studniczka, 'Die archaische Artemisstatue aus Pompeji', *RM* 3 (1888) 277–302. Reuterswaard, *Polychromie* 184, note 518. W. Fuchs, *Die Skulpturen der Griechen* (1969) 241f.

94

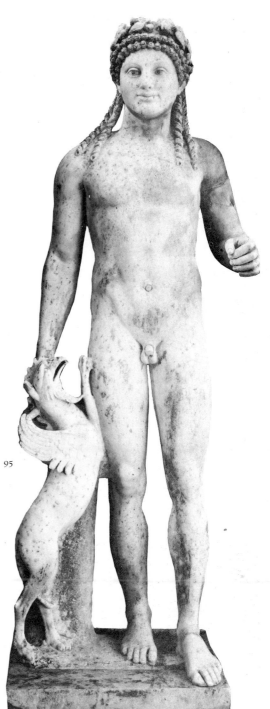

95

95
Statue of the youthful Apollo in the Archaic style.
Illustrated previous page.
Pentelic marble.
Height 1.05 m.
Naples Museum, inv. 146103.
Found in the House of the Menander
(1, 10, 4) in the northern corridor of the
peristyle, near the *tablinum*.

The figure of the god, supported by a tree
stump and socketed into a rectangular
plinth, is accompanied by a griffin. His right
hand appears to hold a *plectrum*, which
strongly suggests that the left arm (which is
carved in a separate piece of marble and
attached with an iron dowel) held a lyre.
The front part of the left foot, where it
overlaps the plinth, is another added piece,
the sculptor having slightly miscalculated
the size of the statue in relation to the block
of marble. There are clear traces of original
colouring: on the eyeballs a faint circle of
black for the iris and a large black dot spotted
with white for the pupil; reddish brown for
the eyebrows, and carmine red for the
corners of the mouth. The dirty brown
colour on the hair is the decayed remains of
the substance used as a base for a golden
yellow colouring, possibly gilding. The tree
stump was bluish grey.

Both the treatment of the head and the
rigidly frontal pose derive directly from the
conventions of Archaic statuary, but the
generally more naturalistic treatment of the
body, with the weight resting firmly on the
right leg, betrays a knowledge of later, more
sophisticated Greek sculptural traditions.
Apollo holding or accompanied by a griffin
is in any case uncommon in Greek
statuary; there does not seem to be any close
parallel. This is evidently the eclectic work of
Athenian sculptors, producing for the
Roman market around the beginning of the
first century AD and adding the figure of a
griffin from the familiar repertory of late
Hellenistic decorative motifs. The same
workshop may well have produced the
Apollo in the Vatican Museums
(Chiaramonti 285), of which the dimensions
and basic pose are almost identical, but the
position of the arms is reversed and the
griffin is omitted.

No suitable base was found within the
House of the Menander. It has been suggested
that the statue originally stood in the
Temple of Apollo, and that it was removed
temporarily for safe custody during the
restorations after the earthquake of AD 62.
Maiuri, *Menandro* 410 ff.

96
Head of a youth in the Archaic style.
Pentelic marble.
Height 28 cm.
Naples Museum, inv. 109621.
From Pompeii, House VII, 3, 40.

The head is that of a youth with his hair
dressed in a style favoured by the Greek
aristocracy about 500 BC. The sharpness of the
detail and the smooth finish on the face,
however, indicate a date around the
beginning of the first century AD. The base of
the neck is carved for insertion into a body,
perhaps a herm.

The closest parallels to this head are found
on double herms, in association with the
head of a bearded old man with a similar
hairstyle (the forerunner of the theatrical
onkos), e.g. Louvre inv. 198.
M. Bieber, *JdAI* 32, 1917, 85; *Theater* 24.

97

96

98

97

Garden painting: a heron and lizard and a pet dog.
Length 1.30 m; height 55 cm.
Naples Museum, inv. 110877.
From the House of the Epigrams (V, 1, 18).

The painting, on a black ground and divided into two panels by red lines, stood in the south-east corner of the peristyle, where it occupied a position closely resembling that of the very similar paintings in the peristyle of the House of the Menander, except that in this instance the screen wall continued upwards, occupying the entire space between the two columns. On the left is a heron picking at a lizard, and on the right a large green plant; between them, painted over the vertical red framing line, is the figure of a small, terrier-like dog, above the head of which is painted in white, A. SYNCLETVS. The adjoining panel to the left (Naples inv. 110876) shows a heron grappling with a snake.
Bull Inst XLIX (1877) 30.

98

Wall painting of a cat.
Height 33 cm; width 42 cm.
Naples Museum, inv. 8648.
From Pompeii.

A fragment probably cut from the upper zone of a late Third Style wall, which contained Egyptianizing elements. The cat, painted in silhouette, is shown curled up on a low upholstered stool.

99

Wall painting: the Judgement of Solomon.
Width 1.60 m; height 65 cm.
Naples Museum, inv. 113197.
From the House of the Doctor (VIII, 5, 24).

Pygmies enact what appears to be the well-known story of King Solomon giving judgement in a case where two women disputed the ownership of a child. Solomon is shown bearded, seated on a raised dais (*tribunal*) between two counsellors, with a bodyguard of armed soldiers. Before him, the true mother kneels and pleads for her child's life, while the false mother watches with apparent indifference as a soldier prepares to cut it in half. The scene is one of three matching panels that were painted on the parapet wall surrounding a miniature garden peristyle, the other two being Egyptianizing landscapes, one with pygmies fighting off crocodiles and hippopotami, the other with pygmies banqueting beneath a large awning slung from trees.

Pygmies portrayed in Egyptianizing settings are one of the commonplaces of Roman Imperial art. Because of the strong element of caricature, this picture can hardly be ascribed to direct Jewish influence in Pompeii, although there were unquestionably many Jews settled in Campania. If correctly identified it is, rather, evidence at second hand of the strong influence of the very large Jewish community in Alexandria. An alternative possibility is that the picture represents an older, native Egyptian version of some traditional story of royal wisdom, such as that attributed to King Bocchoris.
NSc 1882, 322–3. G. Gatti, 'Il Giudizio di Salomone in un dipinto pompeiano' in *Rivista Antimassonica* IV, 1898. Lumbroso, *RendLinc* ser. III, 11, 1882–3, 303–5. Gutmann, *Antike Kunst* 15, 1972, 122–4.

Model of the House of the Menander
(1, 10, 4).
Scale 1:25.

The poet Menander.

The House of the Menander, which takes its name from a portrait of the poet painted on the walls of an *exedra* opening off the peristyle, occupies the greater part of an insula situated in the heart of the residential quarter that lies to the east of the Via Stabiana and to the south of the Via dell' Abbondanza. A seal found in the quarters of the steward bearing the name of Eros, the freedman or trusted slave of a certain Quintus Poppaeus, tells us that at the time of the eruption the house belonged to a member of the prosperous local family of the Poppaei, the family of which Nero's wife, Poppaea Sabina, was a member and to which the Villa at Oplontis probably belonged. It was excavated by Maiuri from 1927 to 1932.

The site had a long and varied history. At this point the ground slopes quite sharply southwards towards the river Sarno, and although only further excavation could determine its earlier history in any detail, the plan and the masonry still upstanding tell us quite a bit of the story. The earliest visible remains date from the second half of the third century BC, at which time the insula was subdivided into a number of small houses, of which five faced north along the northern frontage. The rest seem to have followed the line of the slope, at least three facing east and two more facing west, of which one, the House of the Lovers at the south-west angle, still retained its separate identity in AD 79. Three rooms of one of these early houses, with remains of First Style wall painting, were found by Maiuri when relaying the floor of the large *triclinium* (Room 18) off the east wing of the later peristyle. The early floors were about six feet deeper than those of the later building, and the walls several degrees out of alignment with it. At this early period the House of the Menandar probably consisted simply of the atrium with, probably, a garden plot behind it.

Some time in the second century BC, this nucleus was modernized and enlarged, with a handsome new facade and the insertion of the Corinthian columns flanking the entrance to the *tablinum*, together with a formalization of the garden area beyond, to which belonged the three central columns of the north wing of the later peristyle. Then, shortly after the middle of the first century BC, came another and more radical development. The old buildings round the atrium were again partly modernized, but the main living quarters were transferred to a new setting around a large rectangular peristyle. To create this, several of the adjoining properties were bought up, and place was made for the peristyle by terracing upwards and outwards across the middle of the insula, leaving only the servants' quarters at the old level. A series of handsome living rooms (14–18) was added along the east side and a bath suite along the southern part of the west side. The old *tablinum* and the rooms to right and left of it now opened southwards on to the north side of the peristyle. The south side, where the terracing did not allow for rooms, was modelled into a series of decorative *exedrae*. With the subsequent purchase of the property at the south-east corner of the insula, for conversion into farm quarters, the house occupied the whole insula except for the House of the Lovers and the buildings at the north-east and north-west corners.

As everywhere else in Pompeii, the earthquake of AD 62 did serious damage here. In AD 79 the atrium area, which had been redecorated in the early Fourth Style manner shortly before the earthquake, was still awaiting restoration, and many of the rooms were found unfurnished; and although work was in progress in the peristyle area and by AD 79 had been nearly completed (only the baths still retain their Second Style ornament), the family had not yet resumed residence. As in the Villa of the Mysteries and at Oplontis, the property was left in the charge of the steward, Eros, who continued to operate the agricultural side of the estate, which may very well have consisted of vineyards and market gardens situated in the belt of substantially open ground that lay immediately to the south, inside the walls between the Stabian Gate and the Palaestra. Except for their positions inside and outside the walls respectively, the House of the Menander and the Villa of the Mysteries in this respect had a great deal in common.

Space does not permit a room-by-room account of the decoration of the house. The wall painting offers a fine range of Fourth Style work, some of it (in the atrium area) painted before the earthquake of AD 62, most of it (in the peristyle and the rooms opening off it) in the later post-earthquake phase. Of the Second Style paintings which once adorned the whole of the peristyle area one can now catch some tantalizing glimpses in the bath suite (notably in the apse of the hot room (*caldarium*) with its frieze of black and white figured panels, simulating stuccoed niches and, above it, a second frieze with three polychrome scenes of women bathing), but most of this earlier work had been ruthlessly stripped off by the Fourth Style decorators. They were, on the other hand, glad to retain the fine mosaic pavements of the earlier period. These include a splendid polychrome Nilotic panel in the 'Green Room' (11) with pygmies and boats in a landscape of river birds, plants and architectural scenery (see page 78) set in a severely simple black and white surround; a sadly damaged panel of a Satyr and Nymph in a double *cubiculum* (Room 21) which in the last period appears to have been converted into a library; and the fine series of pavements in the bath suite. The last-named in particular illustrate the art of decorative paving at a turning point in its Roman development: those of the *caldarium* and of the *apodyterium* still strongly influenced by the sort of Hellenistic work which one finds

on Delos, whereas that of the corridor between them, portraying four strigils, an oil flask, and a Negro slave bearing two *askoi*, clearly foreshadows the 'popular' Italic style of the skeleton mosaic (No. 18). The floor of the atrium vestibule is a fine example of a pavement made entirely of fragments of coloured marble set in a ground of black tesserae.

Of the individual rooms we can only mention Room 4, a symmetrical early Fourth Style scheme incorporating three lively panel pictures with scenes from the Trojan War; the 'Green Room' (11) at the north-west corner of the peristyle, a fine example of the sort of late Fourth Style work which tends to refer back to earlier styles and motifs, including a frieze, 25 cm high, portraying in white on red the rape of the

Lapith women by the Centaurs, a rare survival of a type of figured frieze that was common in the late Hellenistic world; and the large *triclinium* (Room 18), which exemplifies another trend in late Fourth Style painting, one that relied for its effect on the contraposition and repetition of broad sheets of colour, picked out with dainty decorative detail and small, isolated figures. Along the south side of the peristyle the two semi-circular *exedrae* (22 and 24) illustrated Diana hunting (22) and a rustic shrine with an image of Venus (24), both displayed within spacious landscape settings; while the central, rectangular *exedra* (23), the focus of the whole architectural scheme, contained figures of three of the great dramatic poets of the past, or of two of them flanking a central figure of Dionysus. Sadly, two figures are now

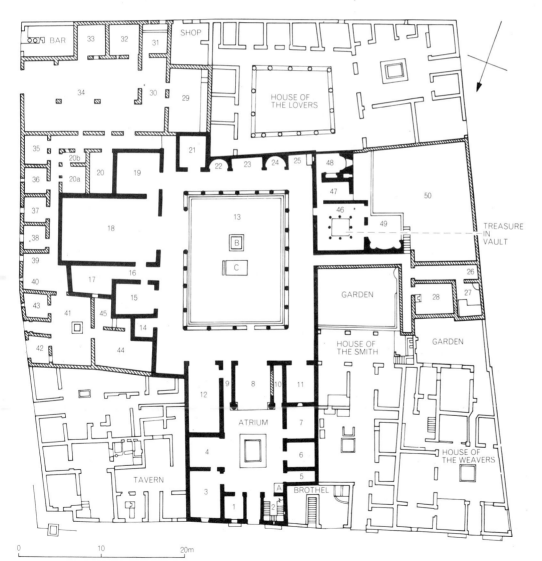

1. Door keeper's lodge.
2. Staircase to upper floor.
3. Bedroom later used as workshop.
4. 'Ala'.
5. Storeroom.
6–7. Bedrooms.
8. Tablinum.
9. Corridor.
10. Cupboard.
11. Green oecus.
12. Large exhedra.
13. Peristyle garden.
14. Store.
15. Red oecus.
16. Corridor.
17. Bedroom.
18. Dining room (triclinium).
19. Yellow oecus.
20, 35–40. Servants' quarters.
21. Day bedroom/library.
22–24 Exhedrae.
25. Exhedra with images maiorum.
26–28. Kitchens.
29. Stable.
30–34. Farm quarters.
41–45. Steward's lodging.
43. Bedroom.
44. Garden.
46. Vestibule to bath suite.
47. Warm undressing room (apodyterium).
48. Hot room (calidarium).
49. Sun terrace.
50. Kitchen garden.
A. Household shrine (lararium).
B. Fountain basin.
C. Wooden dining area (triclinium).

unrecognizable, but the third, on the right-hand wall, is the seated Menander from whom the house takes its name.

Other features of note are the traces of a wooden screen, 2.10 m high, set across the opening between the *tablinum* and the atrium, and of a curtain across the entrance to Room 4; the terracotta surround of the *compluvium* (the opening in the roof); the gabled *lararium* in the atrium, on the right-hand side on entering; and a second household shrine at the south-west corner of the peristyle. This last, in a room decorated with Second Style paintings that may have been retained in the last period as a mark of respect for tradition, consists of a rectangular altar of masonry set in front of a recess, in which were displayed one small seated figure and four small heads or busts, made of wood or of wax, the *imagines maiorum*, symbolic images of the family ancestors (see page 77). Of more specifically architectural interest are the extreme irregularity of the peristyle colonnades, with the columns spaced so as to give the maximum visibility outwards from the principal living rooms, regardless of the architectural proprieties; the lighting of the great *triclinium* (Room 18) by means of a window set high in the walls, above the adjoining roofs (remains of a window frame were found among the masonry fallen from the gable); and the traces of a wooden, open-air *triclinium* beneath a wooden pavilion in the centre of the peristyle garden, as in the House of P. Paquius Proculus (II, 7, 1).

At its greatest extent the residence occupied the whole of the centre of the insula, terraced out at a level corresponding to that of the atrium and of the main entrance in the middle of the north side. Built around and up against this terraced area were the service quarters. To the west of the peristyle, beyond the baths at the end of a long corridor, lay the kitchen, a small vegetable garden and some storerooms. On this side there was no access from the street. To the east, along the street frontage, there were more storerooms and, at an upper level, the quarters of the domestic staff. Alongside this block, at the north end of it, was the steward's lodging, and at the south end, occupying the south-east corner of the insula, were the stables and farm buildings.

The kitchen block (Rooms 26–28) was by any modern standards impossibly remote from the *triclinium* where the food was served, but this does not seem to have worried a Roman householder – what were slaves for, after all? From the corridor, steps led down into an enclosed courtyard at the old ground level, which was used as a vegetable garden. Along the east side of it lay four basement rooms, which constituted the substructures of the bath building. In one of them, under the *caldarium* (and helping to heat it) there was a large bread-oven, and the other three were used as storerooms. It was here, securely protected from recovery after the eruption, that the excavators found the remains of two large chests and their contents. One of these had contained jewellery and the family store of ready cash, forty-six gold and silver coins to a total value of 1432 sestertii together with a collection of family silver, 118 pieces in all, weighing a total of just under 53 lb (24 kg). Many of them were handsomely decorated and included a number of antique pieces. The only comparable find from the Vesuvius area is the Boscoreale treasure (see page 78).

The slaves' quarters, which were accessible from the residence only by a narrow, sloping corridor at the south-east corner of the peristyle, call for little special comment. They had a small independent kitchen and a lavatory. A group of bodies found at the foot of the stairs to the upper storey (between Rooms 19 and 21), one of them carrying a lantern identical to No. 170, are now thought to be those of workmen overcome while engaged in a salvage operation after the eruption. Most of the staff, it seems, got away in time. The steward Eros, on the other hand, died at his post, stretched out on his bedstead in Room 43. This was the living room of a small separate house, with its own entrance leading into a substantial atrium (41) and, beyond it, a tiny garden courtyard (44) with a private kitchen and lavatory. In the steward's room were found his signet ring; a leather purse containing his savings, ninety coins totalling 527 sestertii; some fine bronze vessels; and a large number of iron tools (including fifteen vine-pruning knives) for issue to the farmworkers.

The farm quarters were built round three sides of a courtyard (34) with a wide entrance from the street. Along the north side there was an open lean-to gallery, in which were found the remains of a two-wheeled cart. The far end was occupied by stabling for four animals, together with a cistern and a drinking trough (29, 30), and along the south side were storerooms, a lavatory and a wooden stair up to the farmworkers' quarters (31, 32). The corner of the block, always a valuable property, was let out independently as a bar (*thermopolium*), as was also a single-roomed shop facing on to the street to the south. Although the farm property evidently included vines, it did not press its own wine (as did the Villa of the Mysteries). There was no press, and a stack of forty-three amphoras were all empties awaiting disposal.

The two houses at the north-west corner of the insula both date back to the third century BC, one of them still retaining traces of its First Style painting. Both ceased to be residences after AD 62. One became a weaving establishment, the other the workshop of a smith who also practised carpentry. The miniature two-storey apartment in the angle between the latter and the House of the Menander was, as the *graffiti* make very clear, the lodging of a group of popular call-girls. The houses at the north-east corner, too, seem to have been taken over in this last period for commercial or industrial use, including a cookshop (*caupona*). Thanks to a lively exchange of *graffiti*, we even know the name of the barmaid, Iris, one of whose boyfriends was a weaver from down the street. In the last period before the eruption this was evidently still a lively quarter, but socially it had come down in the world.

One final *graffito*, found just outside the front door of the steward's quarters. It tells the traveller where to find company at Nuceria: *Nucerea quaeres ad porta(m) Romana(m) in vico venerio Novelliam Primigeniam* – 'At Nuceria ask for Novellia Primigenia, in the street of Venus near the Rome Gate.'

101

101
Bronze figure of a donkey.
Length 12 cm; height 9 cm.
Naples Museum, inv. 4955.
From one of the sites in the Vesuvius area.

Hollow cast and carefully worked over after casting to give the effect of coarse hair. A square hole in the belly suggests that the figure was attached to some larger object as a handle or decorative finial.

102
Decorative statuette of a Satyr.
Height (excluding the modern base) 22 cm.
British Museum, inv. WT 1085.
Probably from the Naples area.

Decorative statuette of an exaggeratedly virile, dancing, Satyr-like figure. He is shown naked except for boots, curious hose-like sleeves, and a cloak which is caught up and twisted over his left arm. In his left hand he holds one end of a veil which covers part of his head. On the neck are shown wattles, and the savage, elongated face and forked beard recall the fragment of wall painting, No. 145.

103
Bronze figurine of a deer.
Length 28 cm; height 30 cm.
Naples Museum, old inv. 2134 (base, 109992).
From one of the sites in the Vesuvius area.

Hollow-cast, the body is engraved with a delicate flower design. Although the alabaster on which it stands is ancient, it does not belong; but the figure does seem, rather unusually, to have been a purely decorative piece.

104
Statuette of a Placentarius in gilded bronze and silver.
Height 25 cm.
Naples Museum, inv. 143760.
From the House of the Ephebe (I, 7, 10–12).

One of a group of four identical figures found together in a wooden box in a room off the Atrium. The figure is bronze and the tray silver. They are usually thought to represent *placentarii* (sellers of *placentae*; see Cato, *de Re Rustica*, 76), itinerant piemen crying their wares. The element of caricature is typical of late Hellenistic art. Equally typical of Roman taste is the adaptation of a *genre* type to a functional purpose. These were probably pieces for the service of some special delicacy.
Maiuri, *BdA* 1925, 268–275.

105
Terracotta toad with traces of blue-green glaze.
Length 26 cm; height 9.5 cm.
Naples Museum, inv. 76/166.
From the House of the Tragic Poet (VI, 8, 5).
Found 26 April 1825 (no. 18).

One of a pair, which stood on the edge of the *impluvium* (water basin) in the centre of the atrium (see plan, page 49). Water was fed through a pipe into their hollow bodies by ways of a hole on the underside, and spouted from their mouths into the pool.
    The house is better known as the house of Glaucus in Bulwer-Lytton's *Last Days of Pompeii*.
Von Rohden, 30 figs. 18–19. Kapossy, *Brunnenfiguren*, 48.

105

102

104

103

106–108

Three red pottery (terra sigillata) bowls.
Found in the tablinum of House VIII, 5, 9 on 4 October 1881, together with eighty-seven others of the same forms and thirty-seven pottery lamps, all packed in a wooden crate. The bowls were made by several different Gaulish potters (see page 54), and the lamps were probably made in northern Italy. This suggests that the Pompeian consignee had dealt through an agent in the north rather than directly with the potteries.

106
Diameter 20.5 cm.
Naples Museum, inv. 112974.

Stamped in the centre of the inside by the maker Vitalis, who was active about AD 60–85. There were five of his bowls in the consignment, all of the same form (Dragendorf 29). The decoration comprises an upper frieze of festoons enclosing large rosettes, and a lower one of trellised zig-zag lines with one or two little rosettes in the spaces.
D. Atkinson, *JRS* 4 (1914) 49, no. 28.

107
Diameter 16 cm.
Naples Museum, inv. 112984.

Stamped as No. 106 but by Mommo, one of the most prolific of South Gaulish potters. Twenty-three of his bowls of this form (Dragendorf 29) and ten more of the same shape as No. 108 (Dragendorf 37) were found in the crate. The two bands of decoration are divided into rectangular panels, the upper containing arrowhead shapes alternating with running dogs, the lower *amorini* and stylised flowers.
D. Atkinson, *JRS* 4 (1914) 44, no. 8.

108
Diameter 16.8 cm.
Naples Museum, inv. 112997.

The letters MOM were incised in the mould in large cursive letters under the decoration, probably by the potter Mommo (see No. 107). The form is Dragendorf 37, one of the commonest of the Gaulish forms. Below a band of ovolo mouldings and a wreath of ivy leaves is a broader zone of rectangular panels containing alternately S-shaped patterns above circles and pairs of human figures. Round the bottom runs a chain of V-shaped leaves.
D. Atkinson, *JRS* 4 (1914) 56, no. 54.

109
Glass beaker decorated in relief.
Height 13.2 cm; diameter of lip 7 cm.
Naples Museum, inv. 111412.
From Pompeii, 19 April 1877.

Mould-blown; the glass was formerly clear. The shallow relief decoration includes ivy leaves, petals and dots. Early first century AD. Isings 45, form 31.

110
Tall glass beaker with long oval indentations.
Height 18.5 cm.
Naples Museum, inv. 111405.
From Pompeii, 26 May 1875.

The body was free-blown, the indents being added while the fabric was still soft; the base was blown separately and shaped onto the beaker by pressure from below. This form is found in large numbers at Pompeii in varying sizes, and it continued to be popular throughout the Imperial period.
Isings 49, form 35.

106

107

108

110   111   112

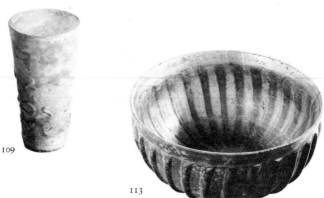

109

113

111
Small bulbous jug in amber-coloured glass.
Height 12.2 cm; diameter of body 7.8 cm.
Naples Museum, inv. 109423.
From the atrium of House VII, 7, 13 (?),
11 January 1872.

An imitation of a fine metal form, free-blown,
with short raised ribs running up from the
base. The attachment of the handle to the
rim is decorated with impressed ridges.
Isings 76, form 57.

112
Stemmed goblet in cobalt blue glass.
Height 14 cm; diameter of rim 15.4 cm.
Naples Museum, 76/215.
From one of the sites in the Vesuvius area.

The body was blown into a mould; two
horizontal wheel-cut lines decorate the
outside. The stem is formed from two large
beads of glass and the foot added separately.
Such drinking cups were used at table; for a
silver version see No. 261.
Isings 50, form 36a.

113
Ribbed blue glass bowl.
Height 8.9 cm; diameter 18.9 cm.
Naples Museum, inv. 13810.
From Pompeii.

These bowls were made by pressing soft
glass into a mould; the interior was polished
on a wheel, the exterior by a second, brief
exposure to fire. Bowls of this form, in
multi-coloured as well as in monochrome
glass, were popular in the first century AD.
Harden, *Camulodunum* 301 ff.

114
Small blue glass jug (askos).
Height 11 cm; length 21.1 cm.
Naples Museum, inv. 109433.
From Pompeii, House IX, 2, 26.

The glass-blower has imitated a shape long
familiar in Greek pottery and in Campanian
bronze ware (Nos. 266, 267). These *askoi* are
commonly found in pairs, and were
evidently so used, and they are often very
finely worked, being blown into a mould
rather than free-blown, as is this example.
Mid first century AD.
Isings 77, form 59.

116
Shallow two-handled glass cup.
Height 3.8 cm; diameter 12.6 cm.
Naples Museum, inv. 133273.
From Pompeii, from the *tablinum* of VI, 16, 28.

One of a pair of identical cups, mould-blown
with formal decoration in relief. Second half
of the first century AD.
NSc 1908, 277.

115
**Small jug (askos) in black and white
marbled glass.**
Height 9.5 cm; length 13.4 cm.
Naples Museum, inv. 118143.
From Pompeii, in IX, 7, 6.

Like No. 114 this is free-blown, but it is
squatter in shape and made in thicker,
opaque glass. It was found in 1888, together
with three other *askoi* in an *aedicula* opposite
the entrance to IX, 7, 6; altogether 23 pieces
of glass, some of them coloured, were found
in this building. Brightly variegated glass in
strong colours was very popular in the early
stages of Roman glass production. Late first
century BC to early first century AD.
Isings 77, form 59.

117
Long-necked glass flask.
Height 15 cm.
Naples Museum, inv. 12435.
From Pompeii.

The form is free-blown, decorated with thin
threads of glass trailed over the bulbous body
as ribs. Such flasks are very common at
Pompeii, though usually undecorated, and
were used for serving liquids or for oils used
in bathing, as No. 231. Inside the flask is a
quantity of black powder, the decayed
remains of its contents. Early first
century AD.
Isings 34, form 16.

116

117

118

114   115

119

118
Dark blue glass jug.
Illustrated previous page.
Height 18 cm.
Naples Museum, inv. 13539.
From Pompeii.

Fine-quality work, free-blown with a
drawn-out spout and an applied handle.
The form clearly imitates that of a bronze
vessel.
Isings 71, form 54.

119
Large glass dish.
Illustrated previous page.
Height 3.5 cm; diameter 22.3 cm.
Naples Museum, inv. 11588.
From Pompeii.

Blown into a mould. A large dish of the same
kind, filled with fruit, is shown in a Fourth
Style still life painting from Pompeii
(Naples Museum, inv. 8645). The form is
copied from *terra sigillata* pottery.
Isings 39, no. 23; cf. Beyen pl. VIII.

120
Fragment of a Second Style wall painting.
Height 1.18 m; width 60 cm.
Naples Museum, inv. 9847.
From the Villa of Diomedes, Pompeii, 1772.

The scheme to which this fragment belonged
was divided into three main panels by four
fluted columns. Between the outer pairs of
columns ran a tall screen wall, over the top
of which could be glimpsed a receding
architectural perspective. A *tholos* occupied
the middle of the central intercolumniation.
The fragment formed part of the right-hand
panel and shows part of one column and of
the red screen wall. Hanging against the
latter is shown a dead hare and, placed on top
of it, the mask of an old father in Greek New
Comedy. To the right of it is part of a column
shown in perspective beyond the screen wall.
Naples Museum, inv. 8594 comes from a
similar wall in the same room (see drawing).
Curtius, figs. 74–76. Webster, *New Comedy*
185, NP3.

121

Wall painting of a silver wine bucket (situla).
Height 77 cm; width 41 cm.
Naples Museum, inv. 9965.
From the peristyle wall in the Villa of Publius Fannius Synistor at Boscoreale.

This *situla* is one of several objects, mostly prizes for athletics, shown as if placed on a dado in front of the painted screen wall of a Second Style scheme. It stands on three low feet in the form of animal's legs, and from the rim spring two tall, ornate handle mounts. Placed diagonally behind it is a trident entwined with a snake.
P. Williams Lehmann, *Roman Wall-paintings from Boscoreale* (Cambridge, Mass. 1953) 11f.

122

Mosaic representing a crab or spider.
Width 41 cm; height 45 cm.
Pompeii, Storerooms inv. 13933.
From House VI, 15, 3.

This naive portrayal of some indeterminate crustacean or spider-like creature represents the opposite extreme of competence and artistic intent to the sophisticated late Hellenistic school of craftsmanship exemplified by Nos. 253, 314. The work of some local craftsman used to laying simple black and white geometrical patterns, it would have been displayed in the middle of a much larger area of white tesserae. Like similar mosaics portraying animals and other symbolic figures, it would have been placed near the entrance to avert ill luck.

123

Wall painting: a leopard.
Width 47 cm; height 21 cm.
Naples Museum, inv. 8650.
From Pompeii.

One of a pair of balancing panels, each supported on a vertical stem, probably from the middle of the lateral panel of a Third Style composition (as in the *tablinum* of the House of M. Lucretius Fronto, see page 70).

122

123

121

124

Tall bronze bowl.

Height 33.7 cm; diameter of rim 31 cm.
Naples Museum, inv. 73146.
From Herculaneum.

The bowl, which has a moulded foot and a frieze of moulded ornament below the rim, has two identical applied handles. Early publications show it as standing on a graceful moulded pedestal, about 23 cm high, with three animal's paw feet, but this has become separated and appears now to be lost. The handles portray two trousered barbarians, moulded in the round, fighting, with their lozenge-shaped shields locked between them. They stand upon, and are attached to the body of the bowl by, a calyx-shaped escutcheon, on which are displayed a pair of crossed spears and two similar shields. At the base of the calyx is an ox-skull (*bukranion*), a common decorative motif in late Hellenistic work of all sorts. Barbarian

shields, in this case oval, are the principal motif also of the frieze on the body of the bowl.

The same earlier publications speak of this piece as a trophy awarded for victory in gladiatorial combat, and the pedestal, to which it appears to have been fastened by a rivet, would indeed suggest some form of ceremonial use. But if these are gladiatorial combatants, they represent an earlier stage of gladiatorial history than the sophisticated, stylized gladiatorial combat of Imperial times, to which alone such trophies would have been appropriate. Barbarians, and in particular Gauls, were one of the commonplaces of Hellenistic art, and pairs of figures fighting were one of the stock themes of Capuan bronzework. From its shape this piece could well be as early as the second century BC.
MB VIII (Naples 1832) pl. XV Ceci, *Piccoli Bronzi* VI, no. 37.

125

Landscape panel of a rustic sanctuary.

Height 34 cm; length 61 cm.
Naples Museum, inv. 9419.
From Herculaneum.

Against the white ground of a lateral panel in a Third Style scheme is a picture framed in red, mounted on a slender support. On a rocky outcrop is a small shrine, behind which is a walled garden with two columns capped with urns, and a large tree. In front of the sanctuary is another column, tied with a garland and supporting a tripod. In the distance are two figures carrying bundles, and the faint outline of another building.
Rostowzew, 'Architektürlandschaft' 84, fig. 50.

126a

Bronze adjustable candelabrum (lamp stand).

Height from 79 cm minimum to 124 cm maximum.
Naples Museum, inv. '61'.
From one of the sites in the Vesuvius area.

This lamp stand is made in three pieces. The base, which can be removed, has three legs, ending in bull's feet, which arch outwards from beneath a plate decorated with three projecting scallop shells. On this base rests a hollow shaft, square in section, topped with a small bearded male herm, wearing a circular crown. The upper part consists of a square rod which fitted into, and was free to move within, the shaft, and which carried the actual lamp support, in the form of a vase. The height of the stand could be adjusted by fitting a small bronze pin, chained to the underside of the herm's right 'arm', into one of a series of holes spaced down the length of the movable rod.

This piece is one of a group, of which the detail of the little herms and of the bases varies considerably, but of which the technical features are so closely related throughout that they are almost certainly the product of a single workshop. About the end of the first century BC.
Pernice IV, 55f., fig. 74.

125

124

126b
Bronze oil lamp.
Height 9 cm; length 20 cm.
Naples Museum, inv. 112331.
From Pompeii.

The two stems of the handle are treated as plant shoots. The single, elongated nozzle meets the body with two small rosettes (as No. 160b) and along the upper surface of the nozzle the figure of a mouse crouches, watching the flame. The motif was doubtless suggested by the fact that mice were a great nuisance, drinking the oil of any lamp that was left unlit.

127
Table support (trapezophorus) with a figure of Attis.
Grey and white Italian marble.
Height 83 cm.
Naples Museum, inv. 120425.
From the atrium of House no. 78 on the Via Stabiana, found 3 March 1866.

Tables of bronze or marble, set against a wall and supported on a single leg, are a common feature of Pompeian house furniture. To the column of marble which constitutes the actual support is often added carved decoration, and coloured marbles were popular. Although the commonest motifs are Dionysiac, the use of a figure of Attis, as here, is by no means uncommon. Identical pieces have been found at Herculaneum and Capua.

Attis, beloved by Cybele, the Great Goddess of Asia Minor, was a beautiful youth whose self-castration, death, and transformation into a pine tree was the subject of the wild rites of annual mourning associated with her cult. He is here portrayed as a shepherd boy, in oriental dress and wearing a Phrygian cap.
Tran tam Tinh (1975) 283. M. J. Vermaseren, *The Legend of Attis in Greek and Roman Art* (Leiden 1966) 14.

128
Wall painting: Pan and the Nymphs.
Height 1.22 m; width 93 cm.
Naples Museum, inv. 111473.
From the left-hand wall of the same *cubiculum* in the House of Jason as No. 132.

Third Style panel showing Pan, pipes in hand, seated on a rock with a goat at his feet. To the left are seated two Nymphs, one of them holding two reed pipes in her hand, while to the right another stands playing a lyre *(cithara)*. Beyond the left-hand Nymphs is a building, set in a rocky landscape, central to which is a pine tree, sacred to Pan.
Schefold, *WP* 265. Peters 97.

128

b

a

126

127

129

131

130

129, 131

Wall paintings: pair of decorative details from a Third Style wall.
Height 2.00 m; width 44 cm.
Naples Museum, inv. 138992–3.
From Room 15 (*cubiculum*) in the Villa of Agrippa Postumus at Boscotrecase, excavated 1903–5.

These are two of the vertical components of the architectonic framework of the side walls (see reconstruction) of which the dado was a dark red and the rest of the background uniformly black. Though reminiscent of the *candelabra* and tripod stands from which much Third Style ornament was derived, they are here reduced to a purely schematic, decorative form. The detail is extremely delicate and includes small sprays of foliage, now largely effaced, sprouting from the vertical stems.
P. von Blanckenhagen and C. Alexander, *The Paintings from Boscotrecase* (*RM* Ergänzungsheft 6 (1962), 14, pl. 3 and 8, 2.

130

Wall painting: temple in a landscape.
Width 65 cm; height 40 cm.
Naples Museum, inv. 9487.
From Pompeii.

Sacro-idyllic landscape, probably from the middle of one of the lateral panels of a Fourth Style wall. It portrays a small temple in a setting of trees. In front of the temple two figures sacrifice at an altar; behind it is a statue in a columnar setting. In the distance can be seen a portico.

132

Wall painting: Europa riding the Bull.
Width 99 cm; height 1.25 m.
Naples Museum, inv. 111475.
From the back wall of a *cubiculum* in the House of Jason (IX, 5, 18).

Third Style central panel portraying Europa, daughter of the King of Phoenicia who, while playing on the seashore with her handmaidens, was approached by Zeus in the form of a white bull, which lured her into seating herself on its back and thereupon carried her off, across the sea to Crete. There, after bearing Zeus three sons, she married the King of Crete, who adopted her sons, one of whom, Minos, became his heir. Europa is shown seated on the bull in a rocky landscape painted in tones of grey on a white ground, against which the figures, which were painted first, stand out in sharp relief.

132

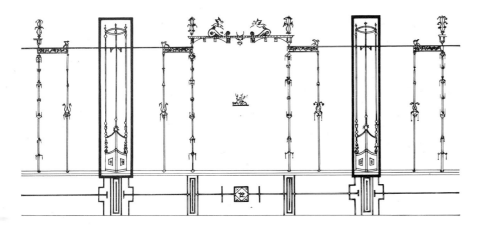

The landscape, with its central oak tree (the tree sacred to Zeus), echoes the central scene.
On the left-hand wall of the same bedroom (*cubiculum*), by the same hand, was the painting of Pan and the Nymphs (No. 128) and on the right-hand wall a painting of Hercules, Deianira and the centaur Nessus. Common to all three paintings was the symbolic use of trees within the landscape.
Schefold, *WP* 263–4. Peters, 96f.

133

Wall painting: Nile landscape.
Width 1.41 m; height 38 cm.
Naples Museum, inv. 8561.
From Herculaneum 1748.

A typical combination of Nilotic flora and
fauna with elements of Egyptianizing
architecture, from the dado (lower zone) of a
Third Style wall. Within a setting of marsh
and river, with date palms and lotus flowers
are, on the left, a crocodile; in the centre, an
island enclosure with buildings made of
reeds, including a tower similar to that
shown in No. 11 and, on the right, a duck and
a hippopotamus on a rocky island.
Pitture di Ercolano I, 50, 263.

134

Three-sided base for a candelabrum.
Pentelic marble.
Height 56 cm.
Naples Museum, inv. 6857.
From one of the sites in the Vesuvius area.

The base, which is carried on the backs of
three crouching rams, is topped with an
inverted capital, in the centre of which is the
socket for a bronze candelabrum. The three
faces are carved in low relief; on one side two
rams reach up to nibble grapes on the top of a
candelabrum with a similarly three-sided
base; on the second side two birds (ravens?)
drinking from a fluted vase (*crater*) hung with
garlands; and on the third a doe suckling a

fawn in the shade of an oak tree. Large
numbers of such ornate pieces of marble
furniture were being produced in the later
first century BC and the first century AD by
Athenian workshops operating within the
academic traditions of late Hellenistic
decorative sculpture. There is a piece
probably from the same workshop in the
Museo Nazionale Romano (inv. 371; *Annali
dell'Inst.* XXII (1850) 6off.).

133

134

135

Bronze candelabrum (lamp stand) and four hanging bronze lamps.
Height 85 cm; base 22.5 cm. square.
Naples Museum, inv. 72191; with lamps, inv. 72159, 72161, 72170 and 110078.
From Herculaneum (the candelabrum and very possibly lamps 72161 and 110078) and from Pompeii (lamps 72159 and 72170).

The candelabrum stands on a square base with four short lion's-paw legs. The shaft is a slender fluted column with an Ionic capital of which the echinus is decorated with a mask – a characteristically South Italian form. Four foliate scrolls curl outwards from the corners of the abacus, forming hooks for the suspension of four oil lamps. Although the record is not certain, it is very possible that two of these (72161 and 110078) were found with the candelabrum; the other two, though of appropriate types, have been added in modern times.

Of the four lamps, 110078 has two spouts placed diametrically opposite each other and joined to the body with griffin-head volutes; 72159 and 72170 have handles in the forms of a leaf and of a horned crescent moon, respectively; while 72161 has no handle at all. All four have small rings for the attachment of the suspension chains.

136

Wall painting: sacro-idyllic landscape with shepherd and goats.
Height 50 cm; width 49 cm.
Naples Museum, inv. 9418.
From Pompeii, exact location unknown.

Landscape from the centre of a wall panel, probably of the Fourth Style. It portrays an idealized rustic shrine, set within a rocky landscape with trees. In the foreground a man is pushing a goat towards the shrine, as if for sacrifice. On a rock to the right stands a shepherd, and on another rock, to the left, two more figures, one of them a statue.
Rostowtzew, 'Architekturlandschaft' 87. Peters 148. *Pitture di Ercolano* 2, 151.

136

137

Large bronze urn (crater).
Height 60.5 cm; diameter of rim 39.8 cm.
Naples Museum, inv. 73098 (vase) and 116002 (stand).
From Pompeii.

The form derives ultimately from metalware vessels of the Classical Greek period, which were widely imitated in pottery, notably in South Italy. The grooved handles end in Silenus heads in Archaic Greek style. The stand (which is ancient but does not belong to this vase) has feet in the form of lion's paws.
Pernice IV, 38.

137

135

138

Relief with scenes from the myth of Telephos.
Pentelic marble.
Length 1.20 m; height 52 cm.
Naples Museum, 76/128.
From Herculaneum, House of the
Telephos Relief.

Originally set into the wall plaster of a small
anteroom to a *triclinium*, the relief shows two
episodes in the history of the Trojan Wars.
Achilles, on his way to Troy, had landed by
mistake on the territory of Telephos, king of
Mysia, who received from Achilles's spear a
wound in the thigh which refused to heal.
Achilles consulted an oracle, which told him
he would only reach Troy if Telephos would
consent to guide him. Telephos too consulted
an oracle and was told that only 'he that
wounded could cure'. In the left-hand scene
Achilles is consulting the oracle. In the
right-hand scene he is scraping rust from his
spearhead ('he that wounded') on to
Telephos's wound, effecting a rapid cure.

The relief belongs to a large series showing
mythological scenes, produced by Athenian
workshops in the later first century BC, for
Roman patrons, who had them set into
decorative painted or marble-veneered
wall schemes in both public and private
buildings. Wall paintings of the Second
Style (e.g. the House of the Lararium, 1, 6, 4,
cubiculum) sometimes incorporated painted
imitations.

There are indications that the relief was
originally brightly coloured.
MdI V (1952) 147. C. Bauchhenss-Thüriedl,
*Der Mythos von Telephos in der Antiken
Bildkunst* (Würzburg 1971) 91. Maiuri,
Ercolano 355.

139

Wall painting: fantasy architecture.
Width 1.32 m; height 1.98 m.
Naples Museum, inv. 9735.
From the Basilica at Herculaneum.

The upper part of the lateral panel of a
Fourth Style composition, comparable to,
though far richer than, that of the end wall of
the Pentheus room in the House of the Vettii
(see page 71). It portrays, in elaborately
receding perspective, an architectural
complex of which such features as the
foliated columns of the monumental
entrance, the *pinakes* within it, and the split
pedimental upper order, are closely derived
from the Second Style. The framing curtain
is a characteristic of Fourth Style wall
painting at Herculaneum rarely found at
Pompeii.
Rumpf pl. 63, 2. Curtius 174f.

140

Fragment of Fourth Style wall painting.
Width 98 cm; height 90 cm.
Naples Museum, inv. 8514.
From Pompeii.

Fragment from the upper zone of an early
Fourth Style wall, including the upper
border and an *aedicula* set in a formal
quasi-architectural scheme of delicate
garlands and slender rods entwined with
tendrils, reminiscent of fine late Third Style
work (as in the White Triclinium in the
House of M. Lucretius, IX, 3, 5). Within the
aedicula is the figure of a woman with flowing
draperies, poised as if flying.

139

140

141a
Bronze candelabrum (lamp stand).
Height 1.12 m.
Naples Museum, inv. 78537.

The tall, gently tapering, fluted stem springs from a three-legged base and carries a lamp stand in the form of a vase (*crater*). Each leg consists of the hind leg of a lion, resting on a low drum and springing from beneath an upward-curling leaf. Ivy leaves fill the angles between the legs. Early first century AD.
Pernice IV, 47f., fig. 60.

141b
Bronze lamp.
Height 11 cm; length 20 cm.
Naples Museum, inv. 72483.
From Pompeii.

The reservoir and nozzle of this lamp are drawn out into an elongated tear-drop shape, which is emphasized by a gentle moulding similar to that on No. 168. The handle is arched over the filling hole and is decorated with a dolphin's head holding a cockle shell in its mouth. This motif is also found on the feet of bronze *candelabra*.

142
Wall painting: Pyramus and Thisbe.
Height 1.05 m; width 80 cm.
Naples Museum, inv. 111483.
From the *triclinium* on the left of the northern *ala* of House IX, 5, 14.

This artless painting, the central panel of a Fourth Style wall, represents the final scene of the story of the unhappy Babylonian lovers, Pyramus and Thisbe, 'the most lamentable comedy, and most cruel death of Pyramus and Thisby', which Bottom the Weaver and his company presented at the court of King Theseus in Shakespeare's *Midsummer Night's Dream*. Pyramus, believing Thisbe dead, has killed himself beneath a mulberry tree; she, finding him dead, is stabbing herself with his sword. The pillar supporting an urn represents the tomb where they were to have met. There is a Third Style version of the same composition in the garden *triclinium* of the House of 'Loreius Tiburtinus' (II, 2, 2–5) and another in a Fourth Style *triclinium* in the House of M. Lucretius Fronto (IV, 11, 1).
Schefold, *WP* 260.

141

b

a

142

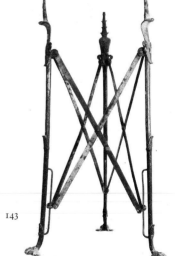

143

143
Bronze folding tripod.
Height 58.2 cm.
Naples Museum, old inv. 1452.
From Pompeii.

The uprights of this tripod consist of three
rods which rest on animal's paw feet; they
are punctuated by three sheath leaves and at
the top each terminates in a decorative finial
in the form of an *uraeus*, crowned with a
lotus bud and springing from two small
bird's heads. Hinged to the inner face just
below the finial are two transverse struts,
each of which is pivoted at the centre to one of
its neighbours and linked to another at the
bottom by means of a ring which is free to
slide up and down the length of a rectangular
loop on the inner face of the upright.
Although the mechanism closely resembles
that of adjustable stands which could
accommodate bowls of various sizes, in
this case there were only two possible
positions: closed, with the uprights and
transverse rods all folded together, or open,
with some circular object, probably a flanged
bowl, resting on the top of the finials and
locking the legs in a fully splayed position.
Ceci, *Piccoli Bronzi*, pl. IV, No. 4. *MB* 5 (Naples
1829) pl. LX.

144
Wall painting: basket.
Height 24 cm; Width 20 cm.
Naples Museum, inv. 8689.
From one of the sites in the Vesuvius area.

The basket, on a white ground, occupied the
centre of one of the lateral panels of a Third
Style wall. The most plausible identification
of the contents is that it represents a work
basket containing spindles of coloured wool,
one of which is shown resting against the rim
of the basket.
Beyen, *Stilleben* 23f. Croisille 44.

145
Wall painting: head of Pan.
Height 19 cm; width 11 cm.
Naples Museum, inv. 9126.
From Herculaneum.

The head has been cut from an ornamental
frieze in a Fourth Style wall.

146
**Wall painting: medallion with busts of
Dionysus and a Maenad.**
Diameter 44.5 cm.
Naples Museum, inv. 9284.
From Herculaneum.

Dionysus, god of wine and of ecstatic
liberation, is shown with a wreath of grapes
and vine leaves; in his right hand he holds a
drinking cup (*cantharos*) and in his left,
resting against his shoulder, the
characteristic Dionysiac staff, or *thyrsus*.
Behind him, her hand on his shoulder, is one
of his attendant devotees, a Maenad; she
wears a mantle and earrings, with flowers in
her hair.

Medallions such as this, containing real or
mythological portraits, were placed in the
middle of the lateral panels of many Fourth
Style compositions (e.g. in the *tablinum* of the
House of the Bicentenary at Herculaneum).
This one, from its subject matter, may have
adorned a *triclinium*; its companion piece
(inv. 9283) showed Dionysus and a Satyr.
Elia no. 304.

144

145

146

147

Bronze stool.
Height 29 cm; length 35 cm; width 25 cm.
Naples Museum, inv. 109506.
From the room to the right of the *tablinum* in
House VII, 7, 10.

The bronze plate across the top is shaped to
hold a cushion. Below it the strengthening
struts between the legs are decorated in
openwork: at each short end a scrollwork
design springing from a central bearded
head and, below it, a crossbar with four
pelta-shaped motifs; and along the two long
sides a formal design made up of open
part-circles framing pendent triangles.

148

Wall painting: Pan and Hermaphroditus.
Width 1.25 m; height 74 cm.
Naples Museum, inv. 27700.
From the Atrium of the House of the
Dioscuri (VI, 9, 6).

Part of the upper zone of a Fourth Style
scheme, from above the doorway leading
from the *fauces* into the Atrium.
Hermaphroditus, one of the more curious
by-products of Greek mythology, was a
minor divinity of bi-sexual form, with
female breasts and male genitals. In this
picture he is seated by a pool, and Pan,
aroused by his apparently female charms,
has just discovered his mistake. Beyond Pan
is a tower within a square enclosure, set in a
rocky landscape. On the right is a statue of
Priapus, standing on a pedestal and holding a
cornucopia.
Richardson pl. 23. 1. Schefold *WP* 116.
Peters 138. Kraus and von Matt no. 276.

149, 151

**Wall paintings: fantasy architecture from a
Fourth Style wall.**
Height 1.88 m; width 52 cm.
Naples Museum, inv. 9710, 9707.
From Pompeii, May 1760.

Narrow vertical panels depicting slender
fantasy architecture in receding perspective
are commonly used to frame the central
panel in one type of Fourth Style wall (see
page 71). On the broad plane surface of the
central panel in the scheme from which
these elements came was painted a small
framed picture of Perseus and Andromeda
(Naples Museum, inv. 8995), and in the
middle of each lateral panel were roundels
(see also Nos. 7, 146). One of these was the
famous 'Sappho' (Naples Museum,
inv. 9084).
A. Allroggen-Bedel, 'Herkunft und
ursprünglicher Dekorationszusammeng-
hang einiger in Essen ausgestellter
Fragmente von Wandmalereien' *Neue
Forschungen in Pompeji* 118f. fig. 95b.

150

**Wall painting: Theseus, slayer of the
Minotaur.**
Width 88 cm; height 97 cm.
Naples Museum, inv. 9043.
From the *exedra* off the Peristyle in the House
of Gavius Rufus (VII, 2, 16).

The central panel of the left-hand wall of a
Fourth Style scheme. It shows Theseus
victorious from his battle with the
Minotaur, the bull-headed monster of Crete
to whom the Athenians had each year to
send a tribute of youths and maidens. The
Minotaur lies dead in the entrance to his lair,
the Labyrinth, and his destined victims press
round Theseus in gratitude. A finer version
of the same Greek original (Naples Museum,
inv. 9049) was found in the Basilica at
Herculaneum. The companion pieces of the
picture at Pompeii were (on the opposite
wall, inv. 9044) Pirithous, the companion of
Theseus, receiving the Centaurs and (on the
rear wall, inv. 9449) Dionysus, Aphrodite and
the Sun god, Helios.
Schefold, *WP* 136. Bianchi Bandinelli 110f.,
illustrating both this piece (fig. 116) and the
piece from Herculaneum (fig. 115).

148

147

149

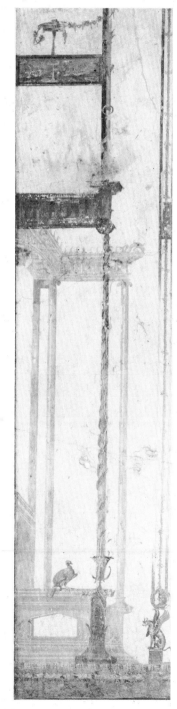

150

151

152

Panel from a painted ceiling.
Width 88 cm; height 82 cm.
Naples Museum, inv. 9973.
From Pompeii.

The design, here reduced to a formal pattern, is reminiscent of a ceiling coffer. A small head of Medusa occupies the centre.

153, 154

Wall painting: pair of sea centaurs.
Height 34 cm; width 24 cm.
Height 30 cm; width 18 cm.
Naples Museum, inv. 8887, 8888.
From one of the sites in the Vesuvius area.

Acroteria from a pair of panels of Fourth Style fantasy architecture similar to those flanking the panel of the Infant Hercules in the House of the Vettii (see page 71). They are shown blowing horns and holding tambourines.

155

Wall painting: woman giving water to a traveller.
Width 44 cm; height 38 cm.
Naples Museum, inv. 9106.
From the *tablinum* of the House of the Dioscuri (VI, 9, 6).

The picture formed part of a longer landscape frieze, with painted mouldings top and bottom, over the side panels of a Fourth Style wall (as in the Atrium of the House of the Menander). In front of a rustic shelter, made of canes, a woman, seated on a circular platform and wearing a conical hat, dips a beaker from a jar and hands it to a traveller, whose dog sits waiting for him. Spinazzola-Aurigemma 580. Richardson 124f. Schefold, *WP* 118. Peters 164.

152

153

154

155

156
Portable pottery brazier.
Height 17 cm; width 32 cm; depth 24 cm.
Naples Museum, 76/198.
From one of the sites in the Vesuvius area.

The brazier is a simple box, with a series of
holes pierced through the top to allow the
heat to escape, and provided with two lug
handles for carrying.

156

157
Wall painting: Phaedra and Hippolytus.
Width 1.03 m; height 1.04 m.
Naples Museum, inv. 9041.
From Herculaneum.

Phaedra, wife of Theseus, King of Athens,
had conceived a guilty passion for her
stepson, Hippolytus, a passion which he
rejected; whereupon Phaedra accused him
of trying to seduce her. He was subsequently
killed while out hunting, and she hanged
herself. In this painting Phaedra's old nurse
tells Hippolytus of her mistress's love, as he
is setting out for the hunt. The scene, of
which there were several variant copies at
Pompeii, is based on a Hellenistic original,
which in turn was inspired by Euripides's
tragedy *Hippolytus*. In this version, from a
Fourth Style wall, Phaedra has been given a
Flavian court hairstyle; it must have been
painted very shortly before AD 79.
Schefold, *WP* 335.

158
Wall painting: the Three Graces
Width 53 cm; height 56 cm.
Naples Museum, inv. 9236.
From the *tablinum* of the House of Titus
Dentatus Panthera (IX, 2, 16).

Panel cut from the middle of a Fourth Style
wall. The Three Graces, or *Charites*,
daughters of Zeus by various mothers,
personified beauty, grace, and intellectual
and moral wisdom. There are innumerable
examples of this group both in painting and
in sculpture, all obviously copied from the
same original, presumably a well-known
Hellenistic sculpture. The Graces are
commonly portrayed, as here, holding or
wreathed with spring flowers. This
explains the presence of flowers in the
landscape setting, a feature not represented
elsewhere in Pompeian mythological scenes.
Schefold, *WP* 242. Peters 139.

157

158

159

Bronze apparatus for heating liquids.
Height 51 cm; base 43 cm square.
Naples Museum, inv. 72986.
From a villa near Stabiae.

Rather like a samovar, this apparatus was
designed to maintain a continuous supply of
hot wine, or any other hot fluid. The liquid
was poured into a gently tapering,
churn-shaped container (A) with a hinged lid;
from this it was free to pass through a tall,
narrow duct (B) into the hollow walls of a
cylindrical fire-box (C), from which it could
be drawn off, as required, through a tap (D)
in the shape of a lion's head. The source of
heat was a charcoal fire in the middle of the
fire-box. Fuel could be stored in the square,
four-legged tray, which also served to
contain the ashes. As long as the level of the

liquid within the main container was kept
above that of the tap, a constant supply was
assured, piping hot. In addition to the tap
there are a number of applied bronze
fittings: on the main container a comic
actor's mask (see No. 174) and a handle in the
form of a miniature bust of Mercury; on the
rim of the fire-box three swans poised for
flight; and on the tray four legs in the form of
Sirens, and four drop handles.
MB 4 (Rome 1841) pl. xx.

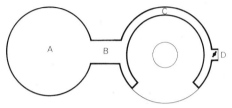

160a

Bronze candelabrum (lamp stand).
Height 1.265 m.
Naples Museum, inv. 78485.
From one of the sites in the Vesuvius area.

The slender shaft is made in the form of a
bamboo cane, which divides into three at the
top to carry the round plate on which the
lamp stood. The three feet arch outwards
from the base of the stem, with long,
tongue-shaped leaves between them. Such
candelabra appear commonly in Pompeian
wall paintings of the Second and Third Style.

160b

Bronze oil lamp.
Height 13 cm; length 20 cm.
Naples Museum, inv. 72490.
From Pompeii.

The two stems of the handle support a
vertical escutcheon in the shape of an
openwork heart. The form is otherwise very
similar to that of No. 126b, but with the
nozzle plain except for the rosettes at the
point of junction. The filling hole is fitted
with a small plug, which is attached to the
base of the handle by means of a chain of
twisted loops of bronze wire.

159

161

Dionysiac scene in marble intarsia.
Slate and coloured marbles.
Length 67 cm; height 23 cm.
Naples Museum, inv. 9977.
From the House of the Coloured Capitals
(VII, 4, 31–51).

One of a pair of Dionysiac scenes found in the *tablinum*, where they were probably used on the walls as panel pictures (*pinakes*). On the left a Maenad dances in ecstacy, with torch and *tympanon*; on the right a Satyr clutches a *thyrsus* and is waving a goat skin; and in the centre is a small shrine. The companion piece portrays a Maenad dancing towards a

Priapus herm; a statue on a pedestal; a nude youth with a panther; and a tree beside a sacred pillar monument or baetyl (as in the sacro-idyllic landscapes).

The technique is that of intarsia, a sophisticated variant of *opus sectile*, composed of shaped and inscribed pieces of coloured marble (*giallo antico* from Africa, *fior di persico* from Euboea, and *paesina verde* and *palombino* from Italy), cut out and fitted into a slate panel. Third quarter of the first century AD.
Mau, *Bull Inst* XLVI (1874), 98. Elia, *BdA* IX (1929) 265ff. Dohrn, *RM* 72 (1965) 131. Kraus and von Matt no. 272.

162

Terracotta lamp.
Length 13.3 cm; diameter 8.2 cm.
British Museum, inv. 1847. 11–8. 1.
From Pompeii.

This and the following three lamps were made in two-piece moulds. Like all Roman lamps, they burned low-grade olive oil with a fibre wick. In low relief on the *discus* (the circular depression with a central filling hole) is Apollo, seated on a rock playing his lyre. Beside him is a griffin (see No. 95). Last third of the first century AD.
BMC Lamps (Walters) no. 776.

163

Terracotta lamp.
Length 12.5 cm; diameter 9.5 cm.
British Museum, inv. 1847. 11–8. 2.
Probably from Pompeii.

In low relief around the filling hole a Satyr chases a Maenad around a flaming altar.
Second half of first century AD.
BMC Lamps (Walters) no. 1060.

164

Terracotta lamp.
Length 12 cm; diameter 9 cm.
British Museum, inv. 1847. 11–8. 7.
Probably from Pompeii.

It has no handle. In low relief on the *discus* is a stork holding a pair of scales, upon which a mouse is shown outweighing an elephant. Although the subject does not seem to be recorded in the surviving literature, it suggests allusion to some familiar fable. There is a stamp on the underside in the shape of a foot, but the name of the maker is illegible. About AD 40 to 70.
BMC Lamps (Walters) no. 596.

165

Terracotta lamp.
Length 11 cm; diameter 7.5 cm.
British Museum, inv. 1971. 4–26. 3.
Reputedly found near Naples 1846.

In low relief on the discus is an erotic scene. Such scenes are quite common on lamps. The couch is of the standard Roman form, of which Nos. 179–184 were part of the decoration. First third of the first century AD.
Unpublished, but see *BMC Lamps* (Bailey) II, Q 828.

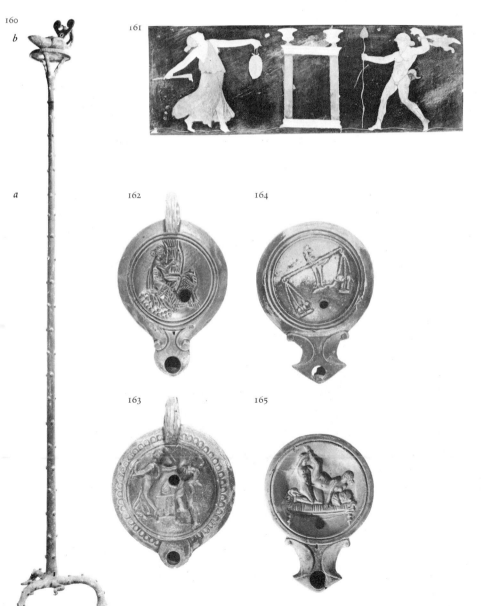

160
b

a

161

162

164

163

165

166
Glazed terracotta lamp with two nozzles.
Height 22 cm; length 37.8 cm.
Naples Museum, inv. 76/165.
From Pompeii.

The vine leaf is a simplified version of that found on bronze lamps (No. 167). The nozzles are joined to the body by large volutes, of which the outer pair end in horse's heads. The well in the middle is decorated with an ovolo border and scalloped fluting radiating from the filling hole.

 The blue-green glaze, coloured with copper oxide, is characteristic of a substantial group of fine terracotta objects, including small statuettes (No. 194) and fountain figures, as well as lamps and pottery vessels. There were several centres of production employing this technique, but it has been suggested that these large lamps with horse's head volutes were imported from Cnidos in south-western Asia Minor, where large numbers of them have been found, and that the glaze was applied by a local potter.

167
Two-nozzled oil lamp on a low stand.
Bronze.
Lamp: height 26.5 cm; length 40.5 cm.
Stand: height 15.8 cm; diameter 14 cm.
Naples Museum, inv. 72284 and 72307.
From Pompeii.

Both the shape of the body and the vine-leaf handle resemble that copied in glazed terracotta in No. 166, except that the volutes linking the nozzles to the body are plain. The vine leaf is also found used decoratively between the legs of lamp stands (e.g. Naples Museum, inv. 72251: Pernice IV, fig. 78).

 The stand (not illustrated) is of a common three-legged type, a more elegant version of No. 168, with a series of openwork volute motifs, enriched with plant ornament, springing from three lion's paw feet. Such lamps stood on side tables, and they are also found on the counters of shops and bars. Pernice IV, 57.

168
Two-nozzled oil lamp on a low stand.
Bronze.
Lamp: height 20.3 cm; length 28 cm.
Stand: height 15.6 cm; diameter 13 cm.
Naples Museum, inv. 72331 and 72212.
From Pompeii.

The lamp is cast in bronze, its ring foot and the ornate handle added as separate castings. The handle consists of a bat-like creature, with a panther's head and spread wings,

perched on the volutes of an acanthus palmette. The small circular stand consists of a moulded top and, below it, twelve equally-spaced, arched projections, three of which are prolonged downwards and end in lion's paws. First century AD.
Pernice IV 58, fig. 79 (the stand).

169
Gold lamp with two nozzles.
Height 15.1 cm; length 23.2 cm.
Naples Museum, inv. 25000.
From Pompeii.

The body bears a design of lotus leaves similar to that found on late Hellenistic bowls in precious metals or their pottery equivalents; it was worked in relief from the outside with a punch, after filling the interior with pitch. The leaf-shaped reflector in front of the handle is similarly worked with a palmette design. The plain spouts and base were cast separately and soldered into place. The lid, now missing, would normally have been the most highly decorated part.

 The discovery of this lamp was one of the sensations of the excavations of 1863.
Breglia no. 1025. Siviero no. 341. *Bull Inst* xxxv (1863), 90–91.

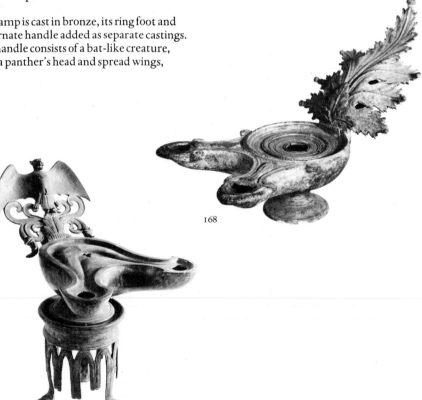

168

166

167

170
Bronze lantern.
Height of lantern only, 21 cm; total height 45 cm.
British Museum, inv. 1912. 5–16. 1.
From Boscoreale.

The wick holder, with a cap which could be removed for cleaning and refilling, is set in the middle of a circular base plate which stands on three small feet. The flame was originally protected by semi-transparent sheets of horn slotted between the double ring of bronze mounted on the base plate and a similar ring above, which is soldered on to the backs of two vertical rods in the form of pilasters with Ionic capitals. To the tops of the latter were attached the rings and chains, linked to the ends of a yoke-shaped cross bar, by which the lantern was held. The lid, a shallow inverted bowl, is pierced with a pattern of holes for ventilation when closed. The lantern could also be carried with the lid raised. A chain attached to the top, ends in a short rod slotted through the main carrying bar, with a ring to stop it slipping too far, and has its own yoke handle. Rings on either side of the lid loop around the main chains to keep the lid centred over the lantern body.
BMC Bronzes no. 1495. Loeschke, *BJb* 118 (1909) 386, fig. 7.

171
Bronze plaque with a lion's-head ring handle.
Width 19.5 cm; height 12.8 cm.
Naples Museum, inv. 72738.
From Pompeii.

One of a pair. The four holes show that it was attached to some large wooden object, probably a door. Although appearing also on other large objects such as chests or vats, handles of this form are very common in representations of doors in classical art.

172
Bronze drop handle.
Mounting plate: width 19 cm; height 3.3 cm.
Handle: width 17.5 cm; drop 7.7 cm.
Naples Museum, inv. 72980.
From Pompeii.

The ends of the handle are in the form of elongated animal's heads, perhaps intended to portray hounds with their ears pressed flat against their necks. The absence of nail-holes shows that this piece was probably soldered on to some portable bronze object, such as a brazier or a heating apparatus (see No. 159).

173
Bronze door handle.
Length 31.3 cm; width 4.8 cm.
Naples Museum, inv. 70277.
From the Vesuvius area, possibly from the Villa of Publius Fannius Synistor at Boscoreale.

The handle was mounted as shown in the diagram, with the grip fixed through the thin bronze base plate, and through slots in the thicker door plate, to two levers on springs which it could raise or drop by sliding up or down. On the face of the base plate. developing from cusped rectangles below the feet of the grip, are heart-shaped motifs turning into volutes and ending in motifs like the hilt of a sword with a strongly marked rib down the central axis. This combination of motifs is found in Campanian bronzeware as early as the second century BC. It was used on door handles certainly by the early first century BC and enjoyed a long popularity.
Cf. Pernice IV, 63. *JdAI* XIX (1904) 15f.

169

171

172

170

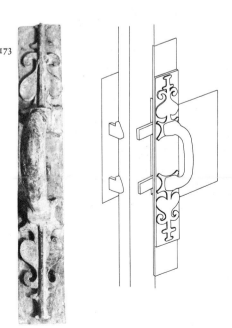
173

174

Bronze ornament in the form of a theatre mask.
Height 5.3 cm.
Naples Museum, inv. '94'.
From one of the sites in the Vesuvius area.

The mask, cast solid, represents a slave in New Comedy. It was probably applied to an elaborate piece of domestic bronze equipment such as the heating apparatus, No. 159.

175

Miniature herm in bronze.
Height 19.5 cm.
Naples Museum, inv. 5343.
Found in Herculaneum, October 1764.

The herm, in the form of a child, is hollow, with an iron rod running down the back of it. It was evidently the foot of some large piece of iron furniture.
Bronzi di Ercolano 2, 356f., pl. LXXXIX.
Cf. K.A. Neugebauer, *Die griechischen Bronzen der klassischen Zeit und des Hellenismus* (Berlin 1951) 27, no. 18.

176

Bronze plaque of a Maenad in high relief.
Height 19.2 cm; width 19.7 cm.
Naples Museum, inv. 120269.
From the debris filling the lower levels of House VIII, 2, 21, found 16 April 1890.

The Maenad, her hair wreathed with ivy leaves, berries and fruit, with a band across her forehead and one breast bared, is displayed against a large vine leaf. Her eyes, now empty, were once filled with silver or cement and coloured glass. Rivets show that the plaque was fastened to some larger, flat object.

Similar bronze plaques, in sets of three, were often used to adorn the fronts of the heavily studded iron chests, with massive locks, which stood in the atrium in many Pompeian houses, containing valuables, family documents and other prized possessions.
Pernice IV, 18, fig. 27.

177

Bronze ring with a Medusa head.
Diameter 11.2 cm.
Naples Museum, inv. 72969.
From Pompeii.

This handle, from the door of a cupboard or a wooden coffer, consists of a grooved ring hinged at the top to a circular base plate, upon which is portrayed in relief the head of Medusa, the snake-haired female monster whose glance turned all who looked upon her to stone and who was slain by Perseus (see No. 316). By an easy extension of ideas a Medusa head was thought to protect the object it adorned. Its shape is well suited to filling circular spaces, and it is used commonly in handles of this sort. The eyes are inlaid with silver, in the centre of which is a hole for the pupil, which may have been made of coloured glass.
Pernice IV, 19.

178

Ivory panel from a piece of wooden furniture.
Height 10.5 cm; width 6 cm.
Naples Museum, inv. 10158.
From one of the sites in the Vesuvius area.

The panel probably formed part of the veneer on an elaborately turned leg of a wooden couch or stool. Its dimensions and slightly tapering convex shape are closely paralleled by ivory plaques in the Chicago Museum thought to have come from a funerary couch.

Carved in relief is the figure of the Muse Terpsichore, patron of the dance, holding a plectrum in her right hand and a lyre beside her left shoulder.
Cf. E. Ransom, *Studies in Ancient Furniture*, I (Chicago 1905) 56f. and 103.

174   175

176

177

178

179, 180
Two bronze mule's head mounts.
Heights, 13 cm and 18 cm.
Naples Museum, inv. 72734, 72736.
From Herculaneum.

Each of these two mounts was applied to the
upper end of the curved arm rest *(fulcrum)* of
a banqueting couch. In a context of
banqueting it was appropriate to portray the
head of a mule, one of the beasts closely
associated with Dionysus, god of wine and
good living. It is shown crowned with a
wreath of ivy leaves (another of the attributes
of Dionysus) and slung over the shoulders is a
saddle cloth, covered with a panther-skin
tied below the neck by its paws. The eyes of
the mules, and very possibly some other
details, such as the ornamental border on the
edge of the cloth, were inlaid with silver.
Similar mounts have been found all over the
Roman world, and at least one, from Asia
Minor, appears to be identical.
Bronzi di Ercolano I, 83 and 279. *RM* 45 (1930)
144, no. 21. *AA* 1904, 30, no. 36.

179   180

181
Bronze bust of a youthful Satyr.
Height 14.5 cm; width 18.2 cm.
British Museum, inv. WT 767.
From 'Torre Annunziata' (probably
Pompeii).

The youthful figure, in high relief, wears a
panther's skin, knotted on his right shoulder
and wrapped around his left arm; in the
folds he carries a bundle of fruits, including
clusters of grapes. His eyes are inlaid with
white cement for the iris and a circular dot of
blue frit for the pupil. Like No. 182, the bust
was probably attached to the lower end of the
curved fitting *(fulcrum)* on a dining couch.
BMC Bronzes no. 1412.

182
Small bronze bust of a goddess of plenty.
Height 10 cm.
Naples Museum, inv. 5150.
Found in Herculaneum.

Cast bronze fitting, probably from the lower
end of the curved support *(fulcrum)* on a
couch. The figure wears a short veil over
the head, covering a high hair-piece, and
round her neck is a silver necklace of beads
from which hang large lozenge-shaped silver
pendants. Her eyes too are inlaid with silver.
In the folds of her loose tunic she carries a
selection of fruit, identifying her as Pomona,
the Italian goddess of orchards and gardens,
or possibly as Fortuna, goddess of plenty.
Bronzi di Ercolano, I, 47, pl. X *MB* 9 (Rome 1845)
352, pl. XXXVII.

182

183, 184
**Decorative intarsia strips, from a
banqueting couch.**
Length 56 cm, height 3.9 cm; and
Length 56.7 cm, height 4.4 cm.
Naples Museum, old inv. 5451, 70995.
From Pompeii.

Two almost identical panels of bronze,
delicately ornamented with inlaid
silverwork in the long, narrow recessed panel
and in the shorter, flat panels at the two ends.
Comparison with another, longer piece in the
Naples Museum (inv. 70992) shows that the
designs on the end panels, meaningless as
they stand, are abbreviated versions of a
scheme with acanthus leaves and sprays of
tiny leaves set symmetrically about a central
palmette: the craftsman was using repertory
motifs fitted as best they might be within the
space available.

Panels of this sort were used to decorate
and strengthen the long horizontal members
of couches; also sometimes on footstools.
They were recessed into the wood with the
flange uppermost.
Mau-Kelsey 361f., fig. 180.

185
**Decorative intarsia strip, from a piece of
furniture.**
Silver on bronze.
Length 61.7 cm; height 3.8 cm.
Naples Museum, inv. 70990.
From Pompeii.

Despite the obvious resemblance of this
piece to Nos. 183 and 184, the absence of any
flange along the upper edge suggests that it
was let into some other piece of wooden
furniture, such as a table. The vine scroll of
the two long recessed panels would have
been appropriate to a table or stool used in a
dining room. The central panel contains an
elaborate formal rosette, the two end panels
a section of a latticework design with
simpler, eight-petalled rosettes.

181

183

184

185

Hall of the Mysteries, Pompeii.
see No. 204.

186

Wall painting: the arrival of Io at Canopus.
Height 80 cm; width 66 cm.
Naples Museum, inv. 9555.
From the room north of the atrium in the
House of the Duke of Aumale (VI, 9, 1).

From the centre panel of a late Third Style
scheme, the painting illustrates a scene from
the story of Io, the virgin priestess of Hera at
Argos, who had the misfortune to attract the
amorous eye of Zeus. Transformed by Hera
into a white heifer, she was watched over by
the hundred-eyed herdsman Argus, until the
latter was slain and Io released by Hermes.
After interminable wanderings she found
haven in Egypt, where she was kindly
received by Isis and resumed human form,
giving birth to Epaphos, legendary ancestor
of, among others, the royal house of Argos.
Within the Isiac cult she tended to be
assimilated with the cow goddess Hathor.

In this painting Io is borne by the river god
of the Nile into the presence of Isis, who is
shown enthroned in her great sanctuary at
Canopus, near Alexandria. Isis holds the

royal cobra of Egypt in her left hand; her feet
rest on a crocodile and, facing her, a small
sphinx symbolises the land of Egypt. Behind
her are two white-robed attendants who hold
sistra (see Nos. 196, 197) and the messenger's
staff (*caduceus*) of Hermes; and at her side,
finger to his lips, stands the child god
Harpocrates (see Nos. 191, 192). Io's past
wanderings are symbolized by the pair of
horns on her forehead. Another painting of
this scene, larger and of superior quality,
clearly derived from the same Hellenistic
original, was found in the Temple of Isis
(Elia, *Mon Pitt* 27–30).
Curtius, fig. 129.

187

Section of a painted frieze.
Length 2.18 m; height 82 cm.
Naples Museum, inv. 8546.
From the portico wall of the Temple of Isis.

The frieze, on a black ground, represents an
ornate acanthus plant scroll, in the spirals of
which are lotus-flower heads alternating
with pygmies and with animals and birds
associated with Isis: from left to right, a
pygmy running, a cobra, a hippopotamus
and an eagle. Below the frieze is part of the
central zone of the wall (see page 59) including
the top of the frame of one of the panels,
which contained a landscape similar to
No. 11. In the frame is a small panel
containing a theatre mask.

187

188

Wall painting: seated figure of Bes.
Width 66 cm; height 1.14 m.
Naples Museum, inv. 8916.
From the Temple of Isis, from the west wall of the smaller of the two rooms at the west end of the sanctuary (see also No. 189).

This inner room, possibly used for initiations, was decorated on the west, north and east walls with figures relating to the cult of Isis, all very broadly executed on a white ground with little or no attempt at relative scale.

The Egyptian god of the dance, characteristically portrayed as a squat, obese figure, seated nude on a throne, with his hands on his knees and a large flower on his head. See also No. 194.
Tran tam Tinh, *Pompéi* 145, no. 52. Elia, *Mon Pitt* III. 4, 21.

189

Wall painting of an ibis.
Width 56 cm; height 82 cm.
Naples Museum, inv. 8562.
From the Temple of Isis, from the north wall of the same room as No. 188.

This large Egyptian ibis occupied the centre of the north wall between representations of the discovery of Osiris and a lion. On the west wall Isis, Serapis and Bes (No. 188) sat enthroned, and facing them were the bull Apis and a number of other sacred animals: monkey, sheep, mole, jackal, sparrowhawk, vulture, cobra, and mongoose (ichneumon). The ibis has a lotus flower on the top of its head and an ear of corn in its beak.
Tran tam Tinh, *Pompéi* 144, no. 48. Elia, *Mon Pitt* III. 4, 22.

190

Bronze statuette of Isis-Fortuna.
Height 30 cm.
Naples Museum, inv. 5312.
From the Vesuvius area.

The base is lost and the whole surface is much corroded. The goddess, heavily robed in a long tunic and mantle, wears an elaborate Egyptian diadem, which incorporates the solar disc and the horns of the goddess Hathor, one of her many manifestations. In her left hand she holds a horn of plenty, symbol of her identification with the Italian goddess Fortuna, who was worshipped as a bringer of good things rather than as a goddess of blind chance. Her right hand, now badly damaged, once held a rudder, symbolizing her protection of seafarers. One of the main annual festivals associated with the cult of Isis was that which marked the opening of the season for navigation.
Tran tam Tinh, *Pompéi* 160–161, no. 98.

188

189

190

191
Bronze statuette of Harpocrates.
Height 8 cm.
Naples Museum, inv. 5329.
From the *lararium* in the House of the
Emperor Joseph II (VIII, 2, 38–39).

Harpocrates, in origin the Egyptian child-god
Harpa-Khruti, son of Isis and Serapis, is
shown in the conventional attitude of
childhood, with his finger on his lips, later
misinterpreted by the Romans as a gesture of
silence. His curly hair is crowned with ivy
leaves and a top-knot. A *bulla* (see No. 48)
hangs round his neck. On his back he has
little wings, a quiver, and a ring for
suspension. He rests his left arm, holding a
cornucopia (horn of plenty) entwined by a
snake, on a knobbly tree trunk.
PAH I, i, 233. *MB* 12 (Naples 1850) pl. XXX. 2.
RM 2, 1887, 119. Boyce 349 note. Tran tam
Tinh, *Pompéi* 162, no. 107.

192
Bronze statuette of Harpocrates.
Height 8.3 cm (12.2 cm with base).
Naples Museum, inv. 5368.
From one of the sites in the Vesuvius area.

Similar to No. 191, but the snake is coiled
round his left thigh and he holds the
cornucopia unsupported. Probably from a
lararium.
Tran tam Tinh, *Pompéi* 164, no. 111.

193
Terracotta figurine of a priest.
Height 18 cm.
Naples Museum, inv. 20477.
From Pompeii (?).

The figure, dressed in long robes edged with
a richly embroidered border, holds some
object, perhaps a key, in his left hand, and is
thought to represent a priest. Which
particular cult he served is uncertain.
Levi, no. 865.

194
Glazed terracotta figure of Bes.
Height 33.8 cm.
Naples Museum, inv. 22583.
From Pompeii.

Bes, the Egyptian god of the dance, is
portrayed in duplicate, back to back, dancing
with bent knees, his hands on his thighs and
his head crowned with lotus leaves (see also
No. 188). Several similar figures have been
found in Pompeii, one in the Temple of Isis,
another set on one of the four marble
colonnettes in the corners of the garden of the
House of the Mosiac Columns, outside the
Herculaneum Gate.
    Terracotta figures with a bluish-green
glaze (as also No. 105) belong to the last
period of Pompeii before AD 79.
Von Rohden 61, pl. L, 2.

193

194

191   192

195
Two figures of ibises.
Marble and bronze.
Length 39 cm; height 25 cm.
Length 41 cm; height 25.5 cm.
Naples Museum, Egyptian Collection, inv.
765 and 766.
Possibly from the Temple of Isis.

The heads, necks and legs of the birds are in
bronze, while the bodies are made of white
marble, following their natural colouring.
The technique of combining such materials
at this date is most unusual.
Tran tam Tinh, *Pompéi* 175 nos. 145 and 146.
Pitture di Ercolano 5, 119.

196
Bronze rattle (sistrum).
Length 22.3 cm.
Naples Museum, inv. 109669.
Found in the atrium of House 1, 2, 10.

The head consists of a broad strip of bronze
shaped into a loop and, strung across it, four
bronze rods, which are looped over at the
ends to hold them in but are otherwise free
to move to and fro, giving a tinkling sound
when shaken. On the top of the loop is a
figure of a cat with a pine cone on her head
and suckling two kittens. The handle is
plain. Though normally of bronze, silver
sistra are known (e.g. Naples, inv. 111770).

The *sistrum*, an instrument of Egyptian
origin, is one of the commonest symbols of
the worship of Isis, who took it over from
Hathor, the Egyptian goddess of music. In
sculpture and painting Isis normally holds a
sistrum in her right hand (see No. 202), and
sistra were carried and shaken by
worshippers as part of the standard rituals of
the cult, to repel the forces of evil or to
express joy or mourning. Apuleius describes
their use vividly in his *Metamorphoses* (XI, 4).
Daremberg and Saglio, s.v. *Sistrum*.

197
Bronze rattle (sistrum).
Height 19 cm.
Naples Museum, old inv. 2386.
From Pompeii.

A smaller version of No. 196. On the top of
the loop is the cat with kittens, and near
the base two small jackals; the ends of the
rods are shaped as duck's heads. The ornate
handle incorporates two sacred cobras and
figures of Bes, Egyptian god of the dance
(cf. nos. 188, 194) and of Hathor, goddess
of music.

198
Pair of small bronze cymbals (cymbalum).
Diameter 11 cm.
Naples Museum, inv. 76943.
From Pompeii.

Two circular sheets of bronze, each concave
internally and surrounded by a broad
flange, linked from the centres by a loose
chain. Cymbals, usually portrayed in
conjunction with tambourines *(tympana)*
and pipes (see No. 319), were commonly
played both at religious and at social
functions (see also No. 204, group IX).
Daremberg and Saglio, s.v. *Cymbalum*.
H. Hickmann, *Annales du Service des
Antiquités de l'Egypte* 49 (1949) 451–545.

195

197

196

198

199

199

Reed-pipe (tibia).
Silver, bone and ivory.
Length 53.7 cm.
Naples Museum, inv. 76894.
From the room to the right of the *tablinum* in
House VII, 2, 18.

The tube is made of bone, cased in bands of
silver and fitted with rings of silver, pierced
with holes, which could be rotated so as to
open or close some of the holes in the tube,
thus varying the range of notes available.
The number of finger holes varies from one
instrument to another: in this case up to
nine, in others up to fifteen. The mouthpiece
consisted of a slightly expanded bulb of
ivory, drilled to the same bore as the tube,
and, fixed into it, a bone holder for the
double reed. The sound would have
resembled that of a primitive oboe.
A variant form (see No. 210), known as the
'Phrygian pipes', combined a straight pipe
with a longer one that turned up at the end,
producing a louder note.

Pipes of this sort were normally played in
pairs (see No. 262), though whether together
or separately is not known. The players
(tibicines) are often shown (as on No. 314)
wearing a mouth band, which supported the
cheek muscles. This piece could well have
been made locally in Campania, witness the
complaints of Seneca (*Letters* 56, 4) at the
horrible noises made by a pipe-maker
(tibiarius) at Baiae testing his instruments.
Howard, *Studies in Classical Phililogy* IV
(1893), pl. II.
Daremberg and Saglio, s.v. *Tibia*.

200

Bronze votive hand of Sabazius.
Height 18 cm; width of base 8 cm.
Naples Museum, inv. 5506.
From Herculaneum, 8 February 1746.

Sabazius was originally a Thracian or
Phrygian divinity of vegetation, and in
particular of barley and wheat. Known in
Greece as early as the fifth century BC, during
the Roman Empire he was worshipped
increasingly in a variety of syncretistic forms,
most commonly as Zeus Sabazius or as
Dionysus Sabazius, but also (just like Isis,
see page 59) taking on the attributes of many
other divinities.

One of the most striking features of his cult
is a series of votive hands, of which the fingers
form the gesture of benediction still familiar
from the Latin Christian rite. Sabazius
himself, bearded and wearing a tunic,
trousers and a Phrygian cap, is seated in the
palm of the hand, his feet on a ram's head and
his hands raised in the same characteristic
gesture. Around him are his major
attributes: on his right, curling up the back of
the hand, his own serpent; on his left, the
pine cone of Dionysus; and above him, the
eagle of Zeus (of which only the claws now
survive) grasping a thunderbolt. On the
wrist is a curious, grotto-like frame,
enclosing the figures of a mother and child.
Elsewhere on the hand are shown a scarab,
two cymbals, a double flute (Phrygian
pipes), a winged staff of Mercury (*caduceus*), a
pair of scales, an owl, a lizard, a frog, a tortoise,
a wine bowl (*crater*), a flaming altar, a whip,
and a little table with another pine cone.

Two very similar hands were found at
Pompeii in 1954, in a shop (II, I, 12)
identified by the excavators as that of a
dealer in small religious and magical objects.
C. Blinkenberg, *Archaeologische Studien*
(Copenhagen & Leipzig 1904) 75, no. E13.
O. Elia, 'Vasi magici e mani pantee a
Pompei', *RAAN* xxxv (1960) 7ff. E. Lane, 'Two
votive hands in Missouri', *Muse* 4 (1970) 43–8.

200

**Wall painting: ceremony in a sanctuary
of Isis.**
Width 85 cm; height 80 cm.
Naples Museum, inv. 8924.
From Herculaneum.

Scene of ritual ceremonial, taking place in
front of a temple set within a garden at the
head of a tall flight of steps. In front of the
doorway, between the sphinxes, stands the
high priest, clad in long white robes, with
shaven head, and holding a golden vessel. He
is accompanied by a priest and a priestess

shaking *sistra* (see Nos. 196, 197). At the foot
of the steps a priest with a wand conducts two
files of worshippers. In the central foreground
another priest fans the flames on a small
horned altar, hung with garlands; to the left
stand a priest and a priestess, shaking *sistra*,
and to the right a rod-bearing priest and a
Negro playing a flute. Four sacred ibises
complete the scene.

The picture is believed to represent the
morning ceremony at which the high priest
poured libations on all the altars in the
temple precinct. There were six such altars in

the temple at Pompeii. The pendant to this
picture (Naples Museum, inv. 8919) shows
what was probably an evening ritual, a sacred
dance performed by a priest dressed as
Bes (see Nos. 188, 194) in honour of Serapis-
Osiris.

Tran tam Tinh, *Pompéi* 101. Tran tam Tinh,
Herculaneum 29f. Apuleius of Madauros, *The
Isis Book (Metamorphoses, Book XI)* ed. J. Gwyn
Griffiths (Leiden 1975) 182, 185f., 199.

201

202

Statue of Isis in Archaic style.
Pentelic marble.
Height of statue, 1.06 m; height of base 95 cm.
Naples Museum, inv. 976.
From the north-west corner of the colonnade in the Temple of Isis.

The goddess's hair is dressed in an elaborate Archaic Greek style, with a garland of five rosettes. She wears a long, clinging tunic in fine material, held tight under her breasts with a belt the clasp of which is formed of two snakes' heads. Over her shoulders, making sleeves, is an equally thin shawl, tucked into the belt. In her right hand she held a *sistrum*, of which only the handle remains, from her left dangles an *ankh*, the Egyptian symbol of life. When found, the statue was rich in traces of its original colouring, with remains of gilding on the hair, rosettes, the collar and hem of her tunic and the snake bracelets on her wrists. She has heavy red eyebrows and pupils, and there are traces of red also on the tree stump beside her left leg and among the folds around the hem of her tunic.

She stands on her original base, which bears the dedicatory inscription: *L. Caecilius Phoebus posuit l(oco) d(ato) d(ecurionum) d(ecreto)* – 'Lucius Caecilius Phoebus set (this statue) up in a place granted by decree of the town council', one of many indications that this temple was official municipal property. L. Caecilius Phoebus was a freedman of the rich Pompeian banking family. The statue is the only complete figure of Isis found in the Temple. Of two others, composite works in wood and marble, only fragments of the marble parts survive.
Mau-Kelsey, 170. Tran tam Tinh, *Pompéi* 156, no. 81. Reuterswaard, *Polychromie* 186f. *CIL* x, 849.

203

Wall painting: Dionysiac cult objects.
Height 46 cm; width 46 cm.
Naples Museum, inv. 8795.
From Pompeii.

Along a narrow ledge at the top of a small flight of steps are, from left to right: a tambourine; a wicker basket, on which are a drinking horn draped with a panther skin, a drinking cup and a *thyrsus*; and a second, taller drinking cup decorated with vine leaves. On the steps are a spray of bay, a pair of cymbals and a small panther grappling with a snake. All these objects are associated with the cult of Dionysus. The picture, which appears to come from the middle zone of a Fourth Style monumental composition (see page 71), is one of several in the Naples Museum portraying attributes of various gods, all of which may have come from the same decorative scheme.
*MB*5 (Rome 1841) pl. LVIII.

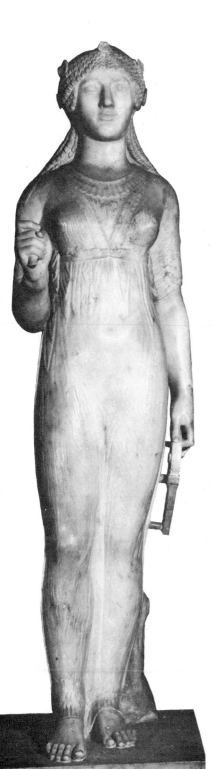

202

203

Painted frieze from the Hall of the Mysteries (reproduction)
Original at Pompeii, Villa of the Mysteries.

Illustration opposite No. 186.

The Villa of the Mysteries was a wealthy suburban residence (*villa urbana*), built towards the middle of the second century BC a short distance outside the walls, between the two roads that converge on the Herculaneum Gate. It was extensively remodelled, modernized and redecorated about 60 BC. During the last years of the town, after the earthquake, parts of it continued to be used as the centre of a farming property under the charge of a steward, who was a freedman of the old Samnite family of the Istacidii, but (just as at Oplontis, see No. 338) the residence, with its magnificent series of early Second Style paintings lay empty. Who the owner responsible for these paintings was we do not know.

The so-called 'Hall of the Mysteries' lay near the south-west corner of the building, entered by a large door in the west wall and with a large window in the middle of the south wall, looking out across a portico towards the Bay of Naples. The walls were covered with nearly lifesize figures, arranged like a frieze against the background of what was still in effect a First Style wall scheme. This background was already in place when the figures were painted, though whether this means that the figures were an afterthought, added at a slightly later date, or whether this sequence merely represents the way the artist chose to lay out and execute his composition, we have no means of telling.

Ever since the discovery of these paintings in 1929–30, their significance has been the subject of lively debate. The suggestion that this was a hall in which the Dionysiac Mysteries were actually celebrated can certainly be excluded. The essence of the Mysteries was that they were secrets, to be guarded jealously from profane eyes, not openly displayed where any passer-by could see them. On the other hand, the paintings are shot through and through with Dionysiac imagery; they reflect in intimate detail the world of ideas to which an initiate of the Mysteries belonged. Side by side with the gods and their attendant train of satyrs, maenads and other Dionysiac followers, there is also a continuous thread of strictly human action, and it is a striking fact that at this human level the small boy reading from a scroll is the only male figure present. This is a women's world, and according to one widely held interpretation the whole

cycle portrays and symbolizes the ceremonies and rituals prior to the wedding of a human bride. There is room for discussion how far one can distinguish the actual physical ceremonials of marriage from portrayals of the symbolic rituals of mystic marriage with the godhead – if indeed the two were clearly distinguishable. But, on this interpretation, the overall intent seems to be clear enough.

There seems to be fairly general agreement that both in its broad conception and in much of its detail the frieze derives from a Hellenistic model or models, and is thus at one remove a unique representation of the lost world of Greek lifesize figured painting (*megalographia*). How closely it followed its sources is open to discussion. It would be pressing coincidence too far to imagine that the available wall space was exactly the same in both cases; and the fact the frieze falls into a number of distinct compositional groups (some of which, such as that of Dionysus and Ariadne (VI), are known from other replicas) would have allowed for a measure of rearrangement, omission or addition. The fact that, despite the unifying hand of the Campanian copyist, one can detect models that were ultimately of different styles and dates, is not in itself significant. Some such assimilation could well have taken place already in the Hellenistic sources. On balance, it seems likely that the relationship between model and copy was a close one but that, as was customary in ancient copying, the process was one of adjustment and adaptation rather than of slavish imitation.

The interpretation which follows, though not free from problems and uncertainties, does offer a plausible and consistent account of these remarkable paintings. It reads from left to right round the room, starting from the small doorway at the north-west corner.

I. Entry of the bride for her initiation. A nude boy reads out a sacred text under the guidance of a woman with a scroll and a writing stylus in her hand. A wreathed attendant, bearing an olive branch, carries in a silver platter of cakes.
II. Preparations for sacrifice. A seated priestess removes a cloth from a basket carried by an attendant, while another attendant pours purifying water on her right hand.
III. The scene shifts to a supranatural level dominated by the figures of Dionysus and Ariadne in the middle of the east wall. An elderly Silenus plays his lyre, resting it on a column. A youthful satyr and his female counterpart are seated on a rock, he playing

the panpipes, she suckling a she-goat.
IV. A woman in an attitude of startled alarm, left hand raised as if to ward off the influence of the scenes that follow on the east wall. This figure cleverly links the two walls, gazing across the corner of the room to bind the two together.
V. A young satyr gazes into a bowl held up before him by an elderly Silenus, while a second young satyr holds up a theatrical mask. The precise meaning is doubtful, but gazing into bowls was a well-known form of divination.
VI. Central to the east wall, dominating the room, Dionysus reclines in the lap of an enthroned Ariadne.
VII. A kneeling woman, with a long torch over her shoulder, reaches out to unveil an object which is almost certainly to be identified as a huge ritual phallus. On the ground lies a winnowing basket. Two women look on.
VIII. A female figure, with dark wings spread, holds up her left hand as if to shut out the previous scene and raises her right, to strike with a whip the kneeling figure of scene IX. Like figure IV, this winged figure, though compositionally part of the previous group of scenes, really belongs with the next group, linking the two walls across the angle of the room.
IX. A half-naked girl kneels, burying her face in the lap of a seated woman, who helps to bare her back to the ritual flagellation inflicted by the winged figure. On their right are two women. One, fully clothed, brings forward a *thyrsus*, the wand of Dionysus and his followers; the other, naked, dances in ecstasy, clashing a pair of cymbals.
X. The bride's toilet. An attendant helps her to dress her hair. A winged Eros holds up a mirror.
XI. Once again the scene is completed across the corner of the room. A second Eros leans on a pillar gazing up at the bride.
XII. The bride, robed and veiled, sits on the marriage couch. On her fourth finger she displays her wedding ring.

A. Maiuri, *La Villa dei Misteri* (Rome, 1931). O. Brendel, *JdAI* 81 (1966) 206 ff. Kraus and Von Matt, 93–6, whose interpretation we follow. For a totally different interpretation see *Guida Archeologica di Pompei*, ed. F. Coarelli (Verona 1976) 340–6.

205

**Inscribed marble slab recording a dedication
by the Ministri Fortunae Augustae.**
Height 70 cm; length 47 cm.
Naples Museum, inv. 76/248.
Found in 1884, loose in the Basilica.

*L(ucius) Numisius Primus, L(ucius) Numisius
Optatus, L(ucius) Melissaeus Plocamus,
ministr(i) Fortun(ae) Aug(ustae), ex d(ecreto)
d(ecurionum), iussu L(ucii) Iuli(i) Pontici (et)
P(ublii) Gavi(i) Pastoris d(uo)v(iri) i(ure)
d(icundo) et Q(uinti) Poppaei et C(aii)
Vibi(i) aedil(um), Q(uinto) Futio (et) P(ublio)
Calvisio co(n) s(ulibus).*
'Lucius Numisius Primus, Lucius Numisius
Optatus and Lucius Melissaeus Plocamus,
ministers of the cult of Fortuna Augusta,
(made this dedication) in accordance with the
decree of the decurions, on the instruction of
Lucius Julius Ponticus and Publius Gavius
Pastor, chief magistrates, and of Quintus

Poppaeus and Caius Vibius, aediles, during
the consulship of Quintus Futius and Publius
Calvisius.'

The cult of Fortuna Augusta, i.e. of the
prosperity of the emperor, was established at
Pompeii by Marcus Tullius, a prominent
citizen who had been a chief magistrate
(*duovir*) and who built a temple of this
dedication shortly before AD 3. Although the
dedicators named in this inscription were all
freedmen of wealthy Pompeian families, the
body of *ministri* might also include slaves. It
seems to have been the practice of this body
to dedicate a new statue shortly after the
accession of each new emperor. The pair of
Roman consuls named here is not recorded
elsewhere, but the inscription is probably to
be dated to the reign of Caligula, *c*. AD 39–40.
CIL x. 187; *ILS* 6384. Castrén 76–8.

206

**Inscribed slab recording a dedication by
the Ministri Augusti.**
Marble, restored from four pieces.
Length 37.5 cm; height 31 cm.
Naples Museum, inv. 3794.
Pompeii, find-spot not known.

*Narcissus Popid(i) Moschi (servus et)
Nymphodotus Capras(ii) Iucundi (servus)
min(istri) Aug(usti) d(ecurionum) d(ecreto)
iussu P(ublii) Vetti(i) Celeris D(ecimi) Alfidi(i).*
'Narcissus, slave of Popidius Moschus, and
Nymphodotus, slave of Caprasius Jucundus,
ministers of the cult of Augustus, (made this
dedication) by decree of the decurions, on the
the instructions of Publius Vettius Celer and
Decimus Alfidius.'

Members of the college of *Ministri Augusti*
held office for one year, and membership was
open to slaves as well as to freedmen.
Dedications such as this one seem to have
marked important events within the
imperial family. The first record of the
college dates from 2 BC (*CIL* x. 890), when one
of the *ministri* was Numisius Popidius
Moschus, a freedman of the influential
Popidius family. The subsequent election to
the college of one of his own slaves,
Narcissus, illustrates very clearly the network
of patronage to which the service of the
Imperial cult gave rise. This inscription
must date from the early years of the first
century AD.
CIL x. 908. Castrén 75.

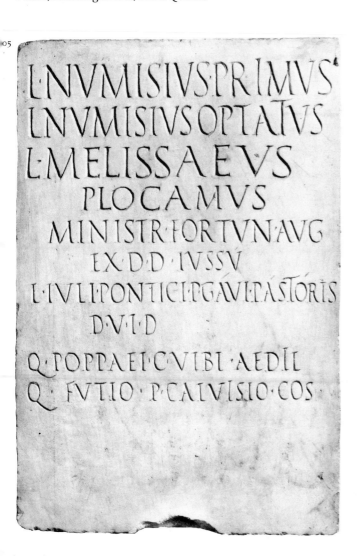

206

207
Wall painting: figure of a priestess.
Height 95 cm; width 43 cm.
Naples Museum, inv. 8908.
From Herculaneum.

The fragment, and its companion piece
showing a youth carrying a stool (Naples
Museum, inv. 9374), were probably cut from
the architectural framework of a Fourth
Style scheme. The woman is veiled and
carries an incense box on a tray in her left
hand.
Helbig no. 1795; cf. *Pitture di Ercolano* IV, 5 pl. I.

208
Wall painting of Mercury.
Height 73 cm; width 49 cm.
Naples Museum, inv. 9452.
From Pompeii.

The youthful god, who was patron of
commerce as well as messenger of the gods,
is shown with wings at his temples and his
ankles and bearing his symbolic staff, or
caduceus (see No. 226) in his left hand. In his
right hand, instead of the usual money bag,
he carries what may be a fish trap, and beside
his right foot is a small tortoise (or turtle).
The most likely position for such a painting
would be in a household shrine or on the
outer wall of a shop, belonging to somebody
who was connected with fishing or the sale of
fish products.
Helbig, 358. *Pitture di Ercolano* V, 89, pl. XIX.

209
Bronze brazier on three legs.
Height 78 cm.
Naples Museum, old inv. 1472.
From one of the sites in the Vesuvius area.

The bowl, which is removable for emptying,
rests on a three-legged stand on animals' paw
feet, and is strengthened with bronze hoops,
a rigid version of the collapsible tripods such
as No. 143. The distinctive shape, in a more
ornate version, the so-called Delphic tripod,
appears frequently in late Second Style
paintings, as on the wall at Oplontis (No. 338).

210
**Wall painting from a household shrine
(lararium).**
Width 1.83 m; height 1.28 m.
Naples Museum, inv. 8905.
Found 6 June 1761 in VIII, insula 2 or 3.

The painting is divided into two registers.
In the upper register, below three garlands,
is a scene of sacrifice. The *genius*, or presiding
divinity of the household, with head veiled
and bearing a cornucopia, symbolic of
plenty, holds a dish (*patera*) out over a marble
altar. He is attended by a small boy carrying a
fillet (a wreath, with ribbons for tying) and a
platter; opposite him a musician plays the
double pipes, beating time with a wooden
clapper beneath his left foot, while a slave

207

208

209

brings forward a pig for sacrifice (see No. 211).
On either side stand the two Lares of the
household, pouring wine from a drinking
horn, or *rhyton*, into a small wine bucket, or
situla. In the lower register two serpents
approach the offerings (of fruit?) upon an
altar. Together with the setting of rich
vegetation, they symbolize the fertility of
nature and the bounty of the earth beneath.
PAH I, 133. *MB* 9 (Rome 1845) 161, pl. XXVII.

211
Small bronze pig on a rectangular stand.
Length 13.5 cm; height 11.5 cm.
Naples Museum, inv. 4905.
From Herculaneum.

Hollow cast, the details sharpened with a
chisel after casting. It is mounted on its
original base which stands on four splayed
cloven hooves springing from formal,
palmette designs. On the pig's left flank are
inscribed the letters HER. VOE. M.L. No
satisfactory interpretation of this abbreviated
text has been proposed. The prominent
position of the letters HER suggest the
possibility of a dedication to Hercules, to
whom a pig was the customary animal of
sacrifice. The figure would in that case have
been placed in a household shrine (*lararium*).
Bronzi di Ercolano I, 83 and 279.

212
Miniature bronze altar.
Height 11 cm; length 19 cm; width 15 cm.
Naples Museum, inv. 74001.
From Pompeii.

The rectangular box in which the
offering was burnt is decorated with simple
profiled mouldings and with crenellations.
It stands on four legs, with wings at the
junction with the body and ending in cloven
animal's hooves. The form is also found on a
much larger scale used as a brazier
(e.g. Naples Museum, inv. 73005).
    Little altars were part of the equipment of
a household shrine (*lararium*). They were
normally built in or made of terracotta, only
rarely of bronze.
Boyce, 16. Gusman, 134.

213
Miniature bronze altar.
Height 13 cm; diameter 15 cm.
Naples Museum, inv. 73997.
From Pompeii.

Beneath a line of tiny crenellations, engraved
with a T-shaped design, alternately upright
and inverted, the circular drum is
ornamented with mouldings of an
architectural character. It stands on three
lion's-paw feet, the shafts of which splay out
into forms that are based on the elements of
an Ionic capital. Like No. 212, this altar is a
miniature version of a shape used also for
braziers (e.g. Naples Museum, inv. 73012) and
would have been made for use in a *lararium*.
MB 3 (Rome, 1839) pl. XXXII.

210

211

212

213

214

Bronze statuette of Apollo.
Height 27 cm.
Naples Museum, inv. 113257.
From the *lararium* in the Atrium of the
House of the Red Walls (VIII, 5/6, 37).

Apollo stands nude, his mantle (*chlamys*)
draped over the column on which he leans
his right arm; his eyes are inlaid with silver,
and he has silver ribbons (*taenia*) in his hair.
A silver-stringed lyre rests against his left leg,
and his left hand probably held the *plectrum*
with which it was plucked, both identifying
him in one of his many roles as patron god of
music. The pose, a rare one derived
probably from a Hellenistic original, is
known in one full-size marble statue in
Florence.
NSc 1882, 420, 437. J. Overbeck, *Griechische
Kunstmythologie* III, 5, 170. Boyce 77, no. 371.

215

Bronze statuette of Hercules.
Height 21 cm.
Naples Museum, inv. 5180.
From Herculaneum.

The Drunken Hercules is shown nude, with a
beard, his club over his right shoulder and his
left hand probably holding a drinking-cup,
now lost. The statuette is of good
workmanship, and the moulded base, which
does not belong to the statuette, is finely
decorated.

216

**Bronze tintinnabulum with five hanging
bells.**
Length, from the wing tips to the lowest bell,
35 cm.
British Museum, inv. WT 1086.
From Pompeii.

Tintinnabula (tinkling bells of the type used
also in some forms of dancing) were hung in
the doorways of houses and shops, often
together with a lamp, as a protection against
evil spirits. This elaborately and aggressively
male object, equipped with wings and the
hind legs of a lion, was a symbol of plenty as
well as a deterrent to evil spirits, and as such
it was a favourite components of such bells.
It is also found, used with the same intent, on
terracotta plaques let into the outer walls of
buildings, particularly at street corners (see
page 56).
Compare Col. Famin, *Musée Royal de Naples:
peintures, bronzes et statues erotiques du cabinet
secret* (Paris 1857) 29f., pls. XXIV, XXVII and
XXVIII.

216

214

215

217
Pottery lamp in the form of a figure of Priapus.
Height 14 cm; length 11.5 cm.
Naples Museum, inv. 27869.
From Pompeii.

The little rustic god of fruitfulness, protector of flocks, bees, vineyards and market gardens, son of Dionysus and Aphrodite, is modelled as a lamp, provided with a ring for suspension, and probably hung from the lintel of an entrance doorway to bring good luck and to ward off evil spirits.
Fiorelli, *Raccolta pornografica* no. 201.

218
Statuette of Aphrodite with Priapus.
Fine white, translucent marble, possibly from Paros.
Height 62 cm.
Naples Museum, inv. 152798.
Found on a table in the *tablinum* of House II, 4, 6.

The group represents Aphrodite preparing to bathe (see No. 219), raising her left foot to remove her sandal and resting her left forearm on the head of a small figure of the god Priapus; a tiny Eros sits below her foot. Aphrodite's left hand, now missing, was carved in a separate piece of marble. The group is remarkable for the extensive remains of gilding as well as some traces of paint. In addition to her necklace, armbands, a bracelet and gilded sandals, Aphrodite wears an exiguous, bikini-like harness. Her eyes are inlaid with cement and glass paste. The hair and pubic hair of both main figures was once gilded (the dark red paint now visible was the underlay) and there are

traces of red paint on the lips of the goddess and on the tree-stump which supports the group; of green on Priapus's pedestal; and of black on the base.

The statuette was found in the large complex of rented accommodation, including a bath-house and tavern, which is known as the villa of Julia Felix. *Graffiti* and other finds suggest that this part of the complex may have served as a brothel in the last years of the town's history.
Reuterswaard, *Polychromie* 184f. *BJb* 170 (1970) 142, M50.

219
Bronze statuette of Aphrodite.
Height 17.5 cm.
Naples Museum, inv. 5133.
Found in Herculaneum, 22 February 1757.

The figure belongs to a large series of representations of Aphrodite (Venus) preparing to bathe (cf. No. 218). She is taking off her left sandal, supporting herself against a narrow tree trunk, around which is curled a dolphin, one of her many characteristic attributes. Her armbands and anklets are made of gold, and the palmette-and-scrollwork decoration on the base is inlaid in silver.
Bronzi di Ercolano 2, 53f., pl. XIV.

218

219

217

220

Replica of the household shrine (lararium) in the House of the Gilded Amorini (VI, 16, 7).
Height 2.07 m; width 1.25 m; depth 74 cm.

This *lararium*, the lower part of which was built of rubble faced with plaster and painted to represent coloured marble veneer, and the upper part constructed of wood and painted stucco and supported on two fluted colonnettes of greenish *cipollino* marble, stood against the north wall of the peristyle. A *lararium* was essentially the shrine of the *lares*, the protecting divinities of the house (see No. 210), who figured in it in association with whatever other divinities the family held in special honour. Within it the master of the house would make small daily offerings, and it was the scene of ceremonial offerings on important family occasions.

The group here displayed (Jupiter, Minerva, Mercury, two *lares* and a lamp; see below), with the exception of the figure of Jupiter, is not that actually found in this particular *lararium*; though absolutely characteristic, it is a composite group, made up from other *lararia*. The *lararium* in the House of the Gilded Amorini contained (along the upper ledge) Jupiter (No. 225) flanked by the other members of the Capitoline triad, Juno and Minerva, and accompanied by Mercury (Hermes; cf. No. 208), the patron god of commerce, who was very popular in this context, and (on the lower ledge) two *lares* and a bronze vessel.
NSc 1907, 565–571; Boyce 57, no. 221.

221

Bronze lamp in the shape of a duck.
Height 8 cm; length 13.5 cm.
Naples Museum, inv. 110674.
From Pompeii, 3 March 1875.

The body of the duck is hollow, forming the reservoir, with a hole for filling in the middle of the back. The tail constitutes the nozzle, and the head looks backward to form the handle. The legs are indicated in shallow relief, tucked up below the wings.

222

Bronze statuette of Minerva.
Height 30 cm.
Naples Museum, inv. 5282.
From Pompeii.

Minerva, the Roman counterpart of Athena, and the goddess of wisdom and good counsel, the arts, sciences, poetry, and spinning and weaving, stands on a rectangular, footed base. She wears a helmet and a tunic loosely tied below her bust with a cord. In her right hand she holds a sacrificial dish, in her left a damaged spear. The statuette probably stood in a household shrine (*lararium*).

221

223

224

223
Bronze statuette of a Lar.
Height 29 cm.
Naples Museum, inv. 5424.
Found at Herculaneum in April 1762, near
the theatre.

The Lares, originally Etruscan divinities of
locality, in Roman times were worshipped as
protectors of the house, usually placed in
pairs within the household shrine (*lararium*;
see No. 220) on either side of the figures of
whatever other gods were specially favoured
by the family. They are regularly portrayed
as youthful figures, wearing short-sleeved
tunics and mantles, often with skirts swirling
in the dance. This example carries a
sacrificial dish and a cornucopia, or horn of
plenty.
Bronzi di Ercolano 2, 197, pl. LII. Cf. *Antike Welt*
6 no. 4 (1975) 26f.

224
Bronze statuette of a Lar.
Height 27 cm.
Naples Museum, inv. 5427.
Found in the earliest excavations at
Herculaneum.

Figure similar to No. 223 but in a more
restrained pose. He carries a wine bucket
(*situla*) and waves a sheaf of wheat.
Bronzi di Ercolano 2, 213, pl. LVI. *MB* 8 (Rome
1844) pl. LXXIII.

225
Bronze statuette of Jupiter.
Height 16.5 cm.
Naples Museum, inv. 133323.
From the *lararium* in the peristyle of the
House of the Gilded Amorini (VI, 15, 7).

This figure of Jupiter sat, enthroned, on the
upper shelf of the *lararium* (see No. 220)
together with the other members of the
Capitoline triad, Juno and Minerva, and with
Mercury the patron of commerce. Jupiter is
bearded, the upper part of his body naked,
the lower half wrapped in a mantle. In his
right hand is a thunderbolt, and the left
probably held a sceptre, now missing.
Boyce 57, no. 221. *NSc* 1907, 565–71.

226
Bronze statuette of Mercury.
Height 19 cm.
Naples Museum, inv. 115553.
From Pompeii, 15 January 1887.

Mercury, the Greek Hermes, messenger of
the gods and patron god of commerce, stands
on a circular, moulded pedestal, with his
cloak draped over his left shoulder, wearing
his characteristic winged hat (*petasos*) and
with wings at his ankles. In his right hand he
holds a money bag, and in his left a winged
staff (*caduceus*) consisting of two intertwined
serpents. Probably from a *lararium*.

222

225

226

227

Painted scenes of tavern life.
Length 2.05 m; height 50 cm.
Naples Museum, inv. 111482.
From the left-hand wall of a tavern
(*caupona*) at Pompeii, VI, 14, 36.

Four scenes of tavern life, annotated in the
colloquial Latin of daily life. Now sadly
faded, even at the time of their discovery,
about 1875, the readings of parts of the
crudely scrawled inscriptions seem to have
been in doubt. This is particularly true of the
first scene, where there were certainly more
letters than have been recorded. We follow
the readings published by Presuhn in 1882,
translating them freely so as to give what
appears to be the general sense.

The scenes are boxed in to form a frieze,
and the apparent continuity of the third and
fourth scenes suggests this is all one story of a
night out on the town. They run as follows,
from left to right:
a. Two men meet and embrace. 'I don't want
it with . . .' (*nolo cum murtal. . . . (?)*).
b. A woman, jug and beaker in hand,
advances to serve the two men. 'Who
ordered? Take it. Come, drink up,
Oceanus(?)' *(qui vol. sumat Oceane(?) veni
bibe)*. One man replies 'Here' *(hoc)*, the other
'No, that's mine' *(non mia est)*.
c. The two men are seated, throwing dice at a
gaming board marked out with two lines of
circles. One says 'I'm out' *(exsi)*, to which the
other replies 'That's a two, not a three' *(non
tria duas est)*.
The board appears to be marked out for the
popular backgammon-type game of *XII
Scripta*, which was played with three dice and
fifteen counters for each player.
d. The two men are ready to come to blows
and the landlord orders them out.
'Nonsense that was a three. I won' (or words
to that effect; the second word is perhaps a
name: *Noxse . . . tia ego fui*). 'You four-letter
bastard, I won' *(Orte fellator ego fui)*. 'Out you
go, fight it out outside' *(Itis foris rixiatis)*.
Maiuri, *Roman Painting* (Geneva 1954) 145.
Bull Inst L (1878), 191. *MemLinc* 1876–77, 104.

228

Inscribed marble slab advertising the Baths of M. Crassus Frugi.
Length 1.15 m; height 57 cm.
Naples Museum, inv. 3829.
Found in 1749, re-used as a shelf within a shrine just outside the Herculaneum Gate.

Thermae M(arci) Crassi Frugi aqua marina et baln(eum) aqua dulci Ianuarius l(ibertus).
'The Baths of Marcus Crassus Frugi. Sea water and fresh water bathing. Januarius, freedman.'

These baths must have been located near the sea shore, probably on the promontory which in antiquity marked the west side of the mouth of the river Sarno, and which is known to have contained thermal springs. The owner was presumably the consul of AD 64, who died a few years later and who is known to have owned another comparable bathing establishment near Baiae (Pliny, *Nat. Hist.* XXXI. 5). This inscription, the first to be found by the eighteenth-century excavators, is best interpreted as a roadside advertisement for the baths, set up by the freedman who had charge of them.
CIL x. 1063; *ILS* 5724. A. Maiuri *RAAN* n.s. XXXIV (1959) 73–9. D'Arms 214–5.

229

Inscribed limestone slab recording the modernization of the Stabian Baths.
Length 84 cm; height 44 cm.
Naples Museum, inv. 3826.
Found in 1857 in the Stabian Baths.

C(aius) V(ulius) C(aii) f(ilius) P(ublius) Aninius C(aii) f(ilius) IIv(iri) i(ure) d(icundo) laconicum et destrictarium faciund(a) et porticus et palaestr(am) reficiunda locarunt ex d(ecurionum) d(ecreto) ex ea pequnia quod eos e lege in ludos aut in monumento consumere oportuit faciun(da) coeraverunt eidemque probaru(nt.).
'Caius Uulius, son of Caius, and Publius Aninius, son of Caius, chief magistrates, put out to contract the construction of a sweating room (*laconicum*) and a scraping room (*destrictarium*) and the reconstruction of the porticoes and the exercise yard (*palaestra*). (This they did) in accordance with the decree of the decurions, out of the money which they were by law due to spend on games or public building. They had charge of the work and they approved it.'

The *laconicum* was a room for sweating under conditions of intense dry heat, and it can be identified with certainty as the still-extant circular room with a conical vault, which was later converted into a *frigidarium*. The *destrictarium*, for cleaning off the oil and dirt accumulated during exercise, which one did with a strigil (No. 230), lay to the north of the *laconicum* and was later eliminated. The porticoes were those of the present *palaestra*. The modernization of the Stabian Baths was undertaken quite soon after the foundation of the colony in 80 BC, and the magistrates in charge of the work were both probably among the original colonists.
CIL x. 829; *ILS* 5706. H. Eschebach *RM* 80 (1973), 235–42.

228

229

230

Set of four strigils and an oil-flask.
Bronze.
Length of strigils, 23 cm.
Naples Museum, inv. 69970–69974, 69927.
From one of the sites in the Vesuvius area.

Before the introduction of fat-based soaps in the late Empire, the cleansing medium used by athletes in the *palaestra* and by bathers of both sexes was a mixture of low-grade olive oil and pumice. This was applied to the body and then scraped off by means of a long, narrow, scoop-like scraper, or *strigil*. A common form of public benefaction was money for a free distribution of such oil. Sets of strigils, often together with a small oil-flask, or *aryballos* (see No. 231), are commonly found attached to a loop which went round the wrist for convenience in carrying.
Cf. Coulon, *De l'usage des strigiles dans antiquité* (Paris 1895) 6 and 45.

231

Blue glass aryballos, or oil flask.
Height 10 cm; diameter 10 cm.
Naples Museum, inv. 133293.
Found at Pompeii in the street (Vicolo dei Vettii) opposite VI, 16.

An imitation in glass of a pottery form, also found in bronze (No. 230). The ring handles on either side of the neck are made in the shape of dolphin's heads. Such flasks contained the oil used in bathing. The bronze chains were for attaching it to the owner's wrist, and for the stopper.
Isings 78, form 61.

232

Three glass unguentaria (perfume flasks).
Heights 9.5 cm; 8.6 cm; 8.5 cm.
Naples Museum, inv. 114890, 12062, 12392.
From Pompeii; 114890 from the *tablinum* of IX, 6, 5 with several toilet articles, including No. 70.

All free blown; such little flasks were among the first articles mass-produced in blown glass, and were sold with their contents; their forms are so varied that it seems that the different shapes were the trade marks of specific types of oils, ointments or perfumes. Later first century AD.
Isings 40, forms 26 and 42, form 28a.

233

Miniature 'test tube' glass perfume bottle (unguentarium).
Length 13 cm.
British Museum, inv. s 284.

The long tubular shape, slightly constricted in the middle, is found in hundreds at Pompeii and Herculaneum, and was one of the most common perfume or ointment bottles of the first century AD. The constriction was for purposes of sealing.
Isings 24, form 8.

234

Bird-shaped perfume bottle in blue glass.
Length 12.8 cm; height 7.7 cm.
British Museum, inv. s 299.

The shape appears to have been the trade mark of producers in north Italy. Some examples have been found containing white or red powder – the decayed remains of perfumes. The flasks were sealed by the beak being melted over a flame at the factory, and opened by the tip of the tail being broken off. Similar flasks have been found at Pompeii (e.g. Naples Museum, inv. 109433).
Isings, 27 form 11.

235

Three bone gaming pieces.
a. Black; on the reverse the number IIII.
b. White; on the reverse the number IIII.
c. White; on the reverse the number XI.
Lengths 4.5 cm, 5.1 cm and 5 cm respectively.
Naples Museum, inv. 109837, 109848, 109854.
From Pompeii.

The shape may represent a trussed fowl. Piece *a.* was found together with ten others of the same form, bearing the numbers I, II, III, VII, VIII, X, XI, XIII, XIV. Pieces *b.* and *c.* were found together with eight others, numbered I, II, III, V, VII, VIII, IX, X. This suggests that in one form of tne game a complete set contained fourteen such pieces, numbered serially. But the discovery in Athens in 1886 of a set of nine similar pieces, numbered I, III, VI, VII, VIII (two examples), X, XII, and found together with a silver gaming board of a scalloped circular design with twelve points, may indicate a variant using only twelve pieces.

A set of six comparable pieces, shaped like boars and numbered I, II, VI, VII, VIII, IX, was found in 1937 in a house at Herculaneum, in a wooden box.
M. Laurent, 'Tessères en os du Musée d'Athènes', *Le Musée Belge* VII (1903) 83ff.

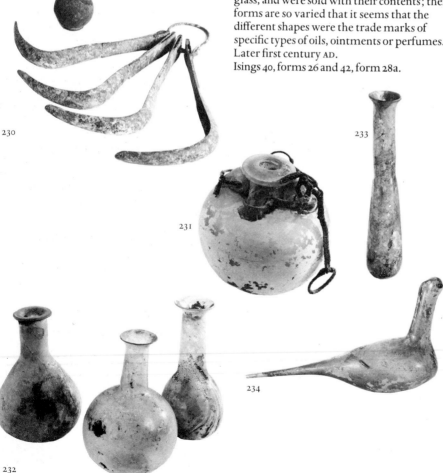

230

231

232

233

234

236
Four knucklebone gaming pieces.
Naples Museum, inv. 76972, 76981, 76987, 76990.
From Pompeii.

Knucklebones, a traditional game already popular in classical Greece, was played with a set of four pieces (*tali*), either *astragali* of sheep or goats or pieces made from terracotta, glass, bronze, or precious materials to the same conventional shape. The pieces were oblong and rounded at the ends, with two wider and two narrower long sides, each of which presented a recognizably different surface and had a different value (1, 3, 4 and 6) and name. There were many variants of the game, but in its simplest and commonest form each player threw the four *tali*, scoring according to the value of the long sides which fell uppermost, not on a simple numerical basis but, as in poker or poker dice, in accordance with certain combinations of numbers. The top throw, a 'Venus' or a 'Royal' (*basileus*), consisted of four faces all different, and the lowest throw, 'The Dogs' or 'Four Vultures', of four plain faces (1); another poor throw was the *senio*, some combination unknown of the twisted face (6) and three other faces. In a version played by the emperor Augustus (Suetonius, *Life of Augustus* 71, 2) any player throwing The Dogs or a *senio* put 4 denarii (small coins) into the pool, which was scooped by the first player to throw a Venus.
Balsdon 155.

237
Four ivory dice.
a. Cube 1.2 cm.
Naples Museum, old inv. 552.
From the Vesuvius area.
b. Cube 2.1 cm.
Naples Museum, inv. 115530.
From Pompeii VIII.
c. Cube 1.3 cm.
Naples Museum, inv. 116480.
From the entrance to IX, 7, 4, one of a pair.
d. Cube 1.4 cm.
Naples Museum, inv. 119371.
From a tavern, VII, 15, 4, one of a pair.

Roman dice (*tesserae*), like modern dice, were small cubes with the values 1–6 in groups of dots or letters on the six faces so arranged that two opposing faces always added up to seven. The Greeks usually played with three dice, but by the beginning of the Empire the Romans started to use only two, shaken in a little cup, although they continued to use three for board games such as *duodecim scripta* (see No. 227). There were probably names for all the different combinations, as in knucklebones (see No. 236).
Balsdon 156.

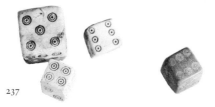
237

238
Cicada in rock crystal.
Length 6 cm.
Naples Museum, inv. 109629.
From House 1, 2, 3, found 12 April 1873.

Found, together with a small crystal duck, a small crystal amphora, and a faceted lump of crystal, in the *tablinum*. Rock crystal, of which the best quality came from India, was prized for its rarity. Other recurrent subjects were fish, shells, walnuts and small vases. It is not known whether these were simply collected as *objets d'art*, given as New Year's presents like Nos. 299–302, had a funerary significance (Gnomon 1976, 519), or whether some were also used as gaming pieces.
Bull Inst XLVI (1874), 202f. Cf. *BMC Gems* nos. 3971–85.

238

239a
Bone tally piece from a board game.
Diameter 3.3 cm.
Naples Museum, inv. 77104.
From Pompeii.

On one side is a hand, palm forwards, with the thumb and forefinger touching to form a ring and the other three fingers clenched. On the reverse, in Roman numerals, XIII. There are several other versions, with different arrangements of the fingers, among the Naples Museum collections (e.g. inv. 77127, 109864). Each side appears to have a different significance, as the numbers on the back (none higher than XXV) bear no relation to the numbers indicated by the fingers on the front. Such pieces may have served as score-counters in some board game, e.g. No. 227 or No. 239.
CIL x. 2. 8069. 101. Henzen, *Annali dell'Inst* XX (1848) 282.

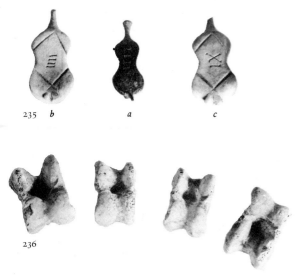
235   *b*   *a*   *c*

236

239a

Four bone gaming counters.

a. Obverse: a female head in profile.
Reverse: IIII/ΛΙΒΙΑ (= *Livia*)/Δ.
Diameter 3.3 cm.
Naples Museum, inv. 77129.
From the Vesuvius area.
CIL x. 2. 8069. 9.

b. Obverse: facade of a building with a statue
in a large niche.
Reverse: ΙΙ/ΕΥΡΟΛΟΧΟΥ (= *Eurolochou*)/B.
There was a village called Eurylochos near
Alexandria.
Diameter 3.0 cm.
Naples Museum, inv. 109586.
From Pompeii, 9 April 1863, 'Portico del
passetto pensile'.
CIL x. 2. 8069. 8.

c. Obverse: seated figure of a woman, her
chin resting on the knuckles of her left hand.
Reverse: ΙΙ/ΦΥΛΙϹ (=*Phylis*)/B.
Diameter 3.2 cm.
Naples Museum, inv. 119383.
From Pompeii I, 1, 6, 31 August 1874.

d. Obverse: head of a youth in profile with a
fillet in his hair.
Reverse: XIII/ΕΡΛΛΗϹ (=*Hermes*)/ΙΓ.
Diameter 3.5 cm.
Naples Museum, inv. 120299.
From the peristyle of v, 4, 1, on 9 October 1890.

The Romans were enthusiastic players of
board games; we find improvised boards
scratched on the pavements of public
buildings throughout the Empire. Of the
two most popular games, *duodecim scripta*
(see No. 227) and *latrunculi*, there is enough
evidence from ancient authors to reconstruct
in broad terms how they were played. But of
others we know very little, beyond the
gaming pieces (e.g. No. 235). The four
counters exhibited here belong to a board
game, possibly invented in Alexandria in the
early Empire, which involved sets of fifteen
counters variously carved on one side with
the heads or busts of gods and goddesses (*d*),
the Imperial family (*a*), famous athletes,
caricatured mythological figures (*c*) views of
buildings in Alexandria (*b*), and victory
crowns from ancient games. On the reverse is
an inscription in Greek identifying the design
on the front. Above the inscription is a
number in Roman numerals (from I to xv)
and below it, its equivalent in Greek (A to ΙΓ).
The heads and busts greatly outnumber the
buildings and crowns, which must have had a
special significance. A set from a child's tomb
in Kertch comprised 12 heads or busts, 1
building and 2 crowns.
Rostovzeff, *Rev. Arch* IV Ser. v (1905) 113.

241

240

240
Large hexagonal glass flagon.
Height 35 cm.
Naples Museum, inv. 13181.
From Pompeii.

The body was blown into a mould, and the
rim turned out and polished. The large flat
handle with combed lines was welded on
separately. Such bottles were used for storing
liquids, and the form is also found in smaller,
short versions.

241
Tall square glass bottle.
Height 41 cm.
Naples Museum, inv. 13009.
From Pompeii.

A taller version of No. 242, but blown into a
mould. The type appears about the middle of
the first century AD. Such bottles were used all
over the Empire for containing liquids, their
shape making them very easy to pack. A
wooden box of them was found in the House
of the Menander.
Isings 66, form 50b. Maiuri, *Menandro* 457f.

242
Low square glass bottle.
Height 21 cm.
Naples Museum, inv. 114835.
From Pompeii, Atrium of IX, 8, 6.

An unusually large version of an otherwise
common form, free blown and squared off
by pressure on a flat marble surface. It was
found together with 3 similar bottles, 6
square storage jars, several cylindrical jars
and other flasks, in a house which in the final
period was used commercially, presumably
by a dealer in whatever these receptacles
contained.
Isings 63f, form 50a.

243
Triangular glass bottle.
Height 16.5 cm.
Naples Museum, inv. 13075.
From Pompeii.

One of a pair. Blown into a mould, the
handle, a flattened bar of glass, welded on
separately. The shape is unusual, as yet only
known at Pompeii.
Isings 66.

244
Two glass bottles in a pottery basket.
Height of bottles: 16 cm and 8.6 cm.
Basket: height 14.5 cm; length 22.5 cm.
Naples Museum, inv. 12845, 12895–6.
From Pompeii.

The two bottles are small, straight-sided
versions of a common cylindrical storage jar,
blown into a mould. The handles, made of
thick flat bars of glass, are welded on
separately.
MB 3 (Rome 1839) 240, pl. II.

245
Two square glass jars.
Height 7.6 cm.
British Museum, inv. WT 1169 and 1170.
Probably from the Naples area.

Small versions of a form which came into
widespread use about the mid-first century
AD and which was used for storage, and
possibly also for preserving things in salt
(cf. Columella, de Re Rustica 12, 4, 4). They
are free-blown, their sides squared by
pressure on a flat surface.
Isings 81, form 62.

246
Two fused bagfulls of silver coins.
Weight 465 grammes.
Musée de Mariemont, inv. B 361.
From Pompeii.

The coins, mainly silver denarii (see No. 247)
of Vespasian and his predecessors, have been
fused together by heat in the shape of the
money bags of cloth or leather that contained
them.
Mariemont, R 73.

245

246

242

243

244

Common denominations of
Roman coinage.
British Museum.

1 Gold Aureus   =   25 Silver Denarii

1 Silver Denarius   =   4 Brass Sestertii

1 Brass Sestertius   =   2 Brass Dupondii

1 Brass Dupondius   =   2 Copper Asses

1 Copper As   =   4 Copper Quadrantes

248

Bronze steelyard balance.
Height (from hook to plate) 73.5 cm;
length of arm 31 cm.
Naples Museum, inv. 74039.
From Pompeii.

The balance operates on the familiar
principle of the steelyard, with an eccentric
fulcrum, the scale pan hanging from the
shorter arm and the counterweight hanging
from a loop which is free to move along a
graduated scale along the longer arm as
described by Vitruvius (x, 3, 4). Commonly,
as in this example, there are two alternative
positions of the fulcrum and two
corresponding graduated scales, one of
which reads (in Roman numerals) from 1 to

14, the other from 10 to 50. The
counterweight is in the form of the bust of a
boy, perhaps the portrait of a young
member of the Imperial family. The eyes
are inlaid in silver.

An inscription punched in dots on the
shorter arm gives the consular date AD 47 and
certifies that the weights are in accordance
with the specifications laid down in that year
by the Roman aediles Marcus Articuleianus
and Gnaeus Turranius, and known as 'the
Articuleiana'. Standard weights and
measures were an important feature of the
Roman commercial system, and in this case
it was the official standards laid up in Rome
which were the point of reference.
CIL x. 2, 8067.2.
Daremberg and Saglio s.v. *Libra*.

249

Bronze balance.
Length of arm, 26 cm; drop of scale-pans,
29 cm.
Naples Museum, inv. 116438.
From the House of the Centenary (IX, 8, 3).

The scales are of the simple equipoise type,
hung from a hook in the centre of the arm.
They were found in the south-west corner of
the western Atrium, along with various
other balances, forceps and pincers, together
constituting what appears to be the
equipment of a doctor. The cup-shaped pans
would have been very suitable for weighing
powders and other loose medical
commodities.

248   249

250

Bronze stamp.
Length 6.8 cm; width 1.5 cm.
Pompeii Antiquarium, inv. 1870–4.
From the entrance to the Thermopolium
(VI, 16, 33) 27 June 1904.

The stamp gives, in abbreviated form, the
name of Lucius Aurunculeius Secundio, a
member of a family which came originally
from Suessa (Sessa Aurunca), a town in
northern Campania, 42 miles from Pompeii.
Such stamps *(signacula)*, bearing the name of
the owner of a workshop or of his agent, were
widely used as trademarks and for
advertisement in the manufacture not only
of bricks, pottery and lamps, but also of more
ephemeral products such as loaves of bread.
Several carbonized loaves in the Naples
Museum are stamped *(C)eleris Q. Grani Veri
ser(vi)*, or '(Made by) Celer, slave of Quintus
Granius Verus'.
NSc 1908, 292. Castrén 141. Mau-Kelsey 497f.

250

251

251

Stucco relief of an athlete.
Height 1.70 m; width 99.5 cm.
Naples Museum, inv. 9578.
From the Villa di S. Marco, Stabiae.

The relief is cut from a large architectural composition in stucco, closely related to Fourth Style painting, which decorated the wall of an *exedra* in the lower peristyle of the villa. The scheme consisted of a central *tempietto* with side panels that included several figures clearly derived from classical statuary, a composition perhaps inspired by the sculpture galleries which were a feature of many wealthy villas. The athlete stands in an attitude of repose holding a beribboned stick in his left hand and resting his left elbow on a hoop. Bowling hoops in various ingenious manners was one of the secondary sports of the *palaestra*. The relief was executed by a workshop active in Campania about the middle of the first century AD. Its work is known also from another villa nearby, at Petaro.
H. Mielsch, 'Neronische und Flavische Stuckreliefs in den Vesuven Städten', *Neue Forschungen* (1975) 125–8.

252

Wall painting of a cargo boat under sail.
Height 97 cm; width 60 cm.
Pompeii, Antiquarium inv. 2212–4.
From Pompeii, shop II, 3, 10, on the left of the doorway.

The picture represents a large merchant ship of the first century AD, of the same type as the more detailed drawing scratched on the peristyle wall in I, 15, 3 (see sketch). Below the ship are painted the words ΑΦΡΟΔΕΙΤΗ CWZOYCA (Aphrodite the Protectoress). Pompeii being a port, a number of merchant sailors and import-export agents must have had offices or shops in the town, in addition to the warehouses and shipyards down by the harbour.
A. Maiuri, 'Navalia Pompeiana', *RAAN* n.s. XXXIII (1958) 18–22. *NSc* 1958, 87 no. 45.

253

Fish mosaic.
Originally about 90 cm. square.
Naples Museum, inv. 120177.
From House VIII, 2, 16.

A studio piece made of very fine tesserae, laid within a tray-like frame of terracotta for use as the central panel (*emblema*) of a larger, less delicate pavement, the design of which is not known. It probably belonged initially to House VIII, 2, 14 and was reused when this was rebuilt in the early Empire and incorporated in this much larger House VIII, 2, 16.

Against a black background is displayed a gallery of edible sea creatures, portrayed with a lively naturalism which enables most of them to be identified, in almost all cases, with species still found and fished in the Bay of Naples. Among the more familiar are octopus, squid, lobster, prawn, eel, bass, red mullet, dogfish, ray, wrasse and a murex shell. The inclusion in the left margin of a small stretch of rocky landscape, which is quite out of character, is perhaps to be explained as a fill-in taken from a different source. There are several other mosaics at Pompeii which are so similar in subject and workmanship that they must be derived from the same original, and are very possibly by the same hand. About 100 BC.
O. Keller, *Die antike Tierwelt* (Leipzig 1913) 393. Pernice VI, 151. A. Palombi, 'La fauna marina nei mosaici e nei dipinti Pompeiani', *Pompeiana* (1950) 427–9.

252

253

254

Still life painting: loaf of bread and two figs.
Width 23 cm; height 23 cm.
Naples Museum, inv. 8625.
From Herculaneum.

Still lifes, rare in the Second and Third Styles, were very popular in the last period, when they were commonly used as parts of larger compositions.

The circular loaf, marked out into seven sections, closely resembles the surviving carbonized examples found at Pompeii and at Herculaneum. The figs are displayed on a window ledge, a favourite mannerism of these still lifes. This little panel probably comes from a Fourth Style architectural scheme.
Beyen, *Stilleben* 81, note 1. Croisille 33, no. 24.

255

Four still life panels.
Width 1.54 cm; height 37 cm.
Naples Museum, inv. 8647.
From Herculaneum.

Each of these panels was originally the centrepiece of a large panel in a Fourth Style wall, as in the peristyle of the House of the Dioscuri. After being cut out, they were framed together to form a frieze. The first two are very different in style from the other two.
a. A plucked chicken or turkey, hung by its feet, and a rabbit hung by one forepaw.
b. Left, strung from a ring by its beak, a partridge. Right, a pomegranate and an apple.
c. Upper shelf, three thrushes. Lower shelf, six pink mushrooms.
d. Upper shelf, two birds, probably partridges. Below, two eels.
Beyen, *Stilleben* 59 ff. Croisille 40, no. 46.

256

Two large painted panels with still lifes.
Height 74 cm; Width 2.34 cm.
Naples Museum, inv. 8611.
From the *triclinium* on the west side of the garden which lies within the property (*praedia*) of Julia Felix (II, 4, 3).

These two still lifes, which are unusually large, come from the upper part of the Fourth Style walls of a dining room.
a (damaged). Lower step, part of a vase, with its lid leaning against it, a strip of woollen material, and a two-handled drinking cup (*calyx*). Upper step, a cockerel with its head dangling, dripping blood.
b. A raised block carrying a large glass bowl full of fruit (apples, pomegranates, grapes, figs). At a lower level, a pottery vase containing dried fruit (prunes?) and, leaning against it, a small amphora-shaped jar, its lid tightly sealed by means of cords attached to the handles.
Beyen, *Stilleben* 30, no. 2. Croisille 30, no. 11.

257

Three painted still life panels.
Width 1.29 cm; height 41 cm.
Naples Museum, inv. 8644.
From Herculaneum.

Each of these panels was originally the centrepiece of a large panel in a Fourth Style wall (cf. No. 256). After being cut out they were framed together to form a frieze.
a. Young bird and a light-coloured pottery jug, over the mouth of which is placed a glass beaker with rilled decoration of a type frequently found in Campania and possibly manufactured at Puteoli (Pozzuoli). On the shelf above are indistinct objects: leaves, material, or possibly sheets of tripe.
b. Silver vase, with a small bird perched on its tall handle; a trident; seafood and shellfish (*frutta di mare*), including murex shells; and a large crayfish. On the shelf above, two cuttle-fish.
c. A rabbit nibbling at a bunch of grapes, and a dead partridge hanging from a ring. In the window, a large red apple.
Beyen, *Stilleben* 72ff. Croisille 39 f., no. 43.

258

Composite picture made up of four separate fragments taken from Fourth Style walls.
Width 49 cm; height 43 cm.
Naples Museum, inv. 9819.
The writing materials and the still life came from Herculaneum, the other two from somewhere in the Vesuvius area.

a. A silver urn, probably from the upper zone of a wall.
b. Left, two book-scrolls of papyrus, one half-unrolled; the titles, on little tags, hang from the wooden baton on which the papyrus is rolled. Right, a diptych, or wooden two-leafed writing tablet (as No. 23).
c. Landscape: a rustic shrine with figures.
d. Half of a still life panel, similar to Nos. 255–257: an apple, a pear and a pomegranate.
Croisille 52.

256

254

255

257

258

259

260

261

262

259, 260

Wall paintings: scenes of banqueting.
Naples Museum, inv. 120092, 120031.
From House v, 2, 4.

Two of three related panels which constituted the centres of the Fourth Style compositions in the *triclinium* at the north-west corner of the peristyle. All three portray the three couches appropriate to a *triclinium*, but the actual □-shaped arrangement is opened out to simplify the composition. Though often interpreted as showing the successive stages of a single feast, the fact that the secondary figures of the side panels of the same walls illustrated personifications of the Seasons suggests rather that they are views of separate banquets held on various occasions. The third scene (inv. 120030), which included musicians and nude dancing girls, is unfortunately not well preserved.

259

Width 66 cm; height 68 cm.
On the left-hand couch a reclining man places his hand on the shoulder of a second man, perhaps a late arrival, also seated, having his shoes removed while a slave offers him a cup. Faintly legible above the figures are the letters SCIO ('I know'). On the middle couch one man lies back raising a large cup while another is helped into his cloak by a slave; above the first man, BIBO ('I drink'). The right-hand couch is empty, and beside it a man, supported by a youth, leans over, apparently being sick.

260

Width 60 cm; height 64 cm.
Apparently a summer banquet, held in a garden under an awning. In the middle is a table set for food and drink and a young slave brings wine in a pair of *askoi* (see Nos. 266, 267). On the left-hand couch reclines a couple, nude from the waist up; the woman raises a drinking horn (*rhyton*) to her mouth, while her companion holds a plate (*patera*). A single figure on the central couch, the host, addresses the company with the words: FACITIS. VOBIS. SVAVITER. EGO. CANTO. ('Enjoy yourselves. I'm singing.') Of the couple on the right-hand couch, the man holds a drinking cup (*cantharos*) and replies: EST. ITA. VALEAS. ('OK. Good luck to you.')
Mau, *Bull Inst.* LVII (1885), 254f. nos. 13 & 12.
Schefold *WP*, 71.

261

Wall painting: woman surprising two lovers.
Width 52 cm; height 60 cm.
Naples Museum, inv. 111209.
From a room beside the *fauces* of House VI, 14, 29.

The scene, of which several other versions are known, comes from a late Fourth Style wall. Its exact significance is unknown. A man and woman recline on a couch, eating bread and fruit from a table; she holds a silver drinking cup (*calyx*). They are looking, in apparent surprise, towards another woman who enters from the left followed by a small attendant carrying a casket.
Sogliano 641.

262

Wall painting: entertainment after a meal.
Width 46 cm; height 44 cm.
Naples Museum, inv. 9016.
From House I, 3, 18 at Pompeii.

The central panel picture (now rather faded) of a Third Style wall. The diners recline on couches, the empty dishes and cups piled on the table and floor. In the centre a girl who has picked up a silver ladle is dancing to the tune of the double pipes, watched by the woman seated on the left. On the right, another seated woman, heavily draped, is perhaps a chaperone, and peeping round the curtain are two small attendants.
   Such scenes are frequently found on Pompeian walls (see No. 261); they derive from Hellenistic originals of which the exact meaning is now lost.
Schefold *WP*, 12 and 334.

263

Large bronze two-handled bowl.
Diameter 34.5 cm; height 12.2 cm
Naples Museum, inv. 73599.
From Pompeii.

The two handles consist of a series of ring mouldings grasped in the mouth of a pair of dolphins, which spring outwards from a Silenus head escutcheon on the underside of the rim.
Pernice IV, 10ff.

263

264
Bronze jug with long spout.
Height 16 cm.
Naples Museum, inv. 69148.
From Pompeii.

Globular jug with a long channelled spout.
The handle, which is decorated with two
swans in low relief, ends in a Medusa head.

265
Bronze jug (oenochoe).
Height 13 cm.
Naples Museum, inv. 69018.
From Herculaneum.

Apart from shallow grooves at the base of the
neck, the rounded body is plain. The mouth
is pinched in to form a deeply lobed spout.
The ornament is concentrated on the
elegant, upstanding handle, which was cast
separately: at the top, facing forward, a lion's
head, and at the junction with the body, in
place of the animal's paw that is usually
found in combination with the lion's head, a
boss in the form of a woman's head in an
Egyptian headdress. Similar pieces found in
central Europe (e.g. A. Radnoti, *Die
römischen Bronzegefässe von Pannonien*,
Budapest 1938, plates XIII, 72, and XLIX, I) are
either actual exports from Campania or are
local pieces influenced by such exports
Cf. *MB* 3 (Rome 1839) pl. XXVII. Pernice *AA*.
1900, 187 no. 14.

266
Bronze askos.
Height 16 cm.
Naples Museum, inv. 116228.
From House VIII, 7, 3, in the Atrium.

The *askos*, a form derived ultimately from
the shape of a half-full leather wine-skin, had
a long history in South Italian pottery,
whence it passed also into metalwork and
glass (see Nos. 114, 115). *Askoi* were
customarily used in pairs, as shown in the
macabre *memento mori* mosaic skeleton (see
No. 18). The handle of this example is in the
form of a lizard.
Pernice, IV, 13f.

267
Bronze askos.
Height 14.5 cm.
Naples Museum, inv. 69164.
From Pompeii.

Bronze *askos* with an elegant scroll handle
ending in a vine leaf.

268
Bronze jug (oenochoe).
Height 20 cm.
Naples Museum, inv. 69046.
From one of the sites in the Vesuvius area.

The elegant vertical channelling was
engraved after casting. An escutcheon in the
form of a Siren perched on a foliated boss
marks the point of junction of the ribbed
handle with the body.

269
Bronze jug (amphora).
Height 35 cm.
Naples Museum, inv. 69629.
From one of the sites in the Vesuvius area.

There are two identical examples of this type
of jug in the Naples Museum. The handles
are made in the form of two ribbed plant
stems with leaves at the lower ends, joined
with volutes to an escutcheon in the form of
the figure of a swan with a snake in its mouth.

269

264

265

268

266

267

270

270

Shallow bronze dish with a short handle (patera).
Diameter 27.5 cm; length of handle 15 cm.
British Museum, inv. 1897. 7–26. 7.
From one of the villas at Boscoreale.

The handle is fluted, with a ram's head terminal and joined to the body of the dish by an inverted calyx with volutes in low relief. The edge of the dish is decorated with bead and egg-shaped ornament. In the centre is a relief medallion on which is portrayed, within a formal border, a scene that is probably to be identified as the companions of Odysseus being devoured by Scylla, the bloodthirsty monster who guarded the straits between Italy and Sicily. Her body ends in splayed fish tails, from between which project the foreparts of three dogs who are attacking the companions. Scylla's tails and the eyes of the dogs and men are inlaid with silver.
BMC Bronzes no. 882. *Monumenti Antichi* VII, 513 fig. 75.

271

Bronze two-handled serving dish.
Length 36 cm; height 12.5 cm.
British Museum, inv. WT 632.
From Torre Annunziata (possibly Pompeii).

A number of identical dishes has been found (e.g. Mariemont R 37 and *AA* 1904, 16 fig. 1) and the distinctive form must have served a particular purpose. When picked up the front end of the dish naturally dips down, and it has been suggested that it was used to serve meat or fish, cooked in a liquid sauce which could be strained off over the rounded lip of the scoop-shaped end.
  The handle mounts are decorated with palmettes flanked by elongated animal heads.

272

Bronze handle from a jug (amphora).
Length 17.3 cm.
Naples Museum, inv. 72637.
From one of the sites in the Vesuvius area.

One of a pair of cast bronze handles, probably from an amphora of the same shape as No. 269. Along the handle, in low relief, is a plant design incorporating acanthus leaves, and on the escutcheon, where it was soldered to the body of the jug, a bearded male head with wild hair and pointed ears, either Pan or a Satyr. The eyes are laid in silver.
Cf. Pernice *AA* 1900, 184 nos. 9 and 10; Tassinari *Gallia* Suppl. 29 (Paris 1975) no. 187.

273

Curved bronze handle decorated with amorino and sea horses.
Length 13 cm.
Naples Museum, inv. 72972.
From Herculaneum.

A little winged amorino is perched on the curling tails of two sea horses; below them are gently rolling waves. The group originally formed a handle, possibly one of a pair, on the edge of a large flat plate.
MB 9 (Rome 1845) 232, pl. L. *Bronzi di Ercolano* I, 25 and 275, note 15.

274

Pair of handles in the form of human hands.
Bronze.
Overall width 18 cm.
Naples Museum, inv. 123300 and s.n.
From Pompeii.

The hands are linked by a channelled grip, decorated at the mid-point with a ring set with small knobs. Along the base of each hand is a flat strip which ends in two bird's-head volutes. Such handles, sometimes with smooth grips and rosettes on the rings in place of the little knobs, are found on large bowls and, on a much larger scale, on stoves and equipment for heating liquids.
Pernice IV, 31f. H. Willers, *Neue Untersuchungen über die römische Bronzeindustrie von Capua und von Niedergermanien* (Hannover & Leipzig 1907), 72.

275

Bronze scoop with a bone handle.
Length 23 cm.
Musée de Mariemont, inv. AC 210 B.
From Herculaneum.

The handle is decorated with bands of ornament, among them engraved concentric circles like those found on dice. The bowl has a vertical flange round the base, on either side of the handle, to contain the loose or powdered substance for which it was used.

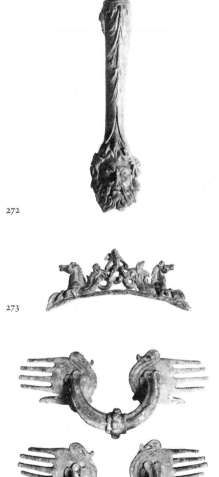

272

273

274

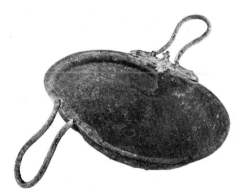

271

275

276
Carpenter's plane of iron.
Length 19 cm; height 10 cm.
Naples Museum, inv. 71964.
From Pompeii.

The tool bears a close resemblance to the traditional carpenter's plane except that the stock was made of iron, possibly with a wooden handle. The angle of the share, or cutting edge, seems to have been adjustable.

277
Iron hammer.
Length 26 cm.
Naples Museum, inv. 71883.
From Pompeii.

As in a modern geologist's hammer, the handle is made in one piece with the head. Ordinary carpenter's hammer-heads, socketed for wooden handles, have also been found at Pompeii, which suggests that this piece may be a specialized tool used by some other type of craftsman.

278
Bronze folding rule.
Length 29 cm.
Naples Museum, inv. 76696.
From Pompeii.

The rule is divided into two equal parts, hinged at the centre. One half carries a small bar on one side, pivoted so as to slot into two hooks on the other half and hold the fully extended rule rigid. Although the length falls just short of a standard Roman foot (about 29.45 cm) this lies well within the margin of error permissible in a system that for most practical purposes depended more on relative proportions than on absolute dimensions.

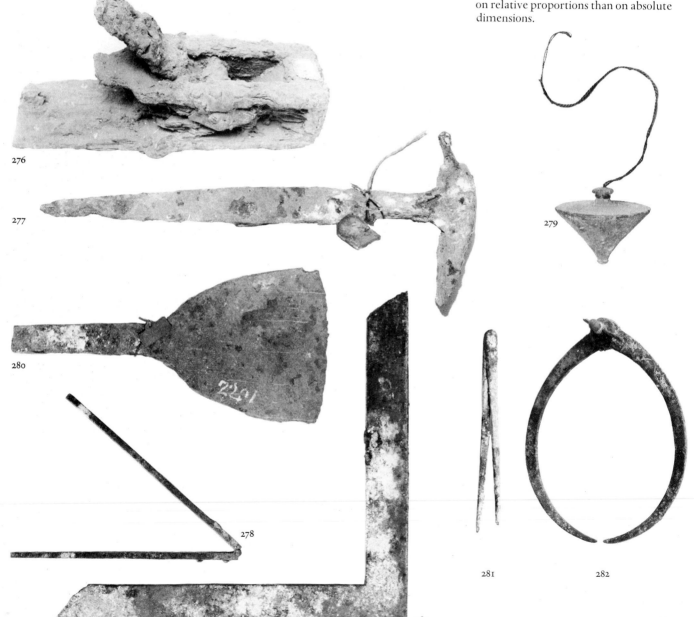

276

277

280

278

279

281

282

283

279
Bronze plumb-bob.
Diameter 5.6 cm; height 4.5 cm.
Naples Museum, inv. 76661.
From Pompeii.

A solid inverted cone of very slightly
concave profile, with a small knob in the
middle of the top to take the string, and
another at the point.

280
Broad mason's chisel of iron.
Length 19 cm; width of blade 9 cm.
Naples Museum, inv. 71771.
From Pompeii.

Although of little use on hard stone, a chisel
of this sort would have been very effective on
the softer local volcanic tufa, both for
splitting and for squaring off the faces.

281
Bronze dividers.
Length 12.3 cm.
Naples Museum, inv. 118226.
From Pompeii, Shop XI, 8, 7.

The form is indistinguishable from the
simpler types in modern use.

282
Bronze callipers.
Length 15 cm.
Naples Museum, 76/266.
From one of the sites in the Vesuvius area.

The form, hinged at the top with two inward-
curving arms, is indistinguishable from that
in use today.

283
Bronze carpenter's or mason's set square.
22.5 cm by 20.5 cm.
Naples Museum, inv. 76689.
From one of the sites in the Vesuvius area.

One arm is longer and narrower than the
other. The ends of the two arms are profiled
and may have been used as templates.

284
Iron stylus.
Length 13 cm.
British Museum, inv. 1968. 2–12. 1.

The *stylus* consists of a shaft, around which is
wrapped a thin sheet of brass, a point at one
end for writing, and a flat eraser at the other.
It was used for writing on a thin film of wax
spread over the inner surface of a writing
tablet, usually made of wood, the form of
which can be seen in Nos. 23 and 258. A
stylus was found among the equipment of the
surveyor Verus in a workshop at Pompeii
(I, 6, 3).

285
Bronze inkpot.
Height 4 cm; diameter 3 cm.
British Museum, inv. WT 682.
From 'Torre Annunziata' (probably
Pompeii).

The pot is made from a rolled strip of bronze
sheet, bent round into a cylinder, to which
the top and bottom discs were applied.

286
**Inscribed slab recording the architect
of the theatre.**
Marble, restored from 3 pieces.
Length 90.5 cm; height 23 cm.
Naples Museum, inv. 3834.
Found in 1792 in the Large Theatre.

*M(arcus) Artorius M(arci) l(ibertus) Primus
architectus.*
'Marcus Artorius Primus, freedman of
Marcus (Artorius, was) the architect.'
   The inscription relates to the major
reconstruction of the Theatre undertaken
during the reign of Augustus. The work on
the seating area and its substructures is
known to have been undertaken by the
Holconius brothers (see page 38f.) around the
turn of the first centuries BC and AD (*CIL* x.
833, 834). The even more radical
reconstruction of the stage building (to
which this inscription may refer) was
evidently financed separately, but was
roughly contemporary.
   The architect was a freedman of the
Artorii, a local Campanian family, and may
well have learnt his profession as a slave,
working with another architect. His name
appears also on a fragmentary marble
epistyle (*CIL* x. 807) which was found,
displaced, to the west of the Temple of
Venus, and which was attributed by
Fiorelli to the columnar structure (*tribunal*)
at the west end of the Basilica.
CIL x. 841; *ILS* 5638a. Castrén, no. 44, 4.

286

284

285

287
Relief showing a coppersmith's workshop.
Italian marble.
Height 42 cm; width 54 cm.
Naples Museum, inv. 6575.
From Pompeii.

The relief was probably set into the wall of a workshop. It illustrates three of the main processes of the coppersmith's craft. In the centre the smith is seated on a bench, holding with a pair of tongs a lump of hot metal on a small anvil, ready to be struck by an assistant who wields a heavy hammer; above are the heavy double doors of the furnace. On the right he is seated at a bench, engraving or embossing a large circular dish. Above him crouches an animal (a watch-dog?), and above that is an assortment of pastry-moulds, dishes, plates and buckets. On the left, he is weighing something out in a large pair of scales. Although there must have been a special charge for his more elaborate pieces, it is likely that, as in many early societies, the simpler pieces were sold by weight.
O. Jahn, *Berichten der phil.-hist. Classe der Königl. Sächs. Gesellschaft der Wissenschaften* 1861, 360ff. H. Blümner, *Technologie und Terminologie der Gewerbe und Kunster* IV (Leipzig 1884), 251.

288–291
In classical times the normal bulk container was the *amphora*, a vessel with a large pointed or rounded body and a very strong neck with two handles. The great majority of these were used for wine and oil, but they could also be put to more specialized uses, e.g. in Campania for soft fruits and for the fermented fish-paste, *garum*, a delicacy which is known to have been produced at Pompeii. There is no direct relationship between the shapes and their contents, and they were commonly re-used for products quite different from those for which they were originally manufactured. The producing areas normally established potteries of their own, and the characteristic shapes and fabrics are an invaluable index of the patterns of commerce.

287

288
Large wine amphora.
Height 1.21 m.
Pompeii, Storerooms inv. 15391.

Amphoras of this form (Dressel IB) were made in Italy during the second and first centuries BC, especially in northern Campania, where they were used to contain Falernian and Caecuban wines. These wines were highly esteemed in their day and are known to have been aged in the amphora. The inside would have been given a coating of pitch to seal the otherwise porous fabric, and the mouth was stopped with a cork disc fixed with *pozzolana* cement.

289
Wide-mouthed amphora (Dressel form 22).
Height 87 cm.
Pompeii, storerooms inv. 15450.

The painted inscription on the neck reads *MAL(a) CVM(ana) VER(a)* ('Real Cumaean fruits') followed by the weight of the contents, LXIIII (64 pounds) and the letters *P.C.Z*, presumably the initials of the owner or consignee. Over the tail of the Z is written the name of the agent or bailiff who packed the amphora, Cornelius (?).

290
Small amphora.
Height 57 cm.
Pompeii, Storerooms inv. 15390.

Small amphoras of this type are hardly ever found in the commercial cargoes recovered from shipwrecks. It was produced for local purposes within the Pompeian area.

291
Cylindrical amphora.
Height 88 cm.
Pompeii, Storerooms inv. 15451.
From a room in the garden of the House of the Centenary (IX, 8, 6).

Recent studies have shown that there are many varieties of cylindrical amphoras of this general form, classified by Schoene (*CIL* IV) as form 11. This particular example falls within the range of Ostia form LIX (Panella, 571–2; 632, nos. 48–49). They were probably made in North Africa and contained olive oil (cf. Beltram Lloris, 522–3). The mouth would have been sealed with a terracotta disc fixed in position with wax.

On the neck is painted the name *L(uci) Helvi Zos(imi)*, possibly that of the agent or shipper.
CIL IV, Supp. 5847.

288   289   290   291

292

Wall painting of a potter at his wheel.
Height 75 cm; width 54 cm.
Pompeii Antiquarium, inv. 2193–4.
From a potter's workshop (II, 3, 7) on the
outside of the south-west corner of the shop.

The potter is shown seated on a low wooden
stool, dressed in the customary short
workman's tunic and working at a tall jug
mounted on a simple kick wheel. Beside
him on the ground are several small jugs and
vases. To the left stands the figure of Vulcan,
Roman god of fire, protector of furnaces and
kilns.

Most of the ordinary pottery in domestic
use at Pompeii (see Nos. 293–298) was made
locally. Several potters' workshops are
attested, including a large one outside the
Herculaneum Gate (Mau-Kelsey 378) and
one, which also made amphoras, in I, 20, 2–3.
NSc 1939, 198ff.

292

293

Large squat one-handled jug.
Height 14 cm; diameter 26 cm.
Pompeii, Storerooms inv. 15397.

Made in thick, coarse pottery, the jug was
probably used for water, the thick walls and
small mouth helping to keep it cool in hot
weather.

294

Pottery jug with trefoil lip.
Height 23 cm.
Pompeii, Storerooms inv. 15396.

Rather finer ware than the other local
domestic pottery exhibited, it was probably
used for serving wine or water in a bar or
tavern, or in one of the poorer private houses.
The form is derived from the Greek *oenochoe*.

295

Cooking pot on a pottery stand.
Height of pot, 28 cm; height of stand, 16 cm.
Pompeii, Storerooms inv. 15398, 15399, 15395.

A slightly larger version of No. 297. Because
the underside was rounded, such pots needed
a stand for serving or for storage.

296

Pottery strainer.
Height 23.5 cm; diameter 26 cm.
Pompeii, Storerooms inv. 15393.

The rounded bottom of the vessel is
perforated by a series of holes, of the size of
knitting kneedles; the handles are designed
for suspension, and the grooved neck would
have been suitable for tying a cloth over the
mouth. A number of vessels of this
specialized form have been found. They may
well have been used for straining curd cheese
to make the *ricotta* which was a major
component of Roman cookery, just as today
it is still very widely used in the preparation
of typical south Italian dishes.

297

Cooking pot on an iron stand.
Height of pot, 26 cm; greatest diameter,
24 cm.
Pompeii, Storerooms inv. 15394, 15394b.

Jars of this distinctive form, with or without
handles and found in varying sizes (see
No. 295) were regularly used for cooking,
placed directly on open charcoal fire or else,
as in this instance, on an iron support.

298

Pottery bowl.
Height 13.5 cm; diameter 27 cm.
Pompeii, Storerooms inv. 15392.

Hundreds of these general-purpose kitchen
bowls, of varying sizes, have been found in
Pompeian houses. They were used for the
storage, preparation and serving of food.

293   294   295   296   297   298

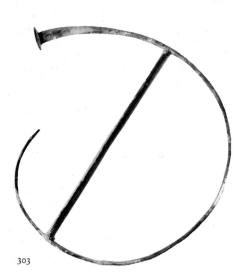

303

299, 300
Two terracotta figurines of gladiators.
Height 13 cm.
Naples Museum, inv. 20340, 20259.
From Pompeii.

Probably from the same mould, one of them (20340) preserving traces of colouring. The figure wears greaves (*ocreae*; see No. 308) on both legs, an unvisored helmet with a crest and a breech cloth, and his exposed right arm is bound with leather thongs; he carries a strongly convex circular shield (*parma*) and is armed with a short sword. His costume and armour are those of a 'Thracian' (*Thrax*) except that the latter was normally armed with a very distinctive, sickle-shaped scimitar. The *Thrax* was usually matched against a heavily-armed *Hoplomachus* or 'Samnite', or the lighter *Myrmillo*. It seems likely that such figurines of gladiators (see also Nos. 301, 302) served the same purpose as Nos. 36–40, namely as small gifts presented on the occasion of the New Year feast of the Saturnalia.
Von Rohden 52 and pl. 41, 1. Levi nos. 851, 852. Winter II, 387, 2b and 2c.

301
Terracotta figurine of a gladiator.
Height 12 cm.
Naples Museum, inv. 20260.

The figure wears a single greave on the left leg and a visored helmet with a tall, angular crest. He carries a large rectangular, curved shield and is armed with a short sword. His armour and weapon indicate that he is one of a rather ill-defined group of heavily-armed gladiators, all of whom seem to be variants of the original 'Samnite' – *Hoplomachus* type.
Von Rohden pl. 41. 1. Levi no. 851.
Winter II, 387, 2d.

302
Terracotta figurine of a gladiator.
Height 14 cm.
Naples Museum, inv. 20341.
From the House of Marcus Lucretius (IX, 3, 5).

Like Nos. 299, 300, he wears two greaves and a crested helmet, but the helmet is visored, his shield, though small, is rectangular and he wears a tunic. His weapon is missing. Perhaps a variant of the *Thrax*.
Von Rohden 52. Levi no. 852.
Winter II, 387, 2c.

303
Bronze horn (cornu).
Height 1.28 m; width 1.10 m;
Diameter 1.20 m.
Naples Museum, old inv. 1277.
From Pompeii.

The tube is approximately 3.3 m long, bent almost into a circle and held by a transverse strut (probably covered in ivory), which rested on the player's shoulder so that the bell of the horn appeared above his head. The mouthpiece (the end is here missing) was detachable. The *cornu* (literally 'horn') was used in the amphitheatre to herald the start of each contest, and also, in combination with pipes, straight trumpets (*tubae*), drums and water organs, to entertain the spectators in the intervals.
Daremberg and Saglio, s.v. *Cornu*. Fiorelli, *Armi antiche* no. 321.

299, 300   302   301

304

304

Bronze gladiator's helmet.
Height 40 cm; width across neck guard,
33 cm.
Naples Museum, inv. 5643.
From Herculaneum.

A heavily-armoured gladiator's fighting
helmet, without decoration. The visor,
which includes a broad flange pierced with
two holes to fasten it down, is made in four
parts, riveted together and strengthened by a
strip of bronze running from the brow to the
chin. It is hinged to the helmet behind the
ears. A broader flange round the base of the
helmet itself protected the back of the neck
and part of the shoulders.
Fiorelli, *Armi antiche*, no. 273.

305

305

Gladiatorial helmet in bronze.
Height 38 cm; greatest width 40 cm.
Louvre, inv. MNC 1674.
From Herculaneum, given by the Queen of
Naples to Josephine in 1802, together with
the following pieces, Nos. 306–308.

A broad flange, rising up over the brow, runs
round the helmet to protect the neck, while
the face is covered by two half-visors formed
from a network of bronze rings, attached at
the sides and provided with tags which slot
into two bands on the cheek guards below.
The high crest ends in a griffin's head, and on
either side of the helmet are sockets for
plumes. Over the forehead is a large Medusa
head in relief.
De Ridder II, no. 1108.

308

Pair of gladiator's greaves.
Bronze.
Height 57 cm.
Louvre, inv. MNC 1666 and 1667.
From Herculaneum.

The guards are long enough to protect most
of the thigh as well as the lower leg. On the
kneecap of each is a gorgon's head; above, on
the left side, is a bearded head within a
lozenge, and on the right, in profile, the
heads of Silenus and a Maenad, placed on a
basket (*cista*). Behind them is a *thyrsus*. On the
knee of MNC 1666 are engraved the letters
NCA, to the left of that M, and at the top of
the greave, punched in dots, upside down,
MP.
De Ridder II, nos. 1169, 1170.

306

Gladiator's bronze arm guard.
Length 33 cm.
Louvre, inv. MNC 1670.
From Herculaneum.

A heavier version of No. 307; decorated in
relief with a figure of Mars, god of war,
wearing a helmet, breastplate and greaves,
and carrying a spear. He stands on a base line,
below a sharply pointed arch ending in small
volutes. On either side of the wrist
indentation are large shield-like bosses.
De Ridder II, no. 1144.

307

Gladiator's bronze arm guard.
Length 28.7 cm.
Louvre, inv. MNC 1669.
From Herculaneum.

Semi-cylindrical guard for the lower
forearm, decorated in low relief with the
figure of a woman wearing a transparent
garment and holding a veil above her head
with her right hand. She is flanked by
scrollwork and rosettes, and on either side of
the indent for the wrist is a *gorgoneion*, or
gorgon's head. The guard was attached with
leather straps.
De Ridder II, no. 1143.

306

307

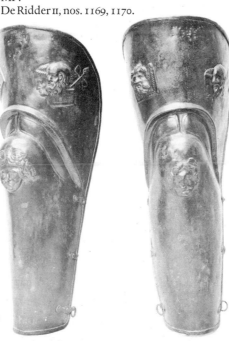

308

309
Bronze gladiator's shield.
Diameter 37 cm.
Naples Museum, inv. 5669.
From Pompeii.

The central silver boss, with a Medusa head in high relief, is surrounded by two concentric olive garlands in low relief and an outer border of olives and single olive leaves. This would have been a dress parade piece, though in shape and size it resembles the actual shields carried by some of the 'Thracian' gladiators (*Thraeces*), also by the mounted gladiators shown in the stucco reliefs on the Tomb of Umbricius Scaurus at Pompeii, now destroyed but known from drawings.
Fiorelli, *Armi antiche* no. 288.

310
Dagger.
Iron, bone and ivory.
Length 30.5 cm; length of blade 19.4 cm.
Naples Museum, inv. 5682.
From Pompeii.

A fighting weapon, with an iron blade of which the tang runs the full length of the grip, which is of bone with a pommel and guard of ivory. Such weapons were carried by the more lightly armed types of gladiator, including the *retiarii* (the net-men), and by the *myrmillones*.
Fiorelli, *Armi antiche* no. 313.

311
Wall painting of a chariot race.
Height 57 cm; length 92 cm.
Naples Museum, inv. 9055.
Probably from the House of the Quadrigae (VII, 2, 25), although the inventory books say from Herculaneum.

The picture, which is bordered below by a red line but is certainly incomplete above and to the left, shows four four-horsed racing chariots (*quadrigae*) and, top left, the legs of the horses of a fifth. The drivers (*aurigae*) stand, as was customary, on a very light two-wheeled frame, dressed in short tunics. The driver on the right wears a red tunic, those in the centre and on the far left both appear to be in green, and the driver at the very top is in white. For protection in the event of a crash (and these were common) they wear tight-fitting leather helmets and a harness of leather thongs on body and legs. On the white ground below the picture there are faint traces of an inscription painted in large letters, which suggests that it comes from a street-front, perhaps of a shop or tavern.

There was no provision for chariot-racing at Pompeii itself, but many cities both in Italy and in the provinces did possess a *circus* or *hippodrome*, and as a spectator sport it rivalled and eventually superseded gladiatorial contests. It was organized into teams, or factions, the support for which was Empire-wide. At first there only two factions, the Reds and the Whites, but early in the first century AD two more were added, the Greens and the Blues; in the long run this proved to be too much for the Romans, who at heart were as clearly two-faction in racing as the British and the Americans are two-party in politics, and by the end of the second century AD the Blues had absorbed the Reds, and the Greens the Whites, a situation which greatly facilitated the expression of rival enthusiasms. It was a clash between the Blues and the Greens which in January 512 reduced the centre of Constantinople to ashes, leaving at least thirty thousand dead behind it – an all-time record for active spectator participation.
B. Maiuri, 'Ludi ginnico-atletici a Pompei' in *Pompeiana* 184–5. Helbig no. 1511.

309

310

312

Terracotta statue of an actor.
Height 1.15 m.
Naples Museum, inv. 22249.
From the entrance to a garden in one of the
houses in VIII, 2 or 3, near the Theatre
(VIII, 3, 14?).

Found with No. 313 and from the same house
as No. 94. The actor, dressed in tunic and
mantle, is wearing the mask of a youth in
tragedy. In its finished form the statue was
brightly painted. The discovery of this pair
of statues, the first terracotta statues to be
found at Pompeii, made a deep impression
on the great German art historian
Winckelmann. Considered to be the work of
the same hand, they have been variously
dated between the last years of the first
century BC and the years immediately before
the eruption.
PAH I, 23 Jan. 1762. Von Rohden 46, pl xxxv. 2.
Deonna, *Les statues de terre cuite* (Paris 1908)
203.

313

Terracotta statue of an actress.
Height 1.11 m.
Naples Museum, inv. 22248.
Found with No. 312.

The mask, which is shown fastened on with a
band decorated with little flowers, is that
proper to a courtesan in tragedy. The figure,
whose left hand was already damaged in
antiquity, was coloured. There are extensive
remains of the white underlay and traces of
brown paint on the hair, and of blue and red
on the drapery.
PAH I, 23 Jan. 1762. Von Rohden 46, pl xxxv. 2.
Deonna, *Les statues de terre cuite* (Paris 1908)
203.

312

313

314
Mosaic panel: rehearsing for a Satyr Play.
Width 55 cm; height 54 cm.
Naples Museum, inv. 9986.
From the *tablinum* of the House of the Tragic Poet (VI, 8, 5).

The rehearsal for a Greek Satyr Play, the characteristic postlude for a Greek dramatic trilogy. The action takes place in front of an Ionic portico hung with *oscilla* (see No. 82) and draped with wreaths and fillets, above which is an attic facade decorated with pilasters, four large golden wine vessels, and a pair of herm-like musicians. The bald and bearded figure wearing a Greek mantle (*himation*) and sandals is the chorus master, possibly the dramatist himself. He watches two actors wearing goatskin loincloths, who appear to be rehearsing dance steps to the notes of the double pipes played by a richly robed and garlanded musician (who would himself have appeared on the stage). On the right an attendant is helping another actor into a shaggy Silenus costume. Behind the seated figure, on a pedestal, is a male tragic mask, and at his feet a female tragic mask and a Silenus mask.

The mosaic, which was the centrepiece of a black and white mosaic pavement decorated with a meander pattern, is a studio piece (*emblema*) derived from a Hellenistic panel painting, perhaps one painted to commemorate a victory in a theatrical contest. In the course of adaptation to its present form the perspective of the architectural setting has become hopelessly confused, with the two flanking pilasters brought forward to constitute a frame. It dates from the years between AD 62 and 79.
E. Pfuhl, *Malerei und Zeichnung der Greichen* (Munich 1923) 841f. Pernice VI, 99f., 171.
Bieber, *Theater* 11f, 20, 130. Kraus and von Matt no. 49.

314

315–318
Wall paintings: four theatrical masks
From the House of the Stags at Herculaneum, where they constituted the lower parts of four of the vertical members which divided the middle zone of the Fourth Style scheme into panels. Each is shown placed at the head of the steps leading up on to a stage, within a frame of garlands with Dionysiac attributes.

315
Mask of a father, in New Comedy.
Length 97 cm; height 65 cm.
Naples Museum, inv. 9838.

The rolled arrangement of the hair, the *speira*, was characteristic of New Comedy. The white hair and beard indicate the role of an old father.

316
Tragic mask of Andromeda.
Length 93 cm; height 64 cm.
Naples Museum, inv. 9850.

Andromeda's mother, Cassiope, claimed that her daughter was more beautiful than the Nereids, and in expiation of this rash boast Andromeda herself was exposed, chained to a rock, to be devoured by a sea monster sent by Poseidon. Perseus, using the Gorgon's head to turn the monster to stone, rescued and subsequently married her. See also the picture of this scene in the House of the Priest Amandus (page 73).

317
Mask of a youth, in New Comedy.
Length 66 cm; height 42 cm.
Naples Museum, inv. 9804.

The same hairstyle as No. 315. Beside the mask is a book basket (*capsa*) and, on the step, a short, curved staff (*pedum*).

318
Tragic mask of a youth.
Length 62 cm; height 62 cm.
Naples Museum, inv. 9805.

His hair is piled high on his head and crowned with a ribbon and a wreath of ivy leaves. Against the steps leans a *thyrsus*.

Bieber *Theater*, 228. Agnes Allroggen-Bedel, *Maskendarstellungen in der römisch-kampanischen Wandmalerei* (Munich 1974) 126–7, nos. 2 (318), 6 (316), 4 (315) and 3 (317).

319

319
Wall painting of a scene from New Comedy.
Height 29 cm; width 38 cm.
Naples Museum, inv. 9034.
From Stabiae.

The panel, which was set into a larger wall
scheme, is almost certainly a *pinax*, or
painted replica of a late Classical or early
Hellenistic Greek panel picture. It portrays
the dance group which in New Comedy took
the place of the chorus in Old Comedy,
consisting in this instance of a dwarf, a
woman playing a double flute and two men
dancing, one of whom holds cymbals while
the other beats a tambourine. The same
Greek original is portrayed in a fine mosaic
panel, signed by Dioscurides of Samos and
datable to the end of the second century BC,
found in the so-called Villa of Cicero at
Pompeii (Naples Museum inv. 9985).
Bieber, *Theater* 95f. Webster, *New Comedy* 192,
NP 54.

315

317

316

318

320
Little silver dish on a silver stand.
Height together 5.5 cm; diameter of dish
8.6 cm, and of stand 7.9 cm.
Naples Museum, inv. 25324 (dish) and
25547 (stand).
From Pompeii.

The little tripod stand has animal's paw feet
and the edge is decorated with an ovolo
moulding with traces of gilding. The dish has
thin crescent-shaped handles decorated
with elongated bird's heads and rosettes
(as on Nos. 327, 330).
Strong 153; cf. Maiuri, *Menandro* 364,
nos. 44–55.

321
Little silver dish on a silver stand.
Height together, 5.8 cm; diameter of dish
6.9 cm, and of stand 8.1 cm.
Naples Museum, inv. 110853 (dish) and
25549 (stand).
From Pompeii, found separately. 110853 was
found 24 November 1875.

Little dishes of this sort were probably used
for serving hot sauces, or (since the form is
found also in glass) small sweetmeats.

322
Small fluted silver bowl.
Height 5.1 cm; diameter 11.7 cm.
Naples Museum, inv. 25553.
From one of the sites in the Vesuvius area.

Inverted conical bowls of this form, with
concave sides decorated with vertical fluting
and a scalloped rim, were common in the
first century AD.
Strong 160.

323
Small fluted silver bowl.
Height 5 cm; diameter 7.9 cm.
Naples Museum, inv. 25557.
From one of the sites in the Vesuvius area.

A smaller version of No. 322. It lacks the
small rounded projections at the ends of the
flutes.

324
Silver spoon.
Length 7.8 cm.
Naples Museum, inv. 25413.
From Herculaneum.

The form of the handle is typical of Roman
spoons. This example has a simple knop
finial and it is fastened to the bowl by a 'rat's
tail' attachment. Spoons were the only form
of cutlery normally used in classical antiquity
since forks were unknown and food was
brought to table in ready-prepared portions,
which did not call for the use of a knife.
Silver spoons are common, and are found
in quite modest households.
Strong 155–6.

325
Silver spoon.
Length 14 cm.
Naples Museum, inv. 25416.
From one of the sites in the Vesuvius area.

A larger version of No. 324, with a more
elaborately moulded baluster knop.
Strong 155–6.

326
Silver egg cup.
Height 8.4 cm.
Naples Museum, inv. 116349.
From House VIII, 2, 23.

The little shallow cup on a short stem,
mounted on a large, lozenge-shaped base,
formed part of a service comprising four
ornate drinking cups, four smaller cups,
several little dishes like Nos. 320, 321, four
plates, four egg cups and various serving
bowls.
Strong 154.

322

323

320

321

326   324   325

327
Two-handled silver drinking cup (cantharos).
Height 8.5 cm; diameter of bowl 12.5 cm.
Naples Museum, inv. 25294.
From one of the sites in the Vesuvius area.

The bowl and the elaborately turned foot are plain except for a bearded border below the rim and a simple stamped motif on the foot. The handle mount terminates in a pair of bird's heads (see No. 330).
For similar cups, see Strong 133–4.

328
Silver plate.
Diameter 17.7 cm; across the handles 22 cm.
Naples Museum, inv. 25297.
From one of the sites in the Vesuvius area.

The plate is in the form of a shallow concave dish without a foot ring. The segmental handles, cast separately and soldered on, are decorated with a central palmette motif, flanked by foliage, ivy leaves and the usual elongated bird's heads.
Strong 148f.

329
Silver jug.
Height 12.5 cm; diameter of mouth 5.3 cm.
Naples Museum, inv. 25692.
From Pompeii.

Tall, rounded shape with a plain, solid, cast handle.
For the form, see Strong 140.

330
One-handled silver dipper, or skillet.
Height 5.7 cm; diameter of lip 11.1 cm;
length of handle 9 cm.
Naples Museum, inv. 25344.
From Pompeii.

The bowl is plain. The handle, which was cast separately and attached to the bowl by means of two curving arms in the form of elongated bird's heads, is decorated in relief with a symmetrical foliate design terminating in a Dionysiac head with large ears, flanked by two duck's heads (see No. 327). Vessels of this shape, usually found in pairs, had a long history, first appearing in the first century AD. They are commonly found also in bronze, and they were most probably used for serving liquids, though not for the actual heating of them.
Strong 147–8.

327

329

328

330

331

One-handled silver dipper, or skillet.
Height 8 cm; diameter of lip 12.7 cm;
length of handle 12.3 cm.
Louvre, inv. Bj 1986.
From the Boscoreale Treasure (see page 78).

Vessel of the same general form and
purpose as No. 330 but the bowl, unusually
for such vessels, is decorated; its profile is
that of a *cantharos*, ornamented with tall
vertical flutes and a frieze of scallop shells and
dots. The handle, which ends in two swan's
heads, is decorated with a *thyrsus*, one of the
attributes of Dionysus, god of wine,
which suggests that this vessel was meant to
be used for serving hot wine.
Héron de Villefosse, no. 47. Strong 148.

332

Silver skyphos (drinking cup).
Height 6 cm; diameter 10.7 (with handles
14.8 cm).
Louvre, inv. Bj 1913.
From the Boscoreale Treasure (see page 78).

One of a pair of matching drinking cups
(*skyphoi*). The body consists of an outer shell,
decorated in high repoussé relief, and a plain
inner shell, with traces of gilding on the
inside and below the lip. The two handles and
the base were made separately. The
decoration consists of a variety of table
furnishings and assorted delicacies, alive and
dead. On one side is a rush basket containing
shrimps, a live goose making towards a dead
hare strung from a staff, grapes spilling from
a wicker pannier, and two dead thrushes. On
the other side, a laurel branch and a basket of
flowers, three turnips, a live boar squatting
in front of an amphora, a large curving knife,
a fluted dish (*patera*) with a swan's head
handle resting on a small stand and
supporting an elegant ewer, and a three-
legged table on which are set another ewer, a
perfume brazier and a small round box
(*pyxis*). Above the hare and staff, in tiny
Greek lettering, is written CABEINOC,
which is presumably the name of the artist,
Sabinus, written in Greek because that was
what fashion called for in such work.
Héron de Villefosse no. 15. Strong 138.

333

Small silver jug.
Height 8 cm.
Louvre, inv. Bj 1901.
From the Boscoreale treasure (see page 78).

One of a pair. The handle, a separate solid
casting decorated in low relief with
scrollwork plant stems and bunches of
grapes, is attached to the rim with the
elongated bird's head motifs which are a
common feature of silver plate. The body is
plain except for a narrow collar of punched
ornament round the neck. On the underside
of the base is scratched the weight, the
equivalent of 425 grammes, which must
refer to the two jugs together. Early first
century AD.
Héron de Villefosse, no. 24. Strong 141, fig.
28b.

334

Miniature silver bust of a woman.
Height 10 cm.
British Museum, inv. 1895. 6-22.1.
From the Boscoreale Treasure (see page 78).

The *emblema* from the centre of a silver dish,
now lost; one of a pair with No. 335. The
woman's hairstyle indicates a date in the first
half of the first century AD.
BMC Silver Plate no. 26.

331

333

332

335
Silver phiale.
Height 5.4 cm; diameter 24 cm;
diameter of central medallion 9.8 cm.
Louvre, inv. Bj 1970.
From the Boscoreale Treasure (see page 78).

In the centre of the dish, which is otherwise
plain, is a medallion (*emblema*) in very high
relief, worked in repoussé. It portrays the
bust of an elderly man. The vogue for such
emblema dishes originated in the third century
BC, and they were enthusiastically collected
by Romans of the late Republic. This piece
was one of a pair with No. 334, very possibly
portraying the original owner and his wife.
On the underside is scratched *Maximae*
('Maxima's'), presumably a mark of
ownership.
Héron de Villefosse no. 2. Strong 151.

336
Two-handled silver dish (kylix).
Diameter 14.5 cm; across the handles 23.5 cm.
British Museum, inv. 1897. 7-26.1.
From the Boscoreale treasure (see page 78).

Around a central boss, on which can be seen
traces of gilding, the bowl of the dish is
decorated with concentric bands of engraved
lotus flower palmettes (*anthemion*). The *kylix*
was made by a Greek artist working in South
Italy about 300 BC, and it is thus one of the
earliest pieces of silver plate found in a
Pompeian family collection.
BMC Silver Plate no. 15. Strong 94.

337
Silver hand mirror: Leda and the Swan.
Diameter 16.7 cm; length of handle 12 cm.
Louvre, inv. Bj 2159.
From the Boscoreale Treasure (see page 78).

The back of the mirror has a border in the
form of an ovolo moulding and, in the centre,
an appliqué medallion in low relief depicting
Leda, seated on a rock and feeding the swan
from a dish (*patera*). The handle is of the
common baluster type. There are traces of
gilding. Richly decorated mirrors of this form
are thought to be associated with the work of
the famous late Republican South Italian
(Campanian?) craftsman Pasiteles. (Pliny
Nat. Hist. XXXIII, 128–130).
Héron de Villefosse, no. 22. Strong 157–8.

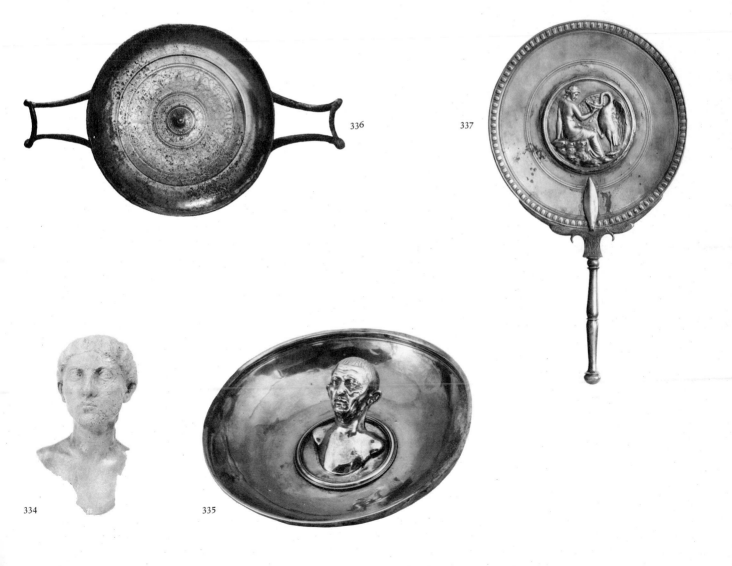

336

337

334

335

Reproduction of one of the painted Second Style walls from the newly-excavated villa at Oplontis.

Length 8.80 m; height 5.60 m.
Reproduced by courtesy of the excavator, Professor Alfonso De Franciscis.

The building to which this painting belongs was part of an opulent seaside villa (*villa marittima*) about three miles west of Pompeii, in the modern Torre Annunziata. The eruption buried it beneath nearly two metres of ash and pumice, then five metres of volcanic mud, and although the site has been known for a long time and was the subject of desultory exploration in 1839–40, it was not until 1964 that systematic excavations were put in hand by Professor De Franciscis.

The remains at present exposed comprise the greater part of the main residential block, together with its domestic service quarters, and to the east of it (not shown on the plan) part of an extensive *villa rustica* annexe. On the north side the main block backed on to a garden. The south facade opened on to a terraced platform, which in antiquity probably fronted directly on to the sea. Viewed from the sea or from the garden behind, the residential block would have been roughly symmetrical about a line of large rooms running north and south, comprising a projecting atrium complex at the south end and, at the north end, beyond a small internal garden courtyard (Room 20), a large *oecus* (Room 21) opening on to the garden between the columns of a gabled porch. These rooms and those to the west of

them constituted the main residence. To the east, screened from the main facade by a row of smaller rooms, were more utilitarian rooms grouped round an inner peristyle. These included the quarters of the domestic staff. Along the south frontage, following the outline of the plan, ran a continuous portico, just as one sees such porticoes in the wall paintings of *villae marittimae* (e.g. No.6).

At the time of the eruption only the servants' wing was occupied. The main residence, stripped of its furnishings, was awaiting modernization and redecoration. Another few years, perhaps months, and the magnificent series of Second Style paintings which are its especial glory would probably have gone the way of the paintings in the large garden *oecus* (Room 21), the walls of which were found already stripped bare. As it is, five rooms retain their original Second Style decoration: the atrium (5); a bed-chamber (11) and a day-room (23) on either side of it; a *triclinium* dining room (14) which adjoins the unusually large and well-appointed kitchen (7); and the large hall (15) which occupied the middle of the south front of the west wing.

No. 338, which covered the whole of the east wall in Room 15, still retains the formal simplicity of the early Second Style schemes, viewed as if through a simple colonnade of lofty Corinthian columns set on a low plinth projecting from the wall behind. But above eye-level the solid wall has been almost entirely eliminated, surviving only as an iconostasis-like screen, with two horizontal architraves and a central arch, which

partition up the receding architectural vistas portrayed beyond them. In the two lateral bays a pair of monumental double colonnades frame the central motif, a Delphic tripod, shown upraised on a tall, slender, circular pedestal and viewed as if through an open gateway leading into a garden. One notes the theatrical masks displayed on brackets; the *pinakes* in their wooden frames perched above the outer ends of the screen; the clever contrast of colour between the upper and the lower colonnades; and in the two narrow outer bays the friezes of shields, a motif repeated both in the atrium and in Room 23. The perspective is not the strict, single-viewpoint perspective of Renaissance and modern practice, but it is a remarkably sophisticated piece of visual illusionism. Painted around 40 BC, it is one of the surviving masterpieces of the fully developed Second Style.

Parts of the building were subsequently modernized a generation or so later. To this time belong the fine early Third Style paintings in the bath suite, perhaps also those of the *cubiculum* in the west wing (Room 38) which still retains its exquisitely painted red ceiling. The north facade in its present form may also be of this period. To the final phase before AD 79 belongs the highly simplified decoration of the inner peristyle of the east wing.

To whom did this villa belong, and can we give it a name? As regards ownership, there is some evidence that its last occupant was the wife of Nero, Poppaea Sabina, who died in AD 65. The Poppaei were a well-known Pompeian family, and it is an established fact that Poppaea Sabina, while empress, owned property within the territory of the city. Her death, followed in 68 by that of Nero, would help to explain why the property, though in good condition and destined for restoration, was still unoccupied in AD 79.

As for the name, Oplontis (or Eplontis), this is found only in two late itineraries and on the Roman map known as the Peutinger Table, where it is marked as a road station between Herculaneum and Pompeii. This may be a survival from pre-eruption times (such documents are notoriously conservative), or denote a later settlement. There are many records of classical finds in Torre Annunziata, in at least one instance coming from what was evidently another luxury villa. The 'Oplontis' villa is a vivid reminder of how much may still await discovery.

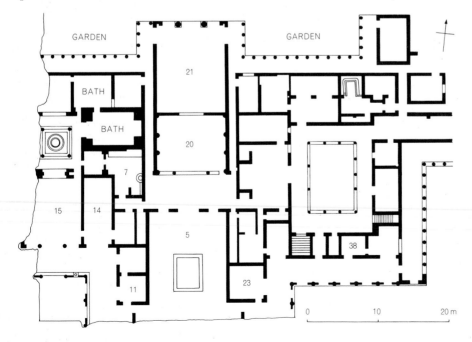

GARDEN   GARDEN

21

BATH

BATH

20

7

15   14

5

38

11

23

0   10   20 m

Glossary

Acroterion (plural *acroteria*) Decorative finial at the apex or the outer angles of a gabled roof.

Aedicula A small ornamental structure projecting from a wall, usually consisting of a gable carried by a pair of colonnettes or pilasters. Often reproduced in the fantasy architecture of Pompeian wall paintings.

Aedile (Latin *aedilis*) One of the pair of junior magistrates elected annually to supervise the day-to-day administration of the city. The office already existed in Samnite Pompeii.

Ala A wing extending to right and left at the far end of the atrium of a typical Pompeian house, giving access to the rooms on either side of the *tablinum*.

Amorino A cupid.

Aphrodite, see *Venus*.

Apollo The Greek god of the arts and music, early absorbed into the Italian pantheon. The principal divinity of Samnite Pompeii.

Artemis The Roman Diana, commonly portrayed as a huntress in her role as the goddess of forests and hills and of wild creatures.

Athena, see *Minerva*.

Atrium The central hall of a traditional Italic house. The roof normally sloped inwards to a rectangular central opening.

Bacchus, see *Dionysus*.

Basilica A colonnaded public hall, usually adjoining the forum, used for commercial and judicial business.

Belvedere A raised building from which to enjoy a view.

Caduceus The wand carried by Hermes (Mercury), with wings and two symmetrically entwined serpents.

Cornucopia A horn overflowing with fruits, symbol of plenty.

Cubiculum (plural *cubicula*) Bedroom.

Dionysus The Roman Bacchus, god of wine and of the theatre, whose cult involved 'mysteries' as well as ecstatic rites. Among his followers were Satyrs, Sileni and Maenads. Satyrs, originally spirits of wild life in the woods and hills, in Roman times were regularly portrayed in youthful human form but with pointed ears, tails and frequently with some of the goat-like attributes of the god Pan. Sileni, like Satyrs, were originally woodland creatures, part-man, part-horse, normally shown as elderly, shaggy, paunchy figures, frequently the worse for wine. Maenads were their female companions, usually portrayed in attitudes of ecstatic abandon.

Duovir (plural *duoviri*) One of the pair of senior magistrates elected annually to represent the city and to act as joint chairmen of the city council. Every fifth year these magistrates had special powers and were called *duoviri quinquennales*. The equivalent magistrates in the Samnite period were called *meddices* (singular *meddix*).

Emblema Strictly, a small panel in fine mosaic, produced separately to be inserted into a larger floor (see No. 72). Also used as the central feature of any larger decorative design, as in the silver dish, No. 335.

Ephebe (Greek *ephebos*) An aristocratic Greek youth who had not yet completed his education.

Escutcheon Term used to indicate a piece of applied decoration, as commonly in metalwork.

Exedra A large rectangular or curved recess opening off a room or corridor.

Hera, see *Juno*.

Hercules Latin form of Heracles, the Greek hero who performed twelve Labours for the king of Argos and was later worshipped as a god for his strength and power to repel evil. Particularly favoured by merchants.

Herm The name derives from early Greek representations of the god Hermes in the form of a rectangular shaft with a carved head. Later, more elaborate versions carried heads also of other divinities and human portraits.

Hermes The Roman Mercury, the messenger of the gods and patron divinity of commerce.

Impluvium The rectangular basin in the centre of the atrium of a Pompeian house, situated beneath the rectangular opening (*compluvium*) in the centre of the roof.

Insula (Latin, 'island') Term used conventionally to denote an ancient city block.

Intarsia (Italian *intarsio*) Shaped designs of wood, stone or metal inlaid into a background that has been cut out to receive them. See Nos. 183–185.

Juno The Greek Hera, the consort of Jupiter and the goddess specially concerned with those aspects of life which affected women (the home, marriage, childbirth, etc.).

Jupiter God of the heavens, whose special attribute was a thunderbolt. The patron divinity of Rome (Jupiter Optimus Maximus Capitolinus) and, with Juno and Minerva, the senior member of the Capitoline triad. Generally equated with the Greek Zeus.

Lararium Household shrine, with statuettes or painted representations of the *Lares*, the traditional guardians of the house, and of other favoured gods. See No. 220.

Lares, see *Lararium*.

Maenad, see under *Dionysus*.

Medusa A mythical female monster with snakes for hair and eyes that turned to stone those who looked upon her.

Mercury, see *Hermes*.

Minerva Goddess of wisdom, learning, and the arts and sciences. With Jupiter and Juno, the third member of the Roman Capitoline triad. Equated by the Romans with Athena.

Oecus (Greek *oikos*) A richly decorated living room.

Onkos Greek hairstyle, found commonly on theatrical masks; see Nos. 315–318.

Opus sectile Paving or wall decoration made of interlocking shaped pieces of coloured marble.

Oscillum (plural *oscilla*) Originally a mask or other ritual object, hung from a sacred tree, which 'oscillated' or spun in the wind. Later used in a variety of shapes in peristyle gardens, hung from the architrave between the columns.

Ovolo (from the Latin *ovum*, an egg) A convex moulding of egg-shaped profile.

Palaestra Open space reserved for exercise and sport. Usually enclosed by colonnades.

Pan A Greek pastoral divinity, responsible for the fertility of flocks, Often shown as half-goat, half-man, playing on his pan-pipe (see Nos. 82, 128).

Peristyle The inner, colonnaded garden court of a Pompeian (or Hellenistic) house, around which the main living rooms of the later houses were grouped.

Pinax (plural *pinakes*) A panel picture painted on wood or marble and often enclosed in a frame which could be closed like a triptych. Few actual *pinakes* have survived, but there are many representations of them in wall paintings.

Priapus Rustic god of fertility, regularly portrayed displaying a huge male organ.

Satyr, see under *Dionysus*.

Silenus, see under *Dionysus*.

Siren A mythological creature, half-woman and half-bird.

Stucco A hard slow-setting plaster based on lime, used for rendering wall surfaces or for moulded architectural detail.

Tablinum The central room at the far end of an atrium house, often with a window opening on to the garden beyond. It was the main reception room, and could be closed off from the atrium by a screen or curtains. In the late houses it opens also on to the peristyle.

Tempietto (Italian) A small temple-shaped building, either circular or gabled, with columns.

Terra sigillata Conventional name for the red-gloss pottery first produced in Italy at Arezzo, and later in many other places both in Italy and the western provinces of the Empire. It is found both in plain forms and with moulded relief decoration, in both cases closely modelled on the shapes and ornament of silverware. See page 54 and Nos. 106–108.

Tesserae (*tessellae*) Small cubes or splinters of coloured stone, glass or paste used to make mosaics.

Tholos A circular columned pavilion or *tempietto*.

Thyrsus A long staff, tipped with a pine cone or with bunches of ivy or vine leaves, carried by Dionysus or his followers.

Travertine Silvery-grey calcareous stone extensively used in the area around Rome, occasionally elsewhere. Most references to 'travertine' at Pompeii refer in fact to the grey limestone of the nearby hills.

Triclinium The dining room of a Roman house or its open-air equivalent. See page 67.

Tufa (Italian *tufo*) A rock formed of hardened volcanic ash, easily worked when freshly quarried.

Uraeus Egyptian cobra sacred to Isis.

Venus The Greek Aphrodite, goddess of love, and patron goddess of Pompeii.

Volute A spiral scroll, as on an Ionic capital.

Zeus The senior member of the Greek Olympian pantheon, in many aspects to be equated with the Roman Jupiter.

1. Periodicals and reference works which appear in the catalogue in abbreviated form.

AA	*Archäologischer Anzeiger* (in *JdAI*), Berlin.
AJA	*American Journal of Archaeology*, New York.
Annali dell'Inst	*Annali dell'Instituto di Corrispondenza Archeologica*, Rome.
AZ	*Archäologische Zeitung*, Berlin.
BdA	*Bollettino d'Arte*, Florence.
BJb	*Bonner Jahrbücher*, Bonn
BMC	*British Museum Catalogue*
Sculpture	A. H. Smith, *A Catalogue of Sculpture*, 3 vols, London 1892–1904.
Bronzes	H. B. Walters, *Catalogue of the Bronzes, Greek, Etruscan and Roman*, London 1899.
Silver Plate	H. B. Walters, *Catalogue of the Silver Plate (Greek, Etruscan and Roman)*, London 1921.
Jewellery	F. H. Marshall, *Catalogue of the Jewellery, Greek, Etruscan and Roman*, London 1911
Rings	F. H. Marshall, *Catalogue of the Finger Rings, Greek, Etruscan and Roman*, London 1907
Gems	H. B. Walters, *Catalogue of the Engraved Gems and Cameos*, 2nd ed. London 1926.
Lamps	H. B. Walters, *Catalogue of the Greek and Roman Lamps*, London 1914.
	D. M. Bailey, *Catalogue of the Lamps in the British Museum I – Greek, Hellenistic and Early Roman pottery lamps*, London 1975
Bronzi di Ercolano	*Le Antichità di Ercolano esposte*, vols v–vi (=*I Bronzi di Ercolano* 1–2), Naples 1767 and 1771.
Bull Inst	*Bullettino dell'Instituto di Corrispondenza archeologica*, Rome.
CIL	*Corpus Inscriptionum Latinarum*.
Daremberg & Saglio	C. Daremberg and E. Saglio, *Dictionnaire des antiquités grecques et romaines*, Paris 1877–1919.
ILS	ed. H. Dessau, *Inscriptiones Latinae Selectae*, 3 vols, Berlin 1892–1916.
JdAI	*Jahrbuch des deutschen archaeologischen Instituts*, Berlin.
JRS	*Journal of Roman Studies*, London.
Kraus & Von Matt	T. Kraus and L. Von Matt, *Pompeii and Herculaneum. Living cities of the dead*, New York 1975 (English translation of *Lebendiges Pompeji*, Cologne 1973)
MAAR	*Memoirs of the American Academy in Rome*, Rome.
Mariemont	*Les Antiquités du Musée de Mariemont*, Brussels 1952
MB	*Real Museo Borbonico*, 1st ed. in 16 vols, Naples 1824–57; subsequent ed. with major alterations, in 9 vols, Rome 1837–45.
MdI	*Mitteilungen des deutschen archäologischen Instituts* (1948), Berlin.
MemErc	*Memorie della Regale Accademia Ercolanese di Archeologia*, Naples 1840–48.
MemLinc	*Memorie dell' Accademia nazionale dei Lincei*, Rome.
Mon Pitt	*Monumenti della pittura antica scoperti in Italia*, Rome
Muse	*Muse*, Bulletin of the Cleveland Museum, Ohio
Neue Forschungen	*Neue Forschungen in Pompeji*, ed. B. Andreae and H. Kyrieleis, Recklinghausen 1975.
NSc	*Notizie degli scavi di antichità communicate alla (Reale) Accademia dei Lincei*, Rome

PAH   *Pompeianorum Antiquitatum Historia*, ed. G. Fiorelli, 3 vols, Naples 1860–64.

Pitture di Ercolano   *Le Antichità di Ercolano esposte*, vols I–V (= *Le Pitture di Ercolano*, 1–5), Naples 1757–1779.

Pompeiana   *Pompeiana. Roccolta di studi per il secondo centenario degli scavi di Pompei*, Naples 1950.

RAAN (Rend Nap)   *Rendiconti dell' Accademia di Archeologia, Lettere e Belle Arti di Napoli.*

RevArch   *Revue Archéologique*, Paris

RM   *Mitteilungen des deutschen archaeologischen Instituts. Römische Abteilung*, Rome (commonly referred to as 'Römische Mitteilungen').

2. General bibliography, listed in alphabetical order under author's name. Any abbreviations used in the catalogue are given below in brackets following the individual entries.

Andreae, B., 'Rekonstruktion der grossen Oecus der Villa des P. Fannius Synistor in Boscoreale', in *Neue Forschungen* 71–92.

Andreae, B., and others, *Pompeji: Leben und Kunst in den Vesuvstädten* (catalogue of exhibition Villa Hügel Essen), Recklinghausen 1975.

Andreau, J., *Les affaires de Monsieur Jucundus*, Ecole Française de Rome, 1974.

Augusti, S., 'La technica dell'antica pittura parietale pompeiana', *Pompeiana* 1950, 313–354.

Barnabei, F., *La Villa Pompeiana di P. Fannio Sinistore scoperta presso Boscoreale*, Rome 1901.

Barnabei, F., *Pompei e la regione sotterrata dal Vesuvio nell'anno LXXIX*, Naples 1879

Beloch, J., *Campanien im Alterthum*, 2nd ed., Naples 1890.

Beyen, H. G., 'The Workshops of the "Fourth Style" at Pompeii and in its neighbourhood'. I. *Studia archaeologica G. Van Hoorn oblato*, Leiden 1951.

Beyen, H. G., *Uber Stilleben aus Pompeji und Herculaneum*, The Hague 1928.

Bianchi Bandinelli, R., *Rome: The Centre of Power. Roman Art to* A.D. 200, London 1970 (Bianchi Bandinelli).

Bieber, M., *History of the Greek and Roman Theater*, Princeton 1939 (Bieber, Theater).

Blanckenhagen, P. H. and Alexander, M., *The Paintings from Boscotrecase*, Heidelberg 1962.

Boyce, G. K., 'Corpus of the Lararia of Pompeii', *MAAR* XIV, 1937.

Breglia, L., *Catalogo delle oreficerie del Museo di Napoli*, Rome 1941. (Breglia).

Carrington, R. C., *Pompeii*, Oxford 1936.

Carrington, R. C., 'Studies in the Campanian "Villae rusticae" ', *JRS* 21 (1931), 110–130.

Casella, D., 'Frutta nelle pitture pompeiane', *Pompeiana* 1950, 355–386.

Castrén, P., *Ordo Populusque Pompeianus: Polity and Society in Roman Pompeii*, Acta Instituti Romani Finlandiae vol. VIII, Rome 1975 (Castrén).

Coarelli, F. ed., *Guida archeologica di Pompei*, Verona 1976.

Comparetti, D. and De Petra, G., *La Villa Ercolanese dei Pisoni, suoi monumenti e biblioteca*, Turin 1883.

Cosenza, G., *Stabia: Memorie storiche ed archeologiche*, Castellamare di Stabia 1890.

Cosenza, G., *Studi archeologici topografici e storici su Stabia*, Trani 1907.

Croisille, J. M., *Les natures mortes campaniennes* (Coll. Latomus, LXXVI), Brussels 1965. (Croisille).

Curtius, L., *Die Wandmalerei Pompejis*, Leipzig 1929; reprinted Darmstadt 1972. (Curtius).

D'Arms, J. H., *Romans on the Bay of Naples*, Harvard 1970 (D'Arms).

Dawson, Ch.M., 'Romano-Campanian Mythological Landscape Painting', *Yale Classical Studies* 9, 1944 (Dawson).

De Franciscis, A., *The Pompeian Wall Paintings in the Roman villa of Oplontis*, Recklinghausen 1975.

De Franciscis, A., *Il ritratto romano a Pompei*, Naples 1951. (De Franciscis).

Della Corte, M., *Case ed Abitanti di Pompei*, Pompei Scavi 1954.

Della Corte, M., *Pompei: I nuovi scavi e l'anfiteatro*, Pompei 1930.

De Ridder, A., *Les Bronzes antiques du Louvre* II, *Les Instruments*, Paris 1915. (De Ridder).

Di Capua, F., 'Sacrari Pompeiani', *Pompeiana* 1950, 60–85.

D'Orsi, L., *Come ritrovai l'Antica Stabia*, Milan 1962.

Elia, O., 'Le pitture della casa del Citarista', *MonPitt: Pompei*, fasc. 1, Rome 1937.

Elia, O., 'Le pitture del Tempio di Iside', *MonPitt: Pompei*, fasc. 3–4, Rome 1942 (Elia *MonPitt*).

Elia, O., *Le Pitture di Stabia*, Naples 1957.

Elia, O., 'Nota per uno studio della decorazione parietale a Pompei', *Pompeiana* 1950, 97–110.

Elia, O., *Pitture murali e Mosaici del Museo Nazionale di Napoli*, Naples 1932 (Elia).

Eschebach, H. 'Die Stadtbauliche Entwicklung des antiken Pompeji', *RM* Erganzungsheft no. 17, Heidelberg 1970.

Eschebach, H., 'Festellung unter der Oberflache des Jahres 79 n. Chr. im Bereich der Insula VII, I – Stabianer Thermen – in Pompeji,' in *Neue Forschungen* 179–190.

Etienne, R., *La vie quotidienne à Pompei*, Paris 1966.

Fienga, F., 'Esplorazione del pago marittimo pompeiano', *Atti del* III *Congresso nazionale di Studi romani*, Bologna 1934, 172–76.

Fiorelli, G., *Catalogo del Museo Nazionale di Napoli, Armi Antiche*, Naples 1869 (Fiorelli, *Armi antiche*).

Fiorelli, G., *Catalogo del Museo Nazionale di Napoli, Raccolta pornografica*, Naples 1866 (Fiorelli, *Raccolta pornografica*).

Fiorelli, G., *Gli Scavi di Pompei dal 1861 al 1872*, Naples 1873 (Fiorelli, *Scavi*).

Gell, W. and Gandi, J. P., *Pompeiana: the topography, edifices and ornaments of Pompeii*, 2 vols, London 1817–19.

Gigante, M., 'La cultura letteraria a Pompei', *Pompeiana* 1950, 111–143.

Gusman, P., *Pompei: La Ville, Les Moeurs, Les Arts*, Paris n.d. 1899?; English ed. *Pompeii: The City, its Life and Art*, London 1900. (Gusman).

Hawkes, C. F. C. and Hull, M. R. *Camulodunum*, 287–306 D. B. Harden 'The Glass', Oxford 1947 (Harden, *Camulodunum*).

Helbig, W., *Untersuchungen über die campanische Wandmalerei*, Leipzig 1873.

Helbig, W., *Wandgemälde der vom Vesuv verschutteten Städte*, Leipzig 1868 (Helbig).

Héron de Villefosse, V., 'Le Trésor de Boscoreale', *Monuments Piot* V, 1899 (Héron de Villefosse).

Higgins, R. A., *Greek and Roman Jewellery*, London 1961 (Higgins).

Ippel, A., *Der dritte pompejanische Stil*, Berlin 1910.

Isings, C., *Roman glass from dated finds*, Archaeologica traiectina II, Groningen 1957. (Isings).

Jacono, L., 'Note di archeologia marittima. I. Il Porto di Pompei?', *Neapolis* I, 1913 fasc. III–IV, 353 ff.

Jashemsky, W. F., 'The Caupona of Euxinus at Pompeii', *Archaeology* XX (1967) 36–44.

Jashemsky, W. F., 'Excavation in the Foro Boario at Pompeii', *AJA* 72 (1968) 69–73.

Jashemsky, W. F., 'The discovery of a market garden orchard at Pompeii', *AJA* 78 (1974) 391–404.

Jashemsky, W. F., 'Pompeian gardens yield their secrets', *American Horticultural Magazine*, spring 1970, 54–63.

Jashemsky, W. F., 'Tomb gardens at Pompeii', *Classical Journal* 66 (1970–71) 97–115.

Jashemsky, W. F., 'From Vesuvius' dust: Pompeii emerges a city of Gardens, Vineyards', *Landscape architecture*, May 1976, 224–230.

Jashemsky, W. F., 'A large vineyard discovered in ancient Pompeii', *Science* 180 (1973) 826.

Johannowsky, W., 'Contributi alla topografia della Campania antica', *RAAN* n.s. XXVII 1952 83–146.

Kapossy, B., *Brunnenfiguren der hellenistischen und römischen Zeit*, Zurich 1969 (Kapossy, *Brunnenfiguren*).

Kirschen, F., *Die Stadtmauern von Pompeji*, (Die hellenistische Kunst in Pompeji VII) Berlin 1941.

Kluge, K. and Lehmann-Hartleben, K., *Die antiken Grossbronzen*, 3 vols, Berlin and Leipzig 1927 (Kluge-Hartleben).

Laidlaw, A., 'A reconstruction of the First Style decoration in the Alexander Exedra of the House of the Faun', in *Neue Forschungen* 39–52.

Lauter, H., 'Zur Siedlungsstruktur Pompejis in Samnitischen Zeit', in *Neue Forschungen* 147–154.

Lauter-Bufe, H., 'Zur architektonischen Gartengestaltung in Pompeji und Herculaneum', in *Neue Forschungen* 169–173.

Lehmann, Ph. W., *Roman Wall-Painting from Boscoreale in the Metropolitan Museum of Art*, Cambridge, Mass. 1953.

Lepore, E., 'Orientamenti per la storia sociale di Pompei', *Pompeiana* 1950, 144–166.

Levi, A., *Le terrecotte figurati del Museo Nazionale di Napoli*, Florence 1926. (Levi).

Maiuri, A., *Ercolano: i nuovi scavi (1927–58) vol I*, Rome 1958 (Maiuri, Ercolano).

Maiuri, A., 'Geologia ed archeologia ad Ercolano ed a Pompei', *RAAN* n.s. XXII 1942–46, 113–140.

Maiuri, A., 'Gli scavi di Pompei dal 1879 al 1948', *Pompeiana* 1950, 9–40.

Maiuri, A., *Herculaneum*, Paris 1932.

Maiuri, A., *La casa del Menandro e il suo tesoro di argenteria*, 2 vols, Rome 1933.

Maiuri, A., *La Villa dei Misteri*, Rome 1947.

Maiuri, A., 'Le pitture delle case di M. Fabius Amandio, del Sacerdos Amandus, di Cornelius Teges', *MonPitt: Pompei. fasc.2*, Rome 1938.

Maiuri, A., *L'ultima fase edilizia di Pompei*, Rome 1942

Mau, A., *Geschichte der decorativen Wandmalerei in Pompeji*, Berlin 1882.

Mau, A., *Pompeji in Leben und Kunst*, 2nd ed. Leipzig 1908; *Anhang zur zweiten Auflage*, Leipzig 1913.

Mau, A., and Kelsey, F. W., *Pompeii, its Life and Art*, New York 1899.

Mustilli, D., 'Botteghe di scultori, marmorarii, bronzieri e caelatores in Pompei', *Pompeiana* 1950, 206–229.

Mustilli, D., 'La villa pseudo-urbana ercolanese', *RAAN* n.s. XXXI 1956, 77–97.

Niccolini, F., *Le Case ed i Monumenti di Pompei Designati e Descritti*, Naples 1854–96 (Niccolini).

Nissen, H., *Pompeianische Studien zur Stadtekunde des Altertums*, Leipzig 1877.

Noack, F. and Lehmann-Hartleben, K., *Baugeschichtliche Untersuchungen am Stadtrand von Pompeji* (Denkmäler antiker Architektur II), Berlin and Leipzig 1936.

Onorato, G. O., 'La data del terremoto di Pompei: 5 febbraio 62 d.C.', *RAAN* ser.8, IV 1949, 644–661.

Overbeck, J., *Pompeji in seinem Gebäuden, Alterthümern und Kunstwerken*, Leipzig 1884.

Packer, J., 'Middle and lower class housing in Pompeii and Herculaneum: a preliminary survey', in *Neue Forschungen* 133–146.

Palombi, A., 'La fauna marina nei mosaici e nei dipinti pompeiani', *Pompeiana* 1950, 425–455.

Pernice, E., *Gefässe und Geräte aus Bronze*, (Die hellenistische Kunst in Pompeji IV) Berlin 1925 (Pernice IV).

Pernice, E., '*Hellenistische Tische, Zisternenmundungen, Beckenuntersätze, Altare, und Truhen*', (Die hellenistische Kunst in Pompeji V) Berlin 1932 (Pernice V).

Pernice, E., '*Pavimente und figürliche Mosaiken*', (Die hellenistische Kunst in Pompeji VI) Berlin 1938 (Pernice VI).

Peters, W. J. T., *Landscape in Romano-Campanian Mural Painting*, Assen 1963.

Presuhn, E., *Pompei: Les dernières fouilles de 1874–1878*, Leipzig 1878.

Pugliese Carratelli, G., 'L'instrumentum scriptorium nei monumenti pompeiani ed ercolanensi', *Pompeiana* 1950, 266–278.

Reuterswaard, P., *Studien zur Polychromie der Plastik: Griechenland und Rom*, Stockholm 1960 (Reuterswaard).

Richardson, L., 'The Casa dei Dioscuri and its Painters', *MAAR* XXIII, 1955.

Rittmann, A., 'L'eruzione vesuviana del 79', *Pompeiana* 1950, 456–474.

Rizzo, G. E., *La pittura ellenistica-romana*, Mailand 1929.

Rocco, A., 'Pompeiana supellex', *Pompeiana* 1950, 278–287.

Rodenwaldt, G., *Die Komposition der pompejanische Wandgemälde*, Berlin 1900.

Rostowzew, M., 'Die hellenistische-romische architekturlandschaft', *RM* XXVI (1911), 1–186 (Rostowzew, 'Architekturlandschaft').

Roux Ainé, H., *Herculanum et Pompei: Recueil general des peintures, bronzes, mosaiques, etc.*, 8 vols, Paris 1870–72.

Ruesch, A., ed. *Guida illustrata del Museo Nazionale di Napoli*, Naples 1908.

Ruggiero, M., *Degli scavi di Stabia dal 1749 al 1782*, Naples 1881 (Ruggiero, Stabia).

Salmon, E. T., *Samnium and the Samnites*. Cambridge 1967.

Schefold, K., *Die Wände Pompejis*, Berlin 1957 (Schefold WP).

Schefold, K., *Pompejanische Malerei*, Basle 1952.

Schefold, K., *La Peinture Pompeienne*, Coll. Latomus no. CVIII, Brussels 1972 (Schefold).

Schefold, K., *Vergessenes Pompeji*, Munich 1962.

Siviero, R., *Gli ori e le ambre del Museo Nazionale di Napoli*, Florence 1954 (Siviero).

Sogliano, A., 'Le Pitture Murale Campagne Scoverte negli Anni 1867–1879 descritte' in *Pompei e la regione sotterrata dal Vesuvio*, vol. II 87 ff., Naples 1879 (Sogliano).

Sogliano, A., *Pompei nel suo sviluppo storico. Pompei preromana (dalle origini alle 80 av.C.)*, Rome 1937.

Spano, G., 'Porte e regione pompeiane e vie campane', *RAAN* n.s. XVII, 1937, 269 ff.

Spinazzola, V., *Le arti decorative in Pompei e nel Museo Nazionale di Napoli*, Milan 1928.

Spinazzola, V., *Pompei alla Luce degli Scavi Nuovi di Via dell'Abbondanza* vols I–III, Rome 1953 (Spinazzola-Aurigemma).

Strong, D. E., *Greek and Roman Silver Plate*, London 1966 (Strong).

Tanzer, H. H., *The Common People of Pompeii* (The Johns Hopkins University Studies in Archaeology no. 29), Baltimore 1939.

Thédenat, H., *Les villes d'art célèbres. Pompei*, Paris 1910.

Tran tam Tinh, V., *Essai sur Le Culte d'Isis a Pompéi*, Paris 1964 (Tran tam Tinh, *Pompéi*).

Tran tam Tinh, V., *Le culte des divinités orientales à Herculaneum* (Etudes préliminaires aux religions orientales dans l'empire romain no. 17), Leiden 1971 (Tran tam Tinh, *Herculaneum*).

Tran tam Tinh, V., 'Les problèmes du culte de Cybele et d'Attis à Pompéi', *Neue Forschungen* 279–83 (Tran tam Tinh, 1975).

Van Buren, A. W., *A companion to the study of Pompeii and Herculaneum*, Rome 1933; 2nd ed. Rome 1938.

Venuti, M., *A Description of the discovery of the Ancient City of Heraclea*, trs. W. Skurray, London 1750 (Venuti, *Heraclea*).

Von Rohden, H., *Die Terracotten von Pompeji*, Stuttgart 1880 (Von Rohden).

Waldstein, C., and Shoobridge, L., *Herculaneum past, present and future*, London 1908.

Webster, T. B. L., *Monuments illustrating New Comedy*, 2nd ed. (University of London, Bulletin of the Institute of Classical Studies, Supplement 24, 1969) (Webster, *New Comedy*).

Webster, T. B. L., *Monuments illustrating Tragedy and Satyr Play*, 2nd ed., (University of London, Bulletin of the Institute of Classical Studies, Supplement 20, 1967) (Webster, *Tragedy and Satyr Play*).

Winter, F., *Die figürlichen Typen der Terracotten*, 2 vols, Leipzig 1903, (Winter).

Witt, R. E., *Isis in the Graeco-Roman World*, London 1971.

Zahn, W., *Die schönsten Ornamente und merkwürdigsten Gemälde aus Pompeji, Herkulanum und Stabiae*, 3 vols, Berlin 1827–59.

Zevi, F., *La casa Reg. IX, 5, 18–21 a Pompei e le sue pitture*, Rome 1964.

3. Some recent books in English.

Boethius, A. and Ward-Perkins, J. B., *Etruscan and Roman Architecture*, chs. 13 and 14 (Pelican History of Art), London 1970.

Brion, M., *Pompeii and Herculaneum: The Glory and the Grief*, London and Toronto 1960.

Bulwer-Lytton, E., *The Last Days of Pompeii*, abridged ed. London 1976.

Clay, E. and Frederiksen, M., *Sir William Gell in Italy: Letters to the Society of Dilettanti, 1831–1835*, London 1976.

Deiss, J. J., *Herculaneum, Italy's buried treasure*, New York 1966.

Grant, M., *Cities of Vesuvius: Pompeii and Herculaneum*, London 1971.

Grant, M., *Erotic Art in Pompeii*, London 1975.

Leppmann, W., *Pompeii in fact and fiction*, London 1968.

McKay, A. G., *Houses, Villas and Palaces in the Roman World*, ch.2, London 1975.

Trevelyan, R., *The Shadow of Vesuvius: Pompeii AD 79*, London 1976.